Carrots and Sticks

Have you ever wondered how a sheepdog, police horse, leopard or octopus is trained? *Carrots and Sticks* brings behavioural science to life, explaining animal training techniques in the language of learning theory. The first sections on instinct and intelligence, rewards and punishers are richly infused with examples from current training practice, and establish the principles that are explored later in the unique case studies.

Drawing on interviews with leading animal trainers, *Carrots and Sticks* offers 50 case studies that explore the step-by-step training of a wide variety of companion, working and exotic animals. It reviews the preparation of animals prior to training and common pitfalls encountered.

The book's accessible style will challenge your preconceptions and simplify your approach to all animal-training challenges. This exciting text will prove invaluable to anyone with an interest, amateur or professional, in the general basics of animal training, as well as to students of psychology, veterinary medicine, agriculture and animal science.

About the authors

PAUL MCGREEVY is Professor of Animal Behaviour and Welfare at the University of Sydney's Faculty of Veterinary Science. His contributions to an evidence-based approach to the training, management, behaviour and welfare of horses and dogs have been recognised with numerous international awards. Detailed information can be found on his website: sydney.edu.au/vetscience/about/staff/pmcgreevy.shtml

ROBERT BOAKES is Emeritus Professor of Psychology at the University of Sydney. His research has focused on the learned behaviour of animals for over 30 years. His current theoretical studies are mainly concerned with learning when reward is delayed. His more applied projects include examining the effects of diet and activity on metabolism, brain and behaviour. Detailed information can be found on his website: sydney.edu.au/science/psychology/staff/bobb

Carrots and Sticks

Principles of Animal Training

Paul McGreevy
Robert Boakes

DARLINGTON PRESS

Published 2011 by Darlington Press
Darlington Press is an imprint of SYDNEY UNIVERSITY PRESS

© Paul McGreevy and Robert Boakes 2011
© Darlington Press 2011

First published in 2007 by Cambridge University Press

Sydney University Press
Fisher Library F03, University of Sydney
NSW 2006 Australia
Email: sup.info@sydney.edu.au

National Library of Australia Cataloguing-in-Publication entry

Author: McGreevy, Paul, 1964-
Title: Carrots and sticks : principles of animal training /
             Paul McGreevy and Robert Boakes.
ISBN: 9781921364150 (hbk.)
Subjects: Animal training.
             Animal training--Case studies.
Other Authors/Contributors:
             Boakes, Robert A.
Dewey Number:
             636.0835

Cover design by Miguel Yamin, the University Publishing Service
Printed in China by Opus Print Group

For Pierre and Margi

Contents

Preface

Throughout history animals have been used to assist humans in work and play or simply to satisfy our curiosity. Several paintings from Ancient Egypt demonstrate that we have been charming, cajoling and exploiting animals for many thousands of years. One example depicts men hand-feeding hyenas that are shown lying on their backs, a feature that strongly suggests that they were tame. There is evidence from the same source that gazelles, ibex and oryx were equally relaxed in human company. In view of the enormous investment of time required for the gentling of non-domesticated species, it is fascinating to speculate about the jobs these animals performed in Ancient Egypt. Some of the uses to which animals have been put in the past may seem unacceptable by modern ethical standards. For example, the Romans tied songbirds to bushes in their gardens and even used animals to torture and execute their enemies.

Animals have long been used to keep vermin such as rats away from human households or grain stores, and to act as guards warning of possible intruders. Across different cultures such guards have included geese, guinea fowl and pigs, as well as dogs. Large species such as horses, donkeys and cattle have for many millennia been used as sources of power. In its crudest form this means traction, as in pulling ploughs, sleds or carts. Later, animals were also used to provide power for primitive machines designed, for example, for milling grain or for raising water from deep wells. Similarly, dogs were forced to run in large wall-mounted wheels to turn roasting-spits.

None of the forms of work mentioned so far required large changes in the animals' behaviour. In contrast to these relatively simple uses of animals, in the domains of hunting and herding humans since pre-history have sought to increase their efficiency by investing considerable time in training animals. Training means changing the frequency with which animals show certain behaviours. Unwelcome behaviours become less likely, while desirable ones become more likely. Ancient Egyptians even tamed cheetahs for hunting, and the work that these big cats performed may have been seen as the most sophisticated and effective hunting tool then available. However, this is a very unusual example. More generally, hunting and herding were the domains in which the dog truly came to the fore as the most trainable of all species.

The role of animals in warfare and in the relative success of different human cultures is often underestimated. The cultures that have prevailed from ancient origins are those that most fully exploited a variety of animals in combat, especially horses. Chief among the peoples that owed their success to the horse were the Mongol hordes. These excellent equestrians used their horses as sources of milk and meat when they were not exploiting their fleetness of foot for lightning raids on unmounted victims. The training of horses to perform

Nubian tribute bearers with a cheetah, giraffe, monkey, baboon and leopard. From the Theban tomb of Rekhmire (TT 100), Eighteenth Dynasty. (After Davies, *The Tomb of Rekh-mi-Rē at Thebes*, II, 1943, plates 17, 19 and 20.)

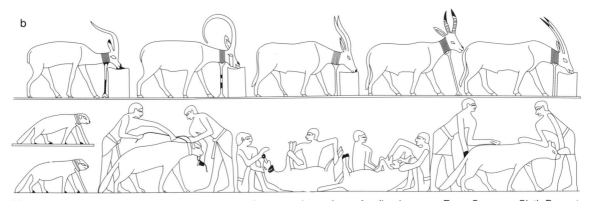

Upper register: antelopes eating from mangers. Lower register: force-feeding hyenas. From Saqqara, Sixth Dynasty. (After Duell *et al.*, *The Mastaba of Mereruka*, II, 1938, plate 153.)

Fig. 0.1 (a) Tethered antelopes eating from mangers and hyenas being force-fed in Ancient Egypt. The animals must have been trained to submit to this treatment. From the Theban tomb of Rekhmire, Eighteenth dynasty. (b) Nubian tribute bearers in Ancient Egypt with a cheetah, giraffe, monkey, baboon and leopard. Animals from all five species appear to have been trained. From the Theban tomb of Rekhmire, Eighteenth dynasty. Reproduced courtesy of R. and J. Janssen.

specific behaviours useful in warfare eventually gave rise to the emergence of military riding academies. The haute-école dressage movements that the Lippizaner stallions of Vienna now perform in their displays were first developed some 400 years ago to vanquish enemies in face-to-face combat. Training and riding skills contributed to the success of armies and the survival of individuals.

Horses are not the only species to have been conscripted into human conflicts. Dogs and pigeons were used to carry messages during the trench warfare of World War I. In World War II the Russians used carefully selected dogs as antitank operatives, while the US Navy trained dolphins to place explosive devices on the hulls of ships. The same war prompted research into the deployment of pigeons to guide what was intended as the world's first smart missile. Three pigeons were strapped into position and trained to peck a spot on recognition of approximations to their target, this peck being transmitted to the guidance system of a missile that was actually never used.

This long tradition of involving animals in human conflict still continues. Dolphins were used to search for mines in the second Gulf War, and dogs are used to detect landmines and are trained to search buildings for terrorists with tiny cameras strapped to their foreheads. Explosive detection is becoming ever more sophisticated these days

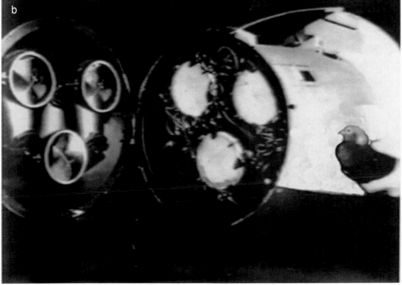

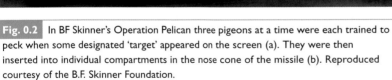

Fig. 0.2 In BF Skinner's Operation Pelican three pigeons at a time were each trained to peck when some designated 'target' appeared on the screen (a). They were then inserted into individual compartments in the nose cone of the missile (b). Reproduced courtesy of the B.F. Skinner Foundation.

with techniques that concentrate volatile substances from a single site and seal them in small airtight capsules so that these can be sent to the dog for his opinion.

Although the behaviour of intensively trained animals can fascinate us, the animals with which most of us have frequent contact are those that have come into our homes as companions. We may be using

Fig. 0.4 A rhino being ridden as part of a circus act. Reproduced with permission from the Captive Animals Protection Society.

animals less in the workplace, but we are not necessarily spending less time with them. Even highly domesticated companion animals need to be trained, although the level of dedication and expertise needed is far below that required to train a Lippizaner stallion or mine-detecting dolphin to perform at a high level.

Over the very long history of training animals, a variety of expert traditions have developed. The language used to describe them is just as varied. For example, the way a shepherd describes how to train his dog is very different from the accounts that might be given by a falconer or by an elephant trainer of how they train their animals. The ways in which these different animals are trained also appear to differ enormously and in turn seems quite different from the advice given in a booklet on 'How to train your pet'. However, the basic idea behind *Carrots and Sticks* is that these differences are superficial ones and that the same general principles apply to any kind of animal training. We reached this conclusion by different routes. One of us (PMcG) trained as a veterinarian and specialised in animal behaviour, with a particular interest in and love of dogs and horses. The other (RAB) trained as a research psychologist, with a particular interest in comparative psychology and learning theory. This book is a result of our collaboration in trying to make clear what we believe these general principles to be.

One set of principles has to do with behaviour that is largely determined by what kind of animal is being trained. We refer to this as *instinctive* behaviour. Although this is an old-fashioned and ambiguous term, it is better than any other label for denoting behaviour more strongly determined by an animal's genes – its *nature* – than by its experience – its *nurture*. Chapter 1 discusses those aspects of instinctive behaviour that are important from the perspective of an animal trainer, and also the way that instinctive behaviour changes as a result of experience; hence the title 'Instincts and their modification'. One of the core principles of training is that based on positive reward: the 'carrot'. The properties of such learning have been extensively studied by psychologists using various kinds of conditioning methods. This research has led to the principles of importance to animal training that are described in Chapter 2. A related set of principles, described in Chapter 3, have been derived from conditioning studies that have employed aversive events – 'sticks' – to find out how punishment works (and sometimes doesn't work) and how avoidance behaviour is learned. Many attempts at training fail because the trainer assumes that animals have very human-like ways of perceiving and thinking about the world. The limitations of this assumption and the realities of animal intelligence are the main topics in Chapter 4.

You are invited to approach the two parts of the book in different ways. The first part can be read in the conventional way from beginning to end, while the second part has a quite different format. It contains a range of case histories to illustrate how the basic principles have been put into practice by trainers. The cases are intended for browsing in no particular order. Since the overall goal of this book is to take the mystery out of training, in the case studies we have unpicked the various processes by which the animals acquired their sometimes amazing behaviours. The accounts of their training are offered as illustrations of training practices. They are not intended as models for readers to emulate. The performances you see represent the end-points of a long process of behavioural modification that may have begun when the animals were very young. Having considered various approaches, you will be better able to decide for yourself whether it is right or wrong that animals are used in these ways. Are certain behaviours undignified? How can animal welfare be ensured when animals are required to work for a living? Should zoos require their animals to perform? Can this enrich their lives? It is possible that your informed response to these questions may then be at odds, say, with your views on riding horses. Regardless of these dilemmas, the information in this book should add to your fascination with the non-human animals with whom we share the world.

The main theme of this book is that, despite huge diversity in the aims of different kinds of training and in the way that trainers explain their methods, all successful training depends largely on the principles we discuss in the four chapters of Part I.

Acknowledgements

A huge contribution to this book was made by the many animal trainers and experts in animal behaviour who generously spent time discussing their methods. In addition to those named in the case studies, these included Sophie Sharp, Emma Lawrence, Steve Austin, Natalie Waran, Herman Raadsma, Bob Cameron, Amanda Warren-Smith, Jenny Lunney, Lynne Roberts-Goodwin, Gabi Hoffman, Susan Wilkins, David Galilee, Peta Clarke, Libby Hall, Kevin Lalande, Kathryn Taylor, Christopher Wathes, Diana Durnam-Walters, Cecilia Lindberg, Jacquii Swinburne, Ellen Cooke, John Black and Ray Joyce, NSW GDBA, Wolfwatch UK, Trevor Goodinson, Dolores Palmer and Dog Aid, Rick Turner at The Big Sheep, Geoff, Chuck, Derek, Chris, and Guy at Seaworld, Australia, Frank Inglese, Peter Crumblin, Bert Tomlin, Dean Corke, Dennis White, Vikki Watts, Ryan Hockley, Ian Robinson, Helen Holdcroft, Ady D'Ettorre, Elle Bombonata, Jenny Gosling, Dan Clarke (GDBA Exeter), Alan Woodward, Stephanie Wehnelt, Andrew Lenihan, Liza Pern, Airey Gargett, Luke Seymour, Philip Swindle, John Randall, Paul Berry, Nancy Coerce, Marie Haskell, John Ravenscroft, Kathryn Tickner, Donna Brander, Christopher Todd, Alan Partington, Dennis Vardy, Nottingham Trent University (Department of Land-based Studies, Brackenhurst campus), Andrew Moss, Grenville Owens, Miranda Stevenson, Georgia Mason, Trevor Poole, Roger Ewbank, Mark Evans, Lynn Hughes, Peter Boyle, Anne McBride, Bob Head, Robin Nicholls and Tonni Harper.

We also wish to thank those who provided us with invaluable help, advice and support in writing this book, including Lynn Cole (for tireless editorial advice), Christine Nicol (for assistance with early drafts), Sandro Nocentini, Pierre Malou, Vanessa Carn, Lucy Angus, Nick Steel, Shirley Bennett, Pamela Staines, Paula French, Stan Burgess, Anne and Pat Stubbs, Nick Copping, Gordon Fitchett, Marianne Gould, Iain Dennis, Claire Weatherall, Karen Lipworth, Natasha Blom, Julia Sumner, Hilary Bugg, Olivia Hassin, Simon Lubans, Judi Wilson, Kathryn Taylor, Danielle Karazinov, Graeme Koetsveld and Margaret Kirkwood.

Part I

General principles

Chapter 1

Instincts and their modification

Species' differences in anatomy, including size, shape and colour, result in their morphological characteristics. Species also differ in behaviour. In this chapter we use the term *instinct* to refer to behaviour that is characteristic of a species.

Some examples of instinctive behaviour in animals, such as the flight response in prey animals, are impulsive and reflex-like. However, many of the actions an animal does that are typical of its species involve complex processes of, for example, spatial learning and memory. One such example is the caching behaviour of the scrub jay that hides food in a variety of locations in the spring and summer and may retrieve it many months later. Such 'caching' is instinctive for the scrub jay in that the behaviour is generally shown by all members of this species but may not be displayed by even quite closely related species. The human capacity for language has been described as an instinct in this sense of the word.

By referring to behaviour as instinctive we do not wish to imply that it is entirely innate and independent of an individual's experience. In this chapter we will discuss a number of different ways in which the normal development of some form of instinctive behaviour depends on a normal environment. When the environment is artificial, the behaviour can develop in a quite different direction. A well-known example of this is imprinting. In many species an individual displays normal adult social behaviour only if it has had contact with other members of the species during a sensitive period when the individual was still young. An essential early ingredient for the successful training of most species is *socialisation*. This means getting the animal to treat human beings as fellow members of its social group. For most species the earlier their contact with humans, the more effective and enduring such socialisation is likely to be. Another process by which an individual's experience can profoundly modify its instinctive behaviour is *habituation*. All species, our own included, have particular ways of reacting to threats, including the potential hazard of something that is new or unexpected, whether an unknown smell, an unfamiliar object, an unexpected movement or a sudden sound. With repeated exposure to empty threats, the response becomes

Fig. 1.1 Scrub jay caching meal worms prior to a later test of its memory for where and when the worms were hidden. Reproduced with permission from N. Clayton and I. Cannell.

progressively weaker. Some of the examples discussed in the case studies (e.g. Case 49: Star the police horse) demonstrate the effectiveness of habituation in getting an animal to tolerate with complete calm events that would traumatise it if it had never previously experienced anything of the kind.

Evolutionary zoology

The principles and phenomena discussed in this chapter have been studied mainly by scientists trained in zoology. Their aim has often been to understand a species' evolutionary history and differences in the way species adapt to their environment. It is, therefore, hardly surprising that most of their research has started with systematic observation in the field. In many cases further understanding of some behaviour depends on experimental research, perhaps initially in the animals' own territory. Sometimes such research takes place in the more easily controlled environment of a laboratory where key factors can be much more easily isolated than in the unpredictable complexity of a natural environment. From such studies animal trainers can gain an understanding of how to work with, rather than against, an animal's instincts.

The hunters and the hunted

In very broad terms animals can be divided into those that hunt and those that are hunted. As both groups have evolved, they have improved their abilities and strategies. With each generation, the genes that survive for breeding purposes are largely those that promote success in either preying or avoiding predation. The killers may refine their stealth, speed, determination, persistence, perceptual abilities or ability to co-operate in the detection and gathering of prey. They may also save energy by maximising the amount of nourishment they gain from each successful pursuit, when most are unsuccessful. Meanwhile the prey become more cautious and athletic. While they must be as vigilant as the next herbivore, they must also calm down as soon as possible after a disturbance so that they can return to grazing or browsing quicker than their fellow herbivores. The combination of genes that makes the next generation of panthers more effective at bringing down antelope may well be matched by improvements in the genes that make the next generation of antelope more flighty. This has been described as an arms race.

In the wild state all animals compete with fellow members of their species – their *conspecifics* – in tests of their biological fitness and their ability to survive and breed. Whether it eats flesh or vegetation, a malnourished individual will not only be slower in the chase but will also be less likely to breed. Unthrifty males are weaker in the power struggles that secure mating rights, while the thinner females in a group may stop cycling and therefore have fewer opportunities to become pregnant. As the hunters and the hunted struggle to be the biologically fittest, both as species and as individuals, the ability to profit from experience can be selected for as well as athleticism or coat colour.

The social and the solitary

Another very general way of classifying animals is between the social and the solitary. The degree to which a human can manipulate the behaviour of a solitary hunter is limited by various aspects of its biology, including the relative weakness of the social bond between the animal and its human colleague (see Fig. 1.2). Solitary hunters have not evolved to co-operate, let alone to take orders. Lone hunters such as hawks and most cats did not evolve to consider other members of their species as team players. On the contrary, they are likely to regard them as competitors. They have less of the hierarchical social structure seen in the truly social species such as dogs and horses. Being predators rather than prey, they do not respond well to coercion. Indeed, while tiger trainers learn to regard their dangerous subjects as fairly predictable, more domestic cats have trained their owners than their owners would care to admit.

It seems that, while many of the predators may be reluctant to take humans seriously as social equals, let alone as superiors, prey animals all too easily revert to regarding humans as predators. When a horse is presented by its trainer with something novel, its likely response is fear. Curiosity follows much later and depends very much on the analogue of a herd effect. Just as heifers are more likely to investigate a new piece of farm machinery in the corner of a field

Fig. 1.2 Mutual grooming between a horse and a human. Being a social species that readily accepts human company, many horses will allogroom (see glossary) humans as they do other horses. With permission from Sandro Nocentini.

Fig. 1.3 Round-pen training of a horse relies on the horse's instinctive response to move away from potential predators. The horse learns that moving towards the trainer leads to the reduction in aversive stimuli such as staring by the trainer. With permisssion from Portland Jones.

if they are in a large group, so is a horse more likely to have the motivation to approach a novel object if it has bonded with its rider. Safety problems arise when the rider overlooks the fear imperative, especially in a novice horse.

Foraging

So far we have considered the hunters and the hunted, and the social as opposed to the solitary. The enthusiasm animals show towards

Fig. 1.4 Dog scavenging from bins; an example of opportunistic feeding. Reproduced with permission from Sandro Nocentini.

different kinds of food and the ways in which they forage provide a third way of classifying species in terms of how easy or otherwise they are to train. Some eat little except freshly killed meat. They are *obligate carnivores*. In the wild at least, herbivores, such as cattle and horses, eat little except grass. In many species choice of food is even more limited. Well-known examples are the Australian koala and its dependence on the leaves from certain types of gum tree and that of the giant panda and its need for particular varieties of bamboo shoots. At the other end of this scale are the omnivores. These are species that eat a wide range of foodstuffs, but still reject some potential foods as beyond the pale. Primates like ourselves that normally accept a wide range of meats, fruits, seeds and vegetables are one example. Many of the species that have flourished in man-made environments are omnivores.

Many omnivores scavenge. Scavengers can detect and consume carrion, faecal material and vegetable matter. They need to be particularly good at learning to avoid potentially toxic foods. Whether scavengers or not, omnivores seem especially resourceful. Their senses, dentition and digestive system allow them to exploit niches unavailable to the specialised eaters. Rather than concentrating on the detection of predators or prey, these species look for any opportunity to supplement their food input. They are opportunists. Pigs, rats and dogs are among the best examples.

Humans provide opportunities for such scavengers (see Fig. 1.4). The first wolves that ventured into early human encampments were exploiting a novel situation for nutrition. They were the ancestors of domestic dogs. Their boldness was rewarded by the nourishment they found in both food scraps and faeces. Both domestic pigs and domestic dogs still consume human faeces when they can gain access to them. Wild pigs, on the other hand, learn rapidly to avoid humans. They can adapt to human hunting patterns and readily change their daily routines to avoid danger. For example, when feral pigs learn that night is associated with the prevalence of shotgun fire, they lie low during the hours of darkness and reserve their foraging activity for daylight.

In very general terms then, the animals that humans have found most trainable are social rather than solitary, and omnivores rather than specialised feeders. Social animals are more likely to accept a human trainer. Omnivores are more likely to possess a wide range of behaviours that, in the wild, allow them to learn to exploit new opportunities and that, in captivity, can be developed by training. Rats have been found to be a wonderfully useful species in the behavioural laboratory partly because they are a convenient size and easy to maintain, but also because of the exceptionally strong tendencies of this social omnivore to investigate any possible opportunity offered by its environment. When trainers attempt to train any kind of animal using food rewards, essentially they are offering the animal a puzzle to solve and a situation to be exploited.

Biological constraints on learning

We have seen that general aspects of an animal's biology, such as what it eats and how sociable it is, are important for training. There are also some highly specific biological constraints on what an animal can be trained to do. Some have to do with the way it perceives the world. It is easy to forget that few animals rival our primate ability to see the world in terms of myriad objects with highly defined colours and shapes. Other constraints operate on the way an animal can manipulate its world. Most animals have limited ways of altering their physical environment and limited equipment for carrying out these alterations. Few birds can use anything but their beaks to pluck at, move or carry objects. Their feet may provide useful support or locomotion when they are not flying, but, beyond this, their use is normally limited to scratching at the ground or moving small objects around. Members of the crow family and of the parrot family are exceptional in their capacity to use their claws. Both in the wild and in captivity crows have been observed to pull up objects suspended on a string, using a relatively complex set of movements that requires one claw to hold one part of the string while the beak pulls on a lower segment (see Fig. 1.5). Many species of parrots are able to go much further than this, so that their ability to manipulate objects with their claws approaches that of a primate using its hands. In contrast, it is very difficult to train a pigeon to do anything

Fig. 1.5 Caledonian crow using a twig to extract food from a cylinder. This is a rare example of the use of a tool by an animal other than a primate. Reproduced with permission from Alex Kacelnik.

Fig. 1.6 Cat leaping to catch ball of paper. The thrill of another chase is used to reward this cat when it retrieves thrown items.

with its feet but tug and scratch. Over many decades pigeons have taken part in some thousands of experiments on learning. With few exceptions these studies have required the birds to indicate what they have learned by movements of their beaks. It is tempting to attribute more intelligence to an animal that can interact with objects in complicated ways and inspect them visually than to an animal that is limited to pushing and sniffing objects or pecking at them. But, of course, such differences merely indicate that the first animal is more human-like in the way it perceives and manipulates objects in its world.

Animals such as dogs that have evolved to hunt readily learn tasks that are related to hunting strategies, while those that have evolved to escape from predators readily learn behaviours that keep them safe and hidden or in contact with their own species. Traditional training of horses exploits their need to avoid agonistic encounters with their companions and reduce stimuli that are potentially painful or aggressive. Therefore horses can be easily trained to move forward in response to contact from a rider's leg, possibly because they have evolved to associate such close contact with danger. The relative ease of training dogs to retrieve derives from the way they evolved to hunt and return with food to feed others in the pack. The social groupings of wild canids offer useful examples of the ways in which leaders dictate the behaviours of the pack members. This phenomenon helps to explain why, of all the animals featured in this book, dogs are the most likely to be described by their trainers as being 'keen to please'.

A dog can be taught to fetch a stick more easily than can a horse. Primarily this is because retrieving flesh and bones is a canine response that enhances fitness. Wild dogs exploit their hugely distensible stomach by gorging themselves as much as possible at the site of a kill and then gathering the best remnants in their mouths for the journey back to the den. Any offspring back at base benefit from this strategy, as well as from the ability of both parents to regurgitate on demand. Horses have their young with them at all times and have no need to retrieve. Furthermore, they lack the dentition that makes stick-holding easy. As you can see in Fig. 1.7, horses have to clench the cross member of a dumb-bell with their teeth. They cannot rest it behind their canines as dogs can because this space is toothless and sensitive.

It is not all bad news for horse lovers. Equids are more useful than dogs for draught purposes because they have evolved to excel at running away from possible threats. Animals that are fast and yet remain sensitive to incoming stimuli are favoured as carriage horses. They thrive on forward movement as their forebears excelled in escape from predators. These ancestors also needed to detect and act upon signals from other members of the herd, telling them to use speeding up, slowing down or veering as escape strategies.

As we will see in the case study of Kodiak, the sled dog (Case 39), the tendency of dogs to look to the pack leader for direction is something that makes them less than ideal as draught animals. Untrained pet dogs that take their owners for a walk may at first seem to

Fig. 1.7 Marvin, a Welsh cob cross, clenching a dumb-bell in his teeth. Training persistence of this novel behaviour is difficult because holding food items for sustained periods is not part of foraging in equidae.

Fig. 1.8 Three ponies being driven over a jump. A unicorn formation promotes sensitivity to signals from other members of the team. Reproduced with permission from Amanda Saville-Weeks, Chariots of Fire Driving Centre.

contradict this point. One needs to remember, however, that these individuals have learned to ignore the pain of the collar because it reduces their ability to travel in their chosen direction. They may pull but are very difficult to direct. Their regard for the human at the other end of the lead is negligible. (Dogs that pull on leads often have poorly defined hierarchies within their social group, the pack of humans with whom they live.)

Domestication

It is a mistake to believe that only domesticated animals can be trained. Indeed, many domestic animals can be quite resistant to training. Hamsters frequently bite the hand that feeds them, and many cats fail to recognise most commands from their owners. In contrast, wild animals such as whales have been taught to assist people in pursuit of seals and have been rewarded with the tongues of their victims. Also, cheetahs have coursed prey for their noble human owners and zebras have been driven four-in-hand.

Elk were ridden in Sweden and Estonia until AD 1400. Indeed, to this day castrated male elk are used for draught purposes in the Pechero-Ilych National Park in the Urals. Although we label as domestic those animals whose ancestors have been selected for their tolerance of us and their suitability for certain functions, we have tried to tame or train almost any animal we can get close to. A ubiquitous effect of the selective breeding of the animals we call domestic has been a steady reduction in their fear responses towards humans. This has made training easier by reducing the crippling fear responses that some wild animals experience when they are in close proximity to humans. Domesticated animals demonstrate a loss of self-preservation and defence skills in general, and this facilitates their interaction with humans. Some interesting side effects of domestication bear consideration. For example, domestication has been accompanied by

Fig. 1.9 Lord Rothschild's zebras being driven in harness. The partially obscured animal on the left at the front does not appear to be a zebra and so maybe a pony was used to lead the team. Reproduced with permission from Natural History Museum, London, UK.

Fig. 1.10 Unattended donkeys carrying panniers full of building materials from a depot to a building site in India. Food and water are used at either end of the journey to reinforce transit back and forth.

some helpful reproductive changes such as earlier puberty (e.g. in dogs), increased fertility (e.g. in sheep), longer lactation period (e.g. in cattle), loss of broodiness (e.g. in poultry) and a loss of pair bonding (e.g. in ducks). While these changes may help breeders turn over their stock and therefore increase the rate at which they can select for improvements in function, the benefits for the animals themselves seem obscure.

Domestication is also associated with lack of choice and dependence on humans for food, shelter and conspecific company. In a form of compensation, domestication brings freedom from the need to search for food and to avoid predation. However, this means that because they leave animals with 'time on their hands', captive conditions may lend themselves to more exploration of novel situations. Such freedom may ultimately be a source of frustration to animals that are not able to adapt to the time-budgets imposed on them by human managers, and can lead to the development of vacuum periods that have to be filled with some form of behaviour. Some of the behaviours animals adopt for these vacuum periods can compromise their welfare e.g. crib-biting in horses can erode their incisors. In a sense, the imposition of intensive husbandry may suit animals that are not only less emotional and therefore more passive in the presence of humans, but that are less frustrated by sub-optimal conditions. There is evidence that in the dog at least domestication may also have resulted in a reduction in brain size. As we shall see (in Chapter 5), it is difficult to measure whether this has had a deleterious effect on problem-solving ability.

Individual variations in learning

Whether an animal learns a task rapidly depends on its species and often on its own individual history. For example, some species, such as pigs, are opportunists and as such will be predisposed to investigate the training apparatus, while others, such as exotic cats, may forage in response to certain stimuli that are difficult to mimic in captive contexts. Similarly, the appropriate reward for any animal also depends both on its evolutionary history as well as on its lifetime experiences. By the same token, aged mice are not selected because physical deterioration can detract from their physical performance while neural degeneration can affect their learning efficiency.

The speed with which an animal learns a new response may also be influenced by its current hormone concentrations e.g. that may make it intent on breeding rather than feeding. Many laboratory experiments with rats use males exclusively, on the assumption that differences in learning in females may occur depending on the stage of their oestrous cycle. Experimenters seem to fear that data from oestrous females can increase the variability of the results and, therefore, increase the numbers of animals required for a given study. However, careful experiments conducted to measure this effect have failed to find any sex differences in learning.

The evolution of hunting animals such as seals can make them reluctant to work for dead fish, especially when the seal is wild-caught rather than captive bred. A lifetime of being led by humans and waiting for them to deliver food may explain why naivety in horses can enhance their learning to use operanda in the presence of humans. While humans may be motivated to learn by the promise of indirect rewards such as money, or even delayed indirect rewards such as the possibility of promotion, animals generally require more closely linked rewards for their labour - at least to start with.

Much of the behaviour of invertebrates such as insects and also that of many vertebrates such as fish is very rigid, showing little dependence on an individual's experience. Complex patterns are made up of a series of response components that are completely invariant and that are elicited only by certain stimuli. Early in the twentieth century, studies of the courting and parenting behaviour of birds and fish gave rise to the terms *fixed action pattern*, to denote the behavioural unit, and *releasing stimulus*, to denote the highly specific signal that is usually needed to trigger a given unit. For the species usually involved in training programmes, notably mammals, the action patterns tend to be more easily modified by experience. Similarly, the stimuli that release these patterns may vary across individuals as a result of past learning. Human verbal commands can sometimes acquire this function. Particularly when working with birds, certain highly specific stimuli can serve to trigger very rigid behaviours. Even with mammals, certain movements or body postures by a human being, including degree and type of eye contact, can inadvertently serve as threat or submission signals. So, when humans make a play bow or lunge towards a dog they have not met before, they are often able to elicit play. These human movements are the most universally recognised by dogs. The art of training largely consists of knowing how to work with such predictable responses rather than against them. In Chapter 2, we will look at examples of *misbehaviour*, disruption produced by the emergence of such patterns in the course of training.

Responses to novel stimuli

Some of the best-defined behavioural patterns are those that animals display when afraid. All animals display fear of what is new, *neophobia*. When the novel event is very sudden, very loud or very large, the fear response is likely to be intense. Fear can also be evoked by particular stimuli that are neither sudden nor intense. A classic example is the fear response evoked in birds such as chickens by a small, silent overhead silhouette in the shape of a hawk. Fear can also be evoked by otherwise innocuous events that have somehow become associated with pain. As described in Chapter 3, learning theorists have used conditioning methods to examine both how fears can be acquired and also how they can be extinguished. Finally, fear can be transmitted; an animal can learn to be afraid of some object as a result of observing a conspecific display fear towards it (see Social learning, Chapter 2).

Reactions to threat have been termed *species-specific defence reactions*. In the rat a predominant one is to 'freeze', meaning, as the term suggests, that the animal remains standing, totally alert, but motionless. Other fear reactions include 'flight' and 'fight'. Which of these reactions the rat displays on a given occasion is likely to depend on the context. If there is an easy escape route, then flight is most likely. If the space is confined and there is no way out, then the rat is likely to freeze for a length of time, which in research settings is commonly taken as a measure of the intensity of its fear. Whether fighting occurs will depend, of course, on whether there is a potential opponent to hand. These fear reactions are found in other species, as is the rat's tendency to avoid open spaces and stay close to a wall when even just slightly anxious. Because of these fear responses, training a rat to avoid a shock ranges from easy to near impossible. It depends on the avoidance response chosen by the trainer to prevent the occurrence of the shock. If the selected response is compatible with one of the rat's natural responses to fear, then avoidance learning can be very rapid. While training a rat to press a lever for food is straightforward, training lever-pressing as an avoidance response is very difficult. On the other hand training a rat to turn a wheel mounted on a wall to prevent a shock arriving turns out to be very easy, because this avoidance response is compatible with its natural flight response.

Habituation and sensitisation

Defence reactions help an animal to survive surprising or novel stimuli until it can learn how relevant they are. Although a whole range of stimuli can evoke fear responses in an animal, in the great majority of cases the reaction will habituate as the stimulus is repeated. Habituation is a decrease in a response that is produced by repeated presentations of the stimulus that initially evoked the response. It can be seen as the simplest form of learning and has been found in every animal that has been tested, even in species like molluscs that get along in life with little more than a thousand nerve cells. A wild goose's flight response to humans decreases after it turns up from a remote winter feeding ground to spend the summer on a lake in a popular park (see Fig. 1.11). Compared to its behaviour when it first flew in, it soon tolerates people approaching it and eventually almost ignores them. It habituates to the stimuli. Consider a police horse,

Fig. 1.11 Graph of behavioural conflict in a duck as it is influenced by the competing drives to approach and avoid the human.

approach

avoid

Fig. 1.12 Two examples of training that combine habituation with counterconditioning: (a) Stunt pony, Mr Pie, galloping through fire; (b) TV dog, Wally, with his head beside flames. Reproduced with permission from Amanda Saville-Weeks, Chariots of Fire Driving Centre.

such as Star (Case 49), who was gradually exposed to more and more of the potentially frightening stimuli that he would later encounter when out on patrol. The people delivering these stimuli in training were familiar to him and started their disturbances at a considerable distance from him. Only when he was ignoring the rumpus at a certain noise level and a certain distance would these variables be made more threatening. Habituation can lead to impressive ignorance of stimuli that are inherently aversive e.g. to flames (see Figs. 1.12a and 1.12b).

The rate at which habituation occurs depends on several factors. One is the strength and effectiveness of the stimulus that initially evokes the response. As might be expected, the weaker the stimulus, the more rapid is habituation. Less obviously, the number of repetitions needed to reduce a response to a low level depends on how rapidly they occur. For example, sounding a loud noise repeatedly at a fast rate may produce a rapid decrease in the initial fear reaction. However, such habituation can be short lived. If, after some delay, the noise is again repeated, the fear reaction may return. On the other hand presenting the noise the same number of times, but with long intervals between each presentation, may produce less of a decrement in fear for each presentation, but it will have a longer lasting effect. In other words, spontaneous recovery of fear is reduced when *spaced* rather than *massed* exposure is given to the initially frightening event. This is why some farm animals, most notably goats, sometimes overcome their fear of electric fences.

Habituation of fear responses does not always occur. While we have found that laboratory rats will come to tolerate very loud, intermittent noise from a speaker close by within less than 20 exposures, the extreme reactions of some dogs to thunder or the sound of fire crackers appear never to weaken. Indeed, under some conditions repeated exposure to a stimulus can produce a heightened response. Such *sensitisation* is the opposite of habituation in that there is an increase in a response with repeated presentations of the stimulus. This usually happens when an individual cannot escape or make an avoidance response to prevent repeated exposure to a stimulus that is intrinsically unpleasant or aversive. If one recalls the magnified unpleasantness of a dripping tap when searching for sleep, the effect of sensitisation becomes clear. Perhaps repeated exposure to the sound of fingernails scraping across a blackboard would have the same effect?

In contrast to an habituation process, the most unlikely response we can make after sensitisation is to ignore the stimulus. Rather like our response to a dripping tap, we normally look for the source of unpleasant stimuli that we have become sensitised towards and focus on ways to avoid them. Like all of the elephants in our case histories, Raja has been sensitised to the hook. He knows the hook hurts and that his keeper will use it if he does not move away from it. In this way the hook can be used to guide Raja, to move individual limbs, to orchestrate meticulous trunk movements and to protect the keepers from an errant foot.

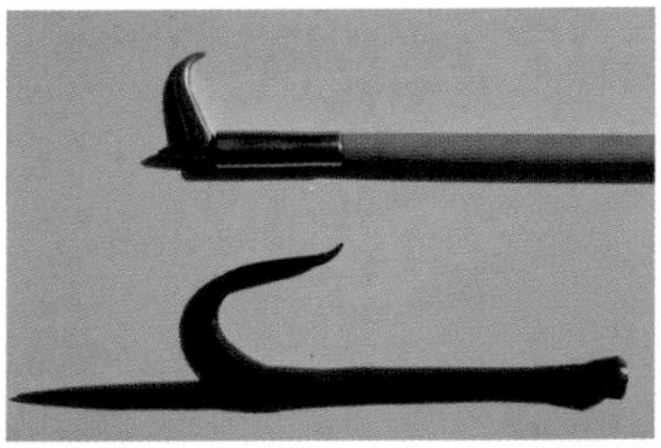

Although research on habituation and sensitisation has concentrated on aversive events, it is clear that these processes also apply to pleasant events. For example, a positive response towards a toy object on the part of a companion animal can often habituate. We may then be tempted to describe the animal as 'bored' with it. In contrast, a well-documented example of sensitisation towards a toy is provided by activity wheels. Certainly in the case of rodents, the more experience they have of running in such a wheel, the more attractive it becomes.

Fig. 1.13 Hooks used in training elephants. The upper one is modern and the lower a traditional hook.

Imprinting

The effects of exposure to certain kinds of stimulation can sometimes be far more dramatic than the examples of habituation and sensitisation we have just given. A generally reliable rule of thumb is that the earlier the experience, the greater its impact on the animal's subsequent behaviour. The best examples of this rule are filial and sexual imprinting.

The essence of filial imprinting has long been recognised. Indeed, Chinese peasants have for centuries used this as a technique to make ducks more effective in the control of snails that otherwise damage rice crops. After exposing ducklings to a special stick until the youngsters show a tendency to follow it, the peasants can then take their brood to the paddy fields as required and, by planting the stick

Fig. 1.14 Konrad Lorenz was the first person to carry out systematic studies of imprinting in young birds. The goslings in this photo are showing a following response to Lorenz's boots. Reproduced with permission from Cambridge University Press.

sequentially in different parts of the plantation, they can ensure that snails in all areas are subjected to predation.

The term 'imprinting' was introduced by Konrad Lorenz, the first person to carry out systematic research on this phenomenon. In what must be the most famous study of animal behaviour of the past 70 years, he compared the behaviour of goslings that after hatching had been isolated from their siblings and mother goose with a group that had had normal post-hatching contact with their conspecifics. The first moving object that the isolated goslings saw was Lorenz. As a result they tended to follow him and would do so even when the opportunity of following a mother goose was presented. Subsequently, the tendency of young animals to form a social bond with anything from some object like a small, moving, noisy toy to an individual from another species has been known as *filial imprinting*. Such a bond is shown not only by a tendency to follow the imprinted object, but also by reduced distress in the presence of the object.

The second important result reported by Lorenz was that when some of his hand-raised birds reached maturity they tended to treat him as a sex object. He noted with some amusement that jackdaws that had imprinted on him would court his favour by presenting him with juicy fresh earthworms and would even attempt to introduce these into his ear holes. However, when not sexually aroused, these birds would happily join other jackdaws in flight. Since then, the influence of early experience on the sexual preference of the adult has been known as *sexual imprinting*.

Lorenz went on to make very strong claims for the generality and unique properties of imprinting. However, his choice of geese was critical for many of the findings he reported. The effects of some brief early experience are rarely as dramatic in other species. Imprinting, as described by Lorenz, is most often seen in *precocial* birds; that is, in birds like geese, ducks and chickens that move around and

Fig. 1.15 Apparatus used to test filial imprinting in ducklings to some arbitrary moving object. By recording how actively the birds follow an object when its properties are altered, the experimenter can determine which of the object's features the ducklings have imprinted upon. Reproduced with permission from Sandro Nocentini (after Introduction to Animal Behaviour by Manning and Dawkins).

feed within a few hours of hatching. However, since his claims about imprinting have been so influential, we will outline these first, before discussing how they need to be modified.

His theory can be likened to the opening of a window of opportunity early in an individual's development. If the animal's experience is normal while this window is open, then its subsequent behaviour both as an infant and as a sexually mature adult will be normal. Thus, if the gosling is in contact with its mother and siblings during this period, it will subsequently follow her on feeding expeditions, seek her out in times of danger and, as an adult, treat other geese as conspecifics and potential sexual partners. If the infant's experience is abnormal, in that it is deprived of normal contact with its conspecifics when the window is open, then the theory predicts that the animal will never behave in a way that is completely normal for its species.

Central to Lorenz's theory was the concept of a sharply defined *critical period*, a window that is abruptly opened wide and later just as rapidly closed. For example, in ducks the period from one to three days after hatching is when the 'following response' by hitherto isolated birds is most easily established. Laboratory experiments testing for such critical periods have used some arbitrary moving object such as a plastic cup rather than the rubber boot that Lorenz's goslings learned to follow. A second claim is that during an individual's development there is only one such window. Other claims are that imprinting is self-terminating and that the effects of what happens during this period are *irreversible*. This means, for example, that once imprinting has occurred to the rubber boot there is no longer a possibility for further imprinting onto other objects, even onto a fellow goose if, a little later, one should pass by for the first time. The theory also implies that whatever the animal experiences during the rest of its life will modify very little the effects of imprinting in its youth. This explains why the jackdaw that imprints on Lorenz would never find another jackdaw quite as sexy.

Lorenz's work inspired a large amount of important research on the effects of early experience. As usually happens, the results have challenged the theory that we have just described in somewhat over-simplified terms. The most important conclusion to draw from these subsequent studies is that there is enormous variation across species in the way that early experience can affect development. In general, filial behaviour, species recognition and mate choice are determined to a far greater degree by the genes than by early experience. For animals that have no contact with conspecifics in infancy, such as parasite birds like cuckoos, choice of a mate has to be entirely dependent on inherited processes that allow them to recognise their own species.

Ducks have been among the favourites for recent research on imprinting and come as close as any species to confirming the original claims made by Lorenz. However, compared to the results he reported for geese, even those for ducks are different. For example, innate factors and what the duckling hears while still in its egg turn out to be extremely important for its behaviour after hatching. Thus, if 24 hours *before* it hatches a duckling is played a duck contentment call, when tested after hatching it will be strongly attracted to a loudspeaker emitting duck calls. Most importantly, it has turned out that critical periods are never very clearly defined; instead, windows tend to open and close quite slowly, and are not always tightly shut thereafter. Furthermore, imprinting is not necessarily self-terminating; thus, a following response that develops first to a relatively weak stimulus may later also develop to a second, stronger stimulus. Initial exposure to a quiet moving plastic cup will not prevent the later development of bonding with a duck-like object emitting duck-like sounds. Many researchers have argued that it is better to abandon the concept of a critical period and instead think of behavioural development in terms of gradual changes in sensitivity to particular kinds of experience.

Another important finding is that such *sensitive phases* usually occur at different stages of development. In general, sexual imprinting occurs at a later stage than filial imprinting. The most extreme example of sexual imprinting that has been studied extensively is that of the male zebra finch. Experiments in which these birds have been fostered by a related species, the Bengalese finch, and then returned to their own species, have found that they will show a lifelong preference for courting Bengalese over zebra finch females, even if they have at some previous stage mated with zebra finches. Such results are, however, rare. This degree of sexual imprinting is not found, for example, even when male Bengalese finches are fostered by zebra finches.

Examples of imprinting as first defined by Lorenz have been difficult to find among mammals. This may be partly because it is harder to identify the critical stimuli. For birds, as for humans, vision and hearing are the most important senses for learning about our social and physical environments, while for most mammals the important sense is smell. A good example of filial imprinting comes from a species of shrew. If a young shrew is fostered during the period

8–14 days after birth, it will subsequently follow a cloth smelling of its foster mother and ignore its biological mother and siblings. Similarly, in some species of mice individuals that have been exposed to a distinctive smell early in development prefer sexual partners with this smell. In precocial mammals, such as sheep or goats, olfaction plays an important role in the acceptance of newborns by the mothers. A nanny will butt and drive away a newborn kid that attempts to suckle, if it carries an odour label signalling that it has already been licked or suckled by another nanny.

Fig. 1.16 Woman wearing a latex hat incorporating super stimuli, evocative of a giant cloaca, that, in combination with characteristic vocalisations, provoke sexual advances and ultimately ejaculation into the depressions in the back of the hat by abnormally imprinted falcons.

Early experience

As with many birds, very young mammals show great distress when alone in an unknown place, but are not frightened by new objects or individuals. As they grow they become more wary of unfamiliar things. This can rapidly develop into full-blown neophobia towards a new object that, if it had been introduced some days earlier, they might have approached. The onset of distress at being placed alone in a strange place often marks the beginning of the period in which rapid socialisation can take place. The later onset of fear of new objects or individuals usually heralds the end of this period, as the young animal becomes more likely to flee than to approach. While a two-day-old duckling placed in a new environment will try to stay close to the equally new, moving toy that is also placed there, a five-day-old will retreat from the toy in apparent terror. However, if there is no escape, its fear will habituate and this older duckling may start to form an attachment towards the toy.

Much the same process has been found for dogs. However, unlike the duckling, being altricial rather than precocial, a puppy is blind and unable to move around for the first few weeks of life. Consequently, there is a much later start to the period during which rapid socialisation can occur in the dog. It begins only when perceptual and motor abilities have matured and lasts a lot longer than the equivalent period for the duck. An influential study of the development of dog–human bonding allowed pups minimal contact with humans, except for a week in which they received three thirty-minute periods of intensive interaction every day. Groups of pups received this special week of treatment at different ages. A handling test given to all animals when they reached 14 weeks of age revealed that the week of human contact had been very effective at making pups sociable with humans, so long as the pups were over two weeks old when treated. Animals that had not been socialised before their test at 14 weeks were very difficult to handle. Depending on the breed, it is around this age that strange individuals come to evoke strong defence reactions, whether flight or attack. Beyond this age, dogs isolated from human contact resemble wild-caught wolves in that persuading them to cope with humans is a slow process of habituation. As with any wild animal this can lead to acceptance of humans, but rarely the close bond that can be formed during infancy.

A social bond between dogs and non-dogs need not, of course, involve humans. Pups isolated from other dogs at four weeks of age and then given minimal human contact have developed attachment to a rabbit companion. Just seeing and smelling a rabbit was sufficient for this to occur, but being able to interact with it produced an even stronger bond. (Incidentally, such interactions were not a great experience for most of the rabbits.) There was no sign in this study that the pups' experience with rabbits had any effect on their behaviour when subsequently reintroduced to other dogs. One of the dogs' many virtues as companions and working animals is that strong bonds with other dogs do not preclude strong attachment to humans, or vice versa.

The dog–rabbit study illustrates general principles of behavioural development, including that of *developmental homeostasis*. This concept is partly based on studies indicating that the otherwise devastating and permanent effects of extended isolation early in the life of a social animal can often be prevented by quite limited contact with other individuals, even ones from another species. Dogs reared in complete isolation for a long period show abnormal social and sexual behaviour thereafter. Yet, just two twenty-minute periods of social contact per week can be sufficient for a pup to develop into a relatively normal

Fig. 1.17 Rats in a standard group housing cage (a) do not have opportunities for the range of activities possible in an enriched environment (b). Reproduced with permission from Darek Figa.

dog. Studies from the 1940s deprived rhesus monkeys of contact with their mother or any other monkey shortly after birth. Extended social isolation in infancy was found to result in lifelong abnormalities of behaviour. However, when such isolated infants had been allowed occasional play periods with their peers, their behaviour as adults appeared normal.

Developmental homeostasis guards only against gross abnormality. When sensitive measures of the social behaviour of rhesus monkeys are used, it turns out that even brief periods in which an infant monkey is separated from its mother and its troop can cause long-lasting disruption. Dogs that are reared and housed together within the same small compound from birth and given minimal custodial care for some months can display what has been called the 'kennel-dog' syndrome. It is easy to spot the difference between a pup that has been reared in the relatively barren environment of a breeding kennel with one that has spent this period in a busy household with other dogs, cats, children, vacuum cleaners and the generally unexpected. 'Kennel dogs' can remain forever fearful and difficult to train. As concluded by John Scott, who spent decades studying the behaviour of dogs, the kennel-dog syndrome, like the isolation syndrome, is largely produced by emotional disturbances which result from a sudden change into an unfamiliar situation for which there has been no preparation in early life'.

Even when domesticated, all former prey species require tact and patience to reduce flight responses, and generally the earlier handling and habituation to humans can take place, the better. Just how early this handling should be is the subject of some debate. Sight, sound and olfactory cues are all employed to ensure that the young animal learns the characteristics of its mother during an early 'sensitive period'. For horses, the time for bonding is the first 48 hours of life when foals learn to follow their mothers who in turn develop a virtually exclusive attachment to their offspring. Some horse breeders advocate the benefits of thorough handling of new born foals, arguing that stimuli that youngsters are exposed to during

Fig. 1.18 Pups learning to socialize with other dogs at puppy preschool. Reproduced with permission from Sandro Nocentini.

an early sensitive period will be accepted as 'normal'. However, care should be taken not to adversely affect the formation of the mare–foal bond during the first days of life. A similar degree of handling of an older foal may be just as effective, although perhaps more difficult as it becomes larger, stronger and more dangerous. It is only recently that sustained research has been conducted on the effects of handling on learning abilities of horses. Results have been mixed but suggest that early handling before 42 days of age improves manageability. Having said that, there is no good evidence that additional human handling or stimulation improves the speed or accuracy of learning.

In many mammalian species there can be an immense difference between an adult whose infancy was spent in a restricted, unchanging setting with limited social contact and one whose infancy included exposure to a broad range of different social and physical settings. Unless times are hard, in most mammalian and some bird species young individuals living in their natural environment spend a great deal of time in play. Although it is difficult to specify the benefits precisely, play clearly does more than promote physical development and perceptual-motor co-ordination. It may enhance social skills, increase emotional stability and improve cognitive ability. When chimpanzees were tested on the classic problem of using a rake to obtain a highly desirable banana that was otherwise out of reach, only individuals with prior experience of playing with sticks solved the problem. Studies of rats raised in enriched cages have shown how beneficial complex environments can be for their ability to learn. However, it is difficult to decide whether these benefits result directly from the extra sensory experience such environments provide, relative to the unchanging simplicity of the home cages most laboratory rats live in, or from the fact that rats play much more in enriched environments.

In conclusion, the instincts that characterise the behaviour of an adult animal of a given species can depend on the occurrence of certain kinds of experience during the individual's development. In natural settings with rich social and physical environments, such critical experience is usually guaranteed to occur. We are able to modify such instincts for human purposes, especially when the animal is still young. In some species there are fairly well-defined windows of opportunity for socialising an animal. Such windows typically begin to close when fear of new objects becomes well developed. In precocial species, such as the horse, there may be lifelong effects from thorough handling of a foal during the first 48 hours of its life. Some of these effects are universally welcome. Others are regarded by traditional horse folk as leading to later insensitivity to some stimuli. With dogs, as already mentioned, the best opportunity for getting them to accept humans as conspecifics is from three to ten weeks. With cats it is a little earlier, from two to seven weeks. The crucial difference between feral and domestic cats is their lack of exposure to human shapes, sounds, movements and smells during this period. Fostering feral kittens over seven weeks of age is largely a fruitless task. The same is true of the exotic cats we encounter in Case studies 25 and 26. More generally, whatever the species, the greater the variety of physical and social stimulation an animal is given from the time it can perceive and move about in its world, the more likely it is to develop into an emotionally stable, trainable and contented adult.

Chapter 2

Learning theory and positive reinforcement

According to tradition there are two ways to change the behaviour of a donkey: use a carrot or a stick. In this chapter we look at various ways behaviour can be modified by the use of carrots or, in the language of contemporary learning theory, *positively reinforcing* events. Given the appropriate motivational state, access to food, water, sex, play, liberty, sanctuary and companionship can all be effective *primary* positive reinforcers. In addition, there are *secondary* reinforcers whose effectiveness depends on their association with primary reinforcers. In Chapter 3 we turn to the complementary set of principles from learning theory that can be applied to behaviour modification based on aversive events, ones comparable to striking with a stick.

Because the final three chapters examine the behaviour of many different species and include interviews with numerous trainers, an important step is to establish a common language for all cases. Barriers to human learning often arise because of a lack of clarity in the definition of terms. During research for this book, it became clear that many excellent trainers are confused about the terms used in what is called learning theory. Since one of our chief goals is to demystify animal training, it is crucial that we agree on the meanings of words, especially technical jargon. This will allow us to consider principles in animal training from a rigorous perspective. For those who might be interested, vernacular terms used by various kinds of professional trainers are included in the glossary at the end of this book. The glossary also contains important technical terms from learning theory.

The definition of learning

Broadly speaking, a stimulus is any change in the environment that can be detected by an animal's sense organs. A response is any behaviour or physiological event. As discussed in Chapter 1, animals have innate or instinctive responses to stimuli. Examples of innate responses include the way newborn mammals move under the influence of tactile and olfactory gradients to find nipples and the way squirrels bury their food when periods of daylight shorten. Learning can be defined as the process whereby experience produces a relatively permanent change in the response to a stimulus. This broad definition encompasses the relatively simple kinds of learning, such as habituation, that were described in Chapter 1. It also includes the acquisition of knowledge, as in *knowing that* two events tend to go together, *knowing where* important places are located in an animal's territory or *knowing when* important events happen. Other kinds of learning underlie changes in habits or the acquisition of skills, as in *knowing how* to move a latch so that a door opens or to send a signal that results in the companion animal's owner opening the door. Whether any animal ever *knows why* a particular event happened is a question we leave until the chapter on animal intelligence (Chapter 4).

Not all changes in behaviour are a consequence of learning. Behaviour can change due to motivational factors, physiological variables or fatigue. A thirsty horse that drinks despite having refused water five hours earlier has changed its behaviour but is not considered to have learned anything in the interim. Instead its motivation to drink has changed as a result of shifts in variables such as blood volume and the concentration of sodium in body fluids. Meanwhile fatigue can change behaviour, transforming a playful kitten into a snoozing ball of fluff, but its effects cannot be described as relatively permanent, whereas they can if a behaviour is learned.

Because the definition of learning has experience as a prerequisite, it excludes permanent changes in behaviour resulting from maturation or debility. So, when male puppies progress from squatting to leg cocking, they have not learned that this new posture elevates the smelly signal they leave for others but are simply maturing and responding to the same increased levels of circulating testosterone that cause them to scrape the ground after elimination. The aged Red

Fig. 2.1 Dog scraping the ground after defaecation. This post-elimination behaviour of mature dogs, especially males, is believed to leave olfactory signals (from glands in the footpads) and some visual evidence of their presence. It is interesting to note that this behaviour, along with various grooming responses, is difficult to train. With permission from Sandro Nocentini.

Deer stag whose roar is ever weaker during the mating season has not learned that the females are unimpressed. Rather the old muscles in his rib cage and belly are beginning to give up the ghost and therefore his vocalisations demonstrate less biological fitness than those of younger, stronger competitors.

Instead of relying solely on invariant behaviour patterns for survival, animals living in changing environments thrive if they are able to respond to change. Learning allows animals to use information about the world to tailor their responses to environmental change. What is pleasant for an animal is generally something that has promoted the survival of its ancestors' genes; what is unpleasant or disgusting is generally something that has put its ancestors' reproductive success at risk. The simplest kinds of animals may possess a limited range of responses, but all show approach towards positive stimuli and withdrawal from those that are potentially harmful. Crucially, such approach and withdrawal responses can often be modified by learning. Invertebrates such as flies, slugs and ants approach stimuli they have learned to associate with positive events and withdraw from those associated with negative events. There are only a few steps of extra complexity between these examples of a simple kind of learned behaviour and that of a commercial broiler chicken that prefers to consume food that contains analgesics presumably because it ameliorates the pain caused by chronic leg weakness.

Animals learn to pick up the slightest cues that alert them to the possibility of a reward. Those in close contact with humans often use the cues that we provide. Seagulls follow trawlers and ploughs with slavish devotion because the activity of either is so regularly associated with a free lunch. Some dogs learn that a trip in the car to the park always ends with the sound of the indicator. This may lead the over-excitable pet to vocalise his excitement every time the driver indicates an imminent change of direction. Similarly cats can learn to associate the sound of a busy tin-opener with their supper but then generalise their response. These are the characters who come running whenever their owner opens a tin of beans. Trainers need to remember that their animals may be alert to - and learn about - many subtle stimuli that have been included quite accidentally within a training programme. For example, obedience-trained dogs that have associated the sound of a choke chain with accurate heel-work may be rather less polished when they know the chain is ineffective - for instance when the lead is not attached.

Quite independently of our deliberate intentions, animals can learn things for themselves in many different ways. As most vets will confirm, fear of needles is something that can be learned very readily. It pays to consider why any animal should ever enjoy a visit to a veterinary clinic. There, the practitioner might manipulate a sore foot until the seat of pain is identified, look down an ear with an auriscope or perform a *per rectum* examination. Apart from the occasional friendly face in the waiting room, there is little that can make the visit a positive learning experience. Dogs learn to mistrust the

Fig. 2.2 (a) Over some decades an increasing number of individuals in a troop of Japanese macaques acquired the habit of washing the sweet potatoes they were given. Although the results of this study had been long accepted as indicating social learning of this behaviour, this claim has been recently queried. Reproduced with permission from Kyoto University Library. (b) A classic example of behaviour that has been spread by social transmission is that of blue tits pecking through the tops of milk bottles to get at the cream. Reproduced with permission from Frank Lane Picture Agency. (c) Rhesus monkey displaying fear for the first time towards a snake-like object after it has watched another monkey showing fear of a snake. Reproduced with permission from Susan Mineka.

smell of the waiting room, while cats may learn to make themselves scarce as soon as their travelling cage is produced.

Social learning

Humans are unusual in their tendency to teach – or train – children and animals in a deliberate way. Indeed, because he sees us as the only species that spends years intentionally passing on information to others, Anthony Barnett has dubbed us *Homo docens* – the teaching ape. It is not clear that there is any other species in which one individual deliberately instructs another. Nonetheless, learning from observation of other individuals is by no means confined to humans. Animals from some species can learn a great deal from each other, a strategy that avoids the costs associated with their own trial and error learning. Fear, for example, can be highly contagious. Monkeys can acquire a fear of snakes simply as a result of watching a video in which another monkey reacts fearfully to a snake. Birds that see a member of their species reacting fearfully to a novel object will learn to mob that object even though they have had no direct experience of it causing a threat (see Fig. 2.3).

More common than the social transmission of food avoidance is that of food selection. For example, in the 1930s in the UK milk delivered to the doorstep started to arrive in bottles with shiny aluminium tops. Within a short period a small bird, the blue tit, learned to peck through these tops to reach the milk. Once a few individuals had learned this independently, the practice rapidly spread via a process known as social transmission to almost the entire population of blue tits in the UK. It is not clear whether this happened as a result of tits learning the trick by watching expert birds perform, that is, by *social learning*. An alternative possibility is that it happened less directly as a result of one individual setting up an occasion that made it easier for the next to learn; for example, by punching a hole in a bottle top that enabled another to reach the cream. Nonetheless, an important role for social learning has often been confirmed. Rats can learn to avoid food giving off a smell that they have detected on the breath of others, if these experienced consumers have been seen to fall ill after returning to the group from a foraging session containing the novel food.

It is important to avoid confusing social learning with the less complex phenomenon of social facilitation, which is the effect one animal can have on others of its species simply by interacting with a resource. An example is when the sight of a chicken pecking at grains on the ground prompts observing chickens to do the same thing even though they may be very well fed and so not especially hungry.

In the absence of any such social transmission of information, learning is based on first-hand experience. To train an animal we normally create an environment and contingencies - relationships between events in that environment - that allow it to learn the target behaviour. When novice plough-horses are harnessed alongside older 'schoolmasters' or young foxhounds are 'coupled' (chained) with older members of a pack, they learn not so much by observation as by having to respond appropriately to avoid discomfort (see Fig. 2.4). Expecting an animal to acquire some behaviour simply as a result of observing members of its own species, let alone by observing human performance, will almost always lead to disappointment.

Associative learning

Almost all forms of training depend on the animal learning associations between particular events. The idea of association can be traced back at least until 350 BC when the Greek philosopher, Aristotle, discussed various principles of association. The most important of these, he suggested, was contiguity, meaning closely touching. He suggested that the more closely two events occur together, the more likely will the thought of one lead to the thought of the other. The links do not have to be made with any logic. When we memorise poetry we see an example of the effect of contiguity. Even a list of nonsense words can become associated so that immediately adjacent items prompt memories of each other. An association between two things can be based on either spatial or temporal contiguity, or both. A dog may associate his bowl with food by their spatial contiguity and the sound of the doorbell with the arrival of visitors by temporal contiguity.

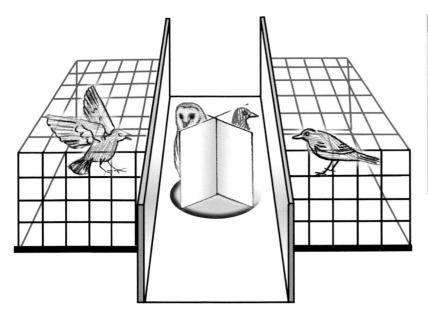

Fig. 2.3 Many small birds will learn to mob a potential predator after seeing a conspecific do so. Apparatus of the kind shown here has been used in experiments that found birds would acquire a mobbing response to an entirely arbitrary object if they were unable to see the object that was evoking mobbing in the 'demonstrator'. Reproduced with permission from Sandro Nocentini.

Over the centuries following Aristotle, many other influential philosophers discussed the principles of association. But it was not until towards the end of the nineteenth century that anyone thought to study them in a systematic way. This research began with experiments on human memory. By the turn of the century the first experiments were carried out on how associations are acquired by animals. At almost the same time, but quite independently, an already famous Russian physiologist, Ivan Pavlov, and a then unknown American student of psychology, Edward Thorndike, carried out the first experiments on learning in animals. As described below, they used quite different approaches and their research provided the basis for what became known as classical and instrumental conditioning, where 'conditioning' refers to a type of learning in which the timing of events is particularly important.

Conditioning can be viewed in two ways. From one perspective it provides a set of techniques for modifying an individual's behaviour. From the other perspective conditioning is a powerful way of studying the nature of associative learning. Over the twentieth century,

Fig. 2.4 Two examples of the strategic use of trained conspecifics in behaviour modification of young working animals: (a) hounds coupled together; and (b) a young horse harnessed with a mature team. Reproduced with permission from Les Holmes.

conditioning research has largely taken place in psychology laboratories. Unlike the research described in Chapter 1, conditioning studies have rarely had the aim of understanding a particular species' behaviour in terms of its ecology or evolutionary history. Instead, the aim has been to find general principles of learning and behaviour that apply across species - including our own - and are independent of variations in stimuli, responses and reinforcing events. As a result, the majority of such studies have used a limited number of species, predominantly rats and pigeons. This has not been because these species have been seen as especially interesting, but rather because they have been viewed as representative, as well as cheap and easy to house and to handle. The strategy of testing a few species over a small range of experimental conditions has turned out to be a successful one both for uncovering general laws of learning and for developing principles of training that apply to all species over a very wide range of conditions.

Classical conditioning

Like many other physiologists of his era, Pavlov studied dogs in order to understand how bodies in general work - including human bodies. During the first half of a very long research career he studied digestion. In 1904 he was awarded a Nobel Prize for this work, the first Russian to gain this honour. By then, however, he had completely switched the direction of his research to what later would be called the neurophysiology of learning. The cause of this change was a phenomenon that Pavlov and his co-workers initially regarded as an obstacle to the study of digestion and then began to see as interesting in its own right. Many of the experiments involved measuring stomach 'juices' as a function of the kind of food a dog was given. When a dog was tested regularly day after day, a complicating factor entered into these functions: digestive juice would begin to flow out of a surgically constructed hole in the stomach as soon as the research assistant approached and well before any food entered the dog's mouth. It seemed that the physiological reaction could be triggered by an association between the arrival of the assistant and the delivery of food. Pavlov and his students eventually realised that this 'psychic reflex' provided a means for studying the formation of associations. An experimental procedure was developed in which to signal the arrival of food various stimuli were selected - the sound of a metronome, visual signals, pressure pads on the dog's body - that were easier to control than the entry of an assistant. At the same time measurement of secretion from the salivary glands replaced digestive juice production as a response. Using this basic procedure over the first three decades of the twentieth century Pavlov laid the foundations for the study of associative learning in animals, becoming more famous for this than for his long forgotten studies of digestion. Although we refer here to the type of learning he studied as classical

Fig. 2.5 In this photograph from 1927 Ivan Pavlov watches his research assistant, Maria Petrova, as she carries out a conditioning experiment. Reproduced with permission from Sovfoto.

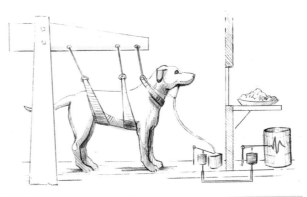

Fig. 2.6 This diagram shows the essential components of apparatus used in Pavlov's laboratory to study salivary conditioning. The experimenter hidden behind the screen can present various stimuli prior to making the meat powder container accessible to the dog. Saliva produced by the stimuli flows through a tube to a device that measures how many drops. Reproduced with permission from Sandro Nocentini.

conditioning, many learning theorists still refer to it as Pavlovian conditioning.

A typical classical conditioning study starts with a neutral stimulus, one having little effect on the animal, and presents this *conditioned stimulus* (CS) repeatedly, and closely followed each time by an *unconditioned stimulus* (US) such as food. Conditioning is said to have occurred when the CS comes to evoke consistently some response, the *conditioned response* (CR) that is related to the US (see Case 44). The term 'conditioned stimulus' derives from a mistranslation into English of Pavlov's original term, '*conditional* stimulus'. The reason for his term was the early finding that the effects of classical conditioning were not irreversible, but rather the ability of a CS to elicit a conditioned response was *conditional* on the continued pairing of the CS with the US. In Pavlov's experiments a buzzer, the CS, that did little when first heard except make the dog prick up its ears, would come to elicit salivation, the CR, after it had been paired many times with meat powder, the US. If the buzzer was no longer followed by the meat powder, it became progressively less effective in eliciting saliva. Crucially, in classical conditioning a CS such as the sound of a buzzer is followed by a US such as food, regardless of what the animal does when it hears the buzzer. The arrival of food is independent of responding. Thus, classical conditioning refers to the process by which an animal learns to associate events over which it has no control. Such learning enables it to predict the occurrence of events in its environment and adapt to them before they happen.

Since Pavlov's time a wide variety of procedures has been used to study classical conditioning. In fact, it is many decades since any researcher employed the conditioned salivation procedure that Pavlov invented. One example of a very different procedure is employed with male quail. In this case the CS is a light and the US is the opening of a window that allows the male subject to see a female. Once switching on the light has been followed several times by opening the window, the male begins to approach the light and to make courtship displays before the window opens.

Outside the laboratory there are many examples demonstrating the role of classical conditioning in learning about sex. Stallions get aroused when they hear the sound of the bridle used to control them in the service pen. Dog breeders capitalise on a similar effect to ensure reliable performance of stud dogs. If they adopt the same routine before taking the dog to the same room prior to every mating, these stimuli produce conditioned sexual arousal. Mohan, the Bengal tiger showcased in the chapter on exotic animals (Case 25), has been used for semen collection and as a result shows an interesting example of this sort of conditioning. On a number of occasions the tiger was exposed to an artificial vagina held in place by Andy, his intrepid trainer. By the end of the breeding season it was clear that Mohan was becoming sexually aroused by the sight of Andy and his latex device.

Another practical example of classical conditioning is seen in cows that release milk when they hear calves calling because they have formed an association between this sound and subsequent suckling of teats. An analogous effect occurs on dairy farms. Initially, the unconditioned stimulus of being milked by a human is needed to produce a milk let-down response. However, with repetition simply being in the milking parlour or sometimes even the collecting yard can cause the milk to begin to drip or even squirt out. The milk let-down shown by dairy cows when they hear the milking apparatus shows that this sound can also become a conditioned stimulus.

A particularly useful variant of classical conditioning is called *counter conditioning*. This refers to a procedure that changes an aversive or noxious stimulus into one that is positive for the animal. The

Fig. 2.7 Two examples of a classical conditioning: a) a Brown Swiss cow in a collecting yard releasing milk in response to the sound of vacuum pumps in the milking parlour; and b) a racehorse conditioned to urinate on straw (and thus provide a urine sample for drug surveillance) in response to whistling by a groom.

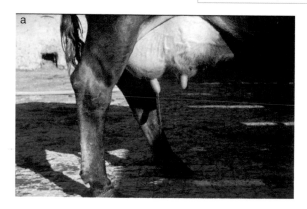

first known example comes from Pavlov's lab. He used a mild electric shock, which initially elicited signs of pain, as a conditioned stimulus. After the shock had been paired repeatedly with food, it came to elicit salivation and there was no sign that it was painful anymore. Counter conditioning can be very useful in animal behaviour therapy and in getting animals to accept painful therapeutic interventions. The condor shown in Fig. 2.8 provides an example of the success of a counter conditioning procedure.

Some of Pavlov's very early experiments confirmed the importance of Aristotle's principle of temporal contiguity. The development of conditioned salivation to a buzzer was much faster if the onset of the buzzer preceded the delivery of meat powder by a few seconds than if the *inter-stimulus interval*, the gap between the two events, were longer. Temporal contiguity has turned out to be a general principle that applies to all forms of classical conditioning. However, the length of the inter-stimulus interval that is optimal for obtaining a conditioned response can vary widely, depending on the species and the nature of the target response. At one extreme is eye blink conditioning. This can be produced by sounding a click before delivering a puff of air to the eye. The best interval for this is about half a second. With a delay between the click and the puff of more than a second or so, it becomes very difficult to get a conditioned blink to the click. On the other hand an interval of several seconds from the onset of a light or sound to the arrival of food to a hungry animal or water to a thirsty one can still allow strong conditioning to these stimuli.

In signal approach learning an animal shows an increasing tendency to approach a localised visual signal if this signal is presented prior to the delivery of food or some other positive reinforcer. This effect is called *sign tracking*. Typically birds are used in such experiments and it is found that they tend to peck at such signals (see Fig. 2.7), an effect known as *autoshaping*. Systematic studies of autoshaping in pigeons have found that strong conditioned pecking can be obtained with intervals of many seconds between the time that a light is switched on behind a translucent response key and the delivery of grain. The optimal interval, however, depends on the interval between trials (as distinct from the interval between stimuli). Thus, if trials occur in rapid succession, it is best to use short intervals – say, around two to four seconds – between the stimulus and the reinforcer. When long inter-trial intervals are used – say, several minutes between the last grain delivery and the next time the light is switched on – an interval of 15 seconds or more between the light onset and the grain can still be very effective.

Fig. 2.8 This condor has been conditioned to place his head in the palm of a gloved hand to be fed. This allows the keeper to administer drops into his eye to treat a chronic disorder.

Impediments to learning

An important feature of classical conditioning is that it is selective. This means that as one particular stimulus, say a buzzer, becomes strongly associated with some important event, such as food, this

Fig. 2.9 Autoshaping a chicken: In experiments designed to determine the degree to which chickens can predict time spans, birds can be trained to expect food rewards after a certain time has elapsed. In the process of shaping the final behaviour, the trainer displayed a dot on the computer screen and then regardless of the bird's behaviour, delivered food down the sloping feed trough after five seconds.

a. Chicken stands in front of computer monitor
b. Waiting for the dot to appear on the screen
c. When the dot appears, the chicken pecks the screen
d. And takes the reinforcer (a poultry pellet) from the hopper.

weakens the associations between other stimuli and food. An example that can be important in training is *overshadowing*. A trainer may intend that the animal learns to associate a certain word with food or with an appropriate response. However, if the spoken word is always accompanied by an unintended hand gesture or body movement, the latter may become the effective conditioned stimulus instead. In other words, the body language signals have overshadowed the spoken signal or command. Consequently, they need either to become the cue in the trainer's mind or to be made less effective by making them less salient or more variable. A very similar example of selective learning is *blocking*. If a stimulus has already become a good signal for a reinforcer, learning about a second stimulus that accompanies the first is retarded or blocked. In the above example, if a hand signal on its own has already become a strong conditioned stimulus, then addition of a verbal command on later occasions, made at the same time as the hand signal, is likely to remain ineffective. Blocking and overshadowing impede training programmes, so good trainers are careful to make sure that only the intended stimulus can serve as a signal to the animal.

Another pervasive characteristic of classical conditioning is that associations between two events are more rapidly acquired if the events are novel. If an animal is exposed to a conditioned stimulus for a number of trials before the conditioning procedure commences, i.e. before it is paired with the US, the acquisition of a conditioned response to that stimulus will be slow. It is as if the animal has simply learned to ignore the stimulus because it has no important consequences. The retardation of learning produced by stimulus pre-exposure is called *latent inhibition*.

As we have seen earlier, Pavlov found that, if a CS such as the sound of a metronome was paired with food as a US, it would continue to make the dog salivate just as long as the CS continued to be followed by the arrival of food. If the metronome was sounded again and again but food no longer arrived, then the process of *extinction* resulted in the disappearance of salivation to the tone. Extinction applies to all the examples of classical conditioning given here. The animal, or person, eventually stops blinking to the click if this is no longer followed by the air puff. The pigeon that has been pecking a lit response key at a rate of two or three pecks a second will soon start to slow down when grain is no longer presented.

All of the above are possibilities that weaken desirable associations and therefore can compromise training programmes. In summary, they demonstrate how inconsistency impedes training.

Instrumental conditioning with positive reinforcement

In 1898, while Pavlov in St Petersburg was still regarding psychic reflexes as an obstacle to the study of digestion, Edward Thorndike in New York was awarded a Ph.D. in psychology for a thesis titled 'Animal intelligence'. This reported the results of a series of experiments on learning in chicks, dogs and cats. Thorndike used mazes to study learning in his chicks. For his dogs and cats he constructed a set of what he called 'puzzle boxes'. The puzzle for these animals

Fig. 2.10 A cat in one of Thorndike's puzzle boxes had no way of knowing what particular response would open the door and allow it to reach the food outside. It could learn what to do only by 'trial-and-error with accidental success'. The response shown here is to pull on a loop hanging from above, but Thorndike obtained the same pattern of results from almost all of the various responses he tried. Reproduced with permission from Sandro Nocentini.

was to find a way of opening the door to reach the food just outside. For one animal the required response might be to pull at a loop of cord in a corner and for another to depress a panel on the floor. After the successful response was made and the food outside collected, the experience was repeated some time later. No matter what response was chosen the result was essentially the same. On the first trial the time from being placed in the puzzle box to when the cat or dog stumbled on the effective response was very long. Over many such trials this time progressively, but somewhat erratically, decreased until the animal performed the response smoothly and with hardly a delay. By plotting these times on a graph Thorndike produced the first learning curves. Because no animal showed an abrupt change from poor to good performance that might have indicated understanding of the task, Thorndike referred to this kind of learning as 'trial-and-error learning with accidental success'. At the time it was widely believed that animals need to understand a problem in order to solve it and that species varied greatly in their ability to reason. In a deliberately provocative manner, Thorndike proposed that all animal intelligence was based on trial-and-error learning and that the capacity for such learning varied very little from species to species.

In Thorndike's puzzle boxes the animal performed a response (e.g. pulling) and obtained a reward (liberty and food) (see Case 24). Unlike the classical conditioning procedure introduced by Pavlov, whether and when a reward occurred in a puzzle box depended on the animal's behaviour. The effect of the reward strengthened the correct response. This is known as *reinforcement*. The term reinforcement refers to the process by which the frequency (or probability) of a particular behaviour increases when a reinforcer follows that behaviour. A piece of carrot functions as a reinforcer if it is given to the donkey each time the animal moves forward and if, as a result, the donkey's speed increases. In general, the kind of learning that is produced by a response–reinforcer relationship – or *contingency* – is now called *instrumental conditioning* since it applies to any procedure in which a response is 'instrumental' in obtaining a reinforcer.

In contrast, a carrot dangled in front of the donkey, but always just out of reach, may function as a lure or 'bribe'. To the extent that this arrangement results in the donkey moving forward, this can be seen as an example of *classical* conditioning. We saw earlier that in the form of classical conditioning called sign tracking an animal will approach a visual stimulus that signals a positive event like food. The donkey may have learned long ago that something that looks like a carrot is likely to taste like a carrot. So, a carrot dangled in front of the animal is likely to elicit the conditioned response of attempting to approach this attractive conditioned stimulus. However, this effect is not likely to last very long if the sight of the carrot is never followed by an opportunity to eat the carrot; extinction of the association will occur, as discussed later in this chapter. Again, we can see how inconsistency impedes learning.

Rocky, the eight-year-old Irish draught-horse in Fig. 2.11, is similar to Thorndike's cats and dogs in that within four weeks of being at his current home he learned that unlocking the bolt on his stable door was reinforced in that it was followed by an improvement of his environment. Although he escaped only four times before his activities were curtailed by the judicious use of a spring clip, he learned that the behaviour had a pleasant result. Interestingly, he shows no attempts to escape if, in place of the closed door, a chain is slung across the threshold of his doorway and loosely tied with a single strand of twine. It appears that the open door affords him a better view and satisfies his motivation to observe the comings and goings of his busy show-jumping home. This theory seems to be borne out when Rocky moves his hay from the dark corner of the stable and munches away in the doorway.

The idea that a large range of events – and not just events with obvious direct biological significance like food or water – can serve as powerful reinforcers was central to the views on instrumental conditioning advanced by B. Fred Skinner. Following Thorndike's pioneering work with puzzle boxes around the beginning of the twentieth century, for some decades research on learning concentrated increasingly on the question of how rats find their way around a maze. Then, in the 1930s, Skinner developed a new research tool that allowed a major advance in the study of instrumental conditioning. The experimental chamber he designed had three main components: something the animal could operate, a *manipulandum*, that was usually a lever for a rat or a plastic pecking disc for a pigeon; a device for delivering reinforcers in the form of, say, small food pellets; and some stimulus source such as a light or loudspeaker that could be used to signal whether a particular response-reinforcer relationship was operating. Everyone except Skinner quickly came to refer to this as a Skinner box. Compared to a maze or a puzzle box, one great advantage was that the experimenter did not have to intervene each time the animal received a reinforcement. Skinner referred to the effects of response-reinforcer relationships on behaviour that can be studied in such a chamber as *operant conditioning*, since

Fig. 2.11   Like the animals in Thorndike's puzzle boxes, this horse has learned by trial-and-error to undo the gate to his loose box. However, in this example of instrumental conditioning, the reinforcer was not the opportunity to escape. It seems that having the gate open was reinforcement enough, since the horse stands happily with just a chain across the threshold.

the behaviour 'operates' on - or makes changes to - the animal's environment. Thus, operant conditioning is a type of instrumental conditioning.

The rat and then the pigeon became the animals favoured by Skinner and other students of operant conditioning. In its Skinner box a pigeon can peck at a plastic disc at its own pace. Reinforcement is delivered, according to some preset arrangement that is automatically controlled. The Skinner box made it feasible for the first time to study the effects of varying the relationship between responses and

Fig. 2.12 An Equiball™ is a container that dispenses food pellets when moved around. It is an example of an extremely simple operant device. The manipulandum is the container itself that must be moved by the horse's muzzle. The container releases food pellets when it is moved appropriately. The sound of pellets in the container serves as a secondary reinforcer and their appearance on the ground as the primary reinforcer.

reinforcement, the various *schedules of reinforcement* that are described later.

The introduction of the Skinner box also made it easier to study the process of *shaping*. Skinner did not wait, as Thorndike had done, until the animal made the required response for the first time and only then deliver reinforcement. Instead, he found that he could train his rats to make some desired response very rapidly if he began by reinforcing very crude approximations to the target behaviour. For example, to train a rat to press a lever, he would start by delivering a food pellet only if the rat moved to the appropriate part of the chamber, then only if it made close contact with the lever, and so on. Shaping can be a way of modifying instinctive responses or of developing some entirely new pattern of behaviour.

In the 50 case studies that appear in our final three chapters, trainers describe the steps in their training methods. Clearly, animals cannot be trained to perform the final step until they are confidently showing the response described in the preceding step. Day-to-day training of behaviours usually proceeds with a series of small increments within these steps, but seasoned trainers happily acknowledge that opportunities to reinforce exceptional improvements may occur serendipitously and so are always prepared to reinforce. Part of the art of training is developing a sense for the optimum size of the increments, a variable that depends on targeted responses, individual subjects and stages in their training.

Crucially, it is the reserving of the reinforcement that makes animals try harder. Trainers who reinforce only what the animal already has learned will be offered those behaviours and no more. Conversely, trainers who wait for tremendous strides usually reinforce too rarely and find their animals lose interest. To train a dolphin to leap over a rod that is three metres above the surface of the water would take a long time using Thorndike's approach. It would be much faster to use a shaping procedure in which the rod starts just above the surface and is raised a little each time the dolphin makes a successful leap. Many examples of shaping can be found in the case histories (e.g. Case 18) described in Part II of this book. Trainers, therefore, probably owe more to Skinner than to Thorndike.

Operant techniques are used very widely. In addition to training, they have been harnessed to study animals' physiological and behavioural needs. Thus, operant devices can be used to determine the preference animals have for certain environmental parameters. For example, pigs placed in a cold chamber will press panels for bursts of infrared heat and work to maintain chamber temperatures at approximately 25 degrees Celsius. Calves, pigs and horses have all been trained to break photoelectric beams to turn on lighting in their accommodation and so indicate the photoperiods they prefer.

The merit of a reinforcer can be measured only in terms of the degree to which it makes the behaviour more likely in future. If a trainer's saying 'good dog' in response to a dog's heel-work has no effect on the dog's future behaviour at heel, then, according to this definition, reinforcement has not occurred. The trainer's words have had a neutral or even confusing effect. The definition does not describe how or why some events act as reinforcers. Whether some event is called a reinforcer is purely a matter of the effect it has. This is why, instead of encouraging owners to give their dogs praise, which can so often be understated and, as a result, ineffective, many of the more enlightened dog schools tell their humans to 'make that dog's tail wag'. While dull vocalisations intended as praise can have negligible impact on a dog's future performance, there are some impressive, if anecdotal, accounts of dogs responding to unintended human responses such as laughter and applause as if they were strongly reinforcing.

Instrumental conditioning is as sensitive to temporal contiguity as classical conditioning. The need for as short as possible an interval between the response and its outcome is central to effective instrumental conditioning. If, when a rat presses the lever in its Skinner box, there is a delay of several seconds before a food pellet arrives, learning will be much slower than if the reinforcement had been immediate. If the delay between response and reinforcer remains long, then even when the response is well learned the rat will continue to press its lever at a much slower rate than it would if immediate reinforcement were available (see Case 31).

A common mistake made by students when first learning how to shape a rat's behaviour in a Skinner box is to be overcautious in pressing the button that releases the food pellet. Their reaction times are slow and consequently the pellet arrives a second or so after the rat has performed the target response. Within this short time the rat may have started doing something else. This can mean that

Fig. 2.13 Place-training a dog involves training it to travel an increasing distance to the desired spot marked by a decreasingly obvious marker. The dog is:

- rewarded for standing in the desired spot on a very obvious marker (1: note the 3 phone books)
- required to wait a short distance from the desired spot mark (2a) and then called to the slightly less obvious marker (2b: 2 phone books) for its reward.
- required to wait a short distance from the desired spot mark (3a) and then called (3b) to the much less obvious marker (3c) for its reward.
- required to wait much further from the desired spot mark (4a and 4b) and then sent to the discrete marker for its reward (4c and 4d). Reproduced with permission from Sandro Nocentini.

the more recent behaviour is followed by immediate reinforcement and as a result becomes stronger than the target behaviour – and can prove very persistent. As discussed in more detail in Chapter 3, a similar issue arises with delay of punishment, as for example in recall training of dogs. The ignorant owner who sees a dog scavenging, calls him back and then hits him is hitting him for coming when he was called, not for chewing chicken bones.

By placing food on or near a lever in a Skinner box, as a so-called lure that increases the salience of the apparatus, trainers can stimulate rats to show interest in that part of their environment. Another form of *stimulus enhancement* may involve the trainers themselves or other animals interacting with the stimulus. The principle of drawing the animal's attention to a given stimulus is central to target training. This involves shaping the animal to retain proximity to a stimulus that can be moved around by the trainer (see Case 18, the hoop-jumping seal and Case 22, the tail-walking dolphin).

Repeatedly placing reinforcers in a certain part of an animal's environment increases the likelihood of it returning to that spot. In exotic animal training it is referred to as the animal's feeding station, and is of tremendous importance in keeping trainers safe by being the destination animals are most likely to head for when they first enter a training pen or after they have performed a given behaviour. On film sets this is known as the animal's place or mark (see Fig. 2.12) and is useful because it means animals can be sent to target without their trainers being in shot. Clearly, when a film script requires more than one animal to move in the same scene, each must be taught its mark individually before they rehearse together. The same principle is at the heart of the only case study that considers the training of sheep (Case 27).

The same result can be achieved by using tiny portable devices that emit characteristic sounds that animals are trained to associate with food. On set, these devices are small enough to be secreted e.g. under carpets, and any sound they make can be edited out in post-production. For small prey species the value of sanctuary is tremendous. This is exploited when training animals such as rats and mice to run from A to B for theatre, television and film purposes, by placing their home cage at B and gradually increasing the distance between A and B (see Fig. 2.14).

If a reinforcer is shown to an animal before it performs a desired response, this is sometimes called a bribe, a term that is rather loaded with negative anthropomorphic implications and seems to presuppose that animals have human minds. What can often happen in training is that the sight, smell or sound of a reward can serve as either a conditioned stimulus heralding the arrival of a reward or as a trigger for an instrumental response (see discriminative stimulus later). Many trainers avoid the use of reinforcers in this way since it can encourage the animals to respond only if they have seen the reinforcers, and it may distract the animals and reduce the likelihood of

Fig. 2.14 For rats in bright sunlight access to a dimly lit home cage is rewarding. By gradually moving the home cage further away, rats can be trained to run a considerable distance along the fence.

their learning novel responses because they interact less with their environment during a training session.

A question that often arises in training programmes based on instrumental conditioning – reward training – is what size of reward to use. The general rule deriving from research that has varied the magnitude of the reinforcer in instrumental conditioning is: the larger the reinforcer, the greater its effect on behaviour. While this may suggest that big is always better, the effectiveness of a reinforcer may decline when many reinforcers need to be given within a short period of time. The obvious example of such a satiation effect is the use of food reward to a hungry animal; with frequent large rewards it will soon lose its appetite. For this reason many trainers use small rewards within a session and then end when the animal completes a 'high note' – that is, performs particularly well – at which point it is given a large reward, a 'jackpot'. Learning theory suggests that jackpots should be used sparingly, since once the animal starts to expect large reinforcers in a given context, small reinforcers may start to lose their effectiveness. Probably the most generally useful practice is to start training with large rewards and short sessions and progressively move towards smaller rewards given in longer sessions. Sometimes

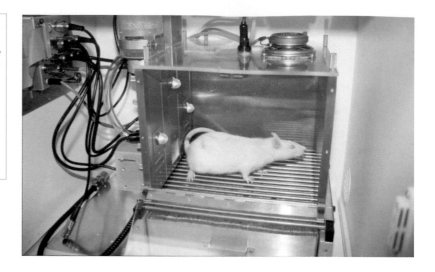

Fig. 2.15 For this rat pressing the lever in the Skinner box switches on the wall lights and only some seconds later the delivery of a pellet. The lights can function as a secondary reinforcer that maintains vigorous lever pressing. In their absence – without such a 'bridge' – the rat would learn more slowly to press the lever for the delayed primary reinforcer.

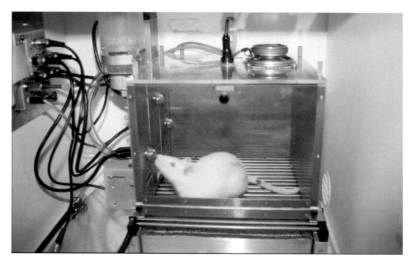

Fig. 2.16 Once the light turns off, the rat moves to collect its delayed reinforcer, the food pellet that drops into the hopper below the lights. The cables connect the Skinner box to a computer that provides automatic control of the lights and reinforcer delivery, while also recording frequency and distribution of lever pressing. The roof of the Skinner box contains the houselight and a loudspeaker for providing an auditory stimulus when required. The floor is a grid of stainless steel bars that can be used for the delivery of shock for experiments using aversive events (see Chapter 3).

animals get over excited by large rewards, so it is preferable to avoid allowing animals to see jackpots before they are given.

Secondary reinforcers

A delay between response and reinforcement is not such a problem for effective training if there is some event that fills the gap. If, when the rat presses the lever, a light is immediately switched on, then the rat may acquire the lever-press response rapidly and continue to perform it at a high rate, even if the food pellet does not arrive for a while. For this to occur, though, the light has to be a consistently reliable signal for the arrival of food. In this case the houselight is said to function as a *secondary*, or conditioned, reinforcer. This contrasts with a *primary*, or unconditioned, reinforcer, which is an event that needs no special training or experience to establish its reinforcing properties. Secondary reinforcing properties are usually acquired through classical conditioning (see Case 29). Like any conditioned stimulus, they are subject to extinction; if the houselight is no longer a reliable signal that food is about to arrive, it will lose its secondary reinforcing property. The concept of secondary reinforcers makes sense in terms of the adaptiveness of behaviour in natural settings. For example, a fox may learn to associate the smell of hens with the meal that sometimes follows. Detection of the smell is then likely to encourage the fox to persist in its hunt.

Consider the way in which horses are often praised using tactile stimuli; they can be either scratched at the withers or patted on the neck. Horses have evolved to find grooming one another rewarding. Indeed horses indulging in the familiar 'I'll scratch your back if you scratch mine' occupation have reduced heart rates that suggest they may be getting pleasure or stress reduction from the stimulation. So, a scratch in the correct part of the withers can represent a primary reinforcer. By comparison, the far more common practice of patting horses on the neck is reinforcing only if the owner has coupled the pat with something pleasant. Because horses have not evolved to enjoy pats on the neck, this kind of tactile stimulation has to be conditioned as a secondary reinforcer. Temporal contiguity is as important for secondary reinforcement as for any other kind of conditioning. Imagine that an owner is trying to turn a pat on the neck into a secondary reinforcer. Giving a sugar lump to a horse two minutes after a pat will not develop a useful association. The pat needs to arrive just before the lump if it is to become reinforcing.

In conclusion, secondary reinforcers are most effectively established when presented before or up until the presentation of a primary reinforcer, just as for any other kind of classical conditioning. Simultaneous presentation of a reward and a novel secondary stimulus is less likely to work because the primary reinforcer will overshadow the new stimulus. Similarly, presentation of the secondary stimulus after the primary reinforcer is unproductive because, although an association will exist between the two, it does not help the animal predict the arrival of a reward.

Clicker training

The best example of a secondary reinforcer used for training purposes is the sound made by a so-called 'clicker'. This was introduced by

Marion and Keller Breland, who studied with Skinner in the late 1930s, just after he had published his first, and subsequently very influential, book, *The Behavior of Organisms*. The Brelands were pioneers in the application of operant conditioning principles to animal training. They developed various feeding devices that made a characteristic sound as a prelude to food. The first step in any kind of training was to have the animal learn to associate this sound with the arrival of food, as shown by the animal reacting with increasing speed and reliability to the sound. Psychology labs studying the learned behaviour of rats or pigeons use the same procedure and call it magazine training. The use of a hand-held clicker was the next step (see Cases 3, 6, 7, 11, 12 and 13 among others). Essentially, the click comes to mean: 'Yes, that's good. Job done! Expect a reward any second now.' The click forms a bridge between the response and reinforcement – that is why it is also sometimes called a bridging stimulus. When a clicker is first used, the correct association is established by making the sound just before giving a delicious reward. Doing this many times convinces the animal of the signal's reliability. A trainer can be sure that an animal has made the association between the clicker and reinforcement when it stops what it is doing at the sound of a click – and immediately travels to the trainer to receive its reinforcer.

Any kind of signal could serve as a secondary reinforcer. One advantage of a commercial clicker device is the sound it makes, which is crisp and distinctive. The crispness facilitates precise reinforcement of brief responses such as the blinking of an eye. Being pocket-sized or attachable to key rings, clickers are convenient but by no means unique. Indeed, as long as they cannot be confused with words that appear in common parlance, human vocalisations (so-called 'clicker words') are even more readily available. As we have seen, experienced trainers are always prepared to reinforce opportunistically and can

Fig. 2.17 The trainer has used a clicker to train this baboon to reach upwards to two target hand-grips and hold its body close to the cage door. When in this position, a non-invasive veterinary procedure can be carried out on the animal.

most easily do so if they are not reliant on having a primary reinforcer instantly to hand and can issue their own secondarily reinforcing sound without having to locate a device. Having said that, clicker devices can make praise universal from one trainer to the next. This is one reason why, for instance, animal actors will perform with humans other than their trainers; because those relative strangers are carrying clickers.

As with students training rats in a Skinner box the tendency is for novice clicker trainers to be overcautious in their clicking. This allows the animal to proceed to a next step in its response to an environment i.e. to stop doing the shaped behaviour. Clicker training courses encourage novices to be generous in their clicks, and this in turn encourages animals to offer responses readily (i.e. to be creative).

Few animals find verbal praise terribly exciting. This is true for dogs, for example, especially when praise is compared to chocolate or a game of chase with a tennis ball. Nevertheless, under many conditions the use of verbal commands and verbal praise is indispensable.

There are plenty of top obedience trainers who choose not to live in the same space as their dogs because this can habituate the dogs to the sound of their trainers' voices and hence decrease the dogs' responsiveness in competition. The common overuse of verbal praise, with the consequent extinction of its effectiveness, is another reason why many trainers use clickers.

If every delivery of a reward depends on the close presence of a human, its effect can quickly become context-specific to human proximity, so that an animal fails to perform the behaviour at any distance from its owner or handler. The cue of a human is an important contingency for these animals. But as we have seen in place-training (see Fig. 2.13, dog being place trained) and the shaping of animals to travel from A to B, it is often important to train movements away from the trainer. So, how do we tell an animal it is doing well, when we are unable to stand beside it and give it food or some other reward?

Clicker training really comes into its own when used to reinforce at a distance (see Tyson, the dolphin in Case 22). As we have seen, clicker training relies on the establishment of a strong association between a singular, unmistakable sound and primary reinforcement. Consistency is extremely important in the early stages of clicker training when the meaning of the characteristic noise should not be blurred. Many trainers abide by the maxim 'the clicker never lies', which reminds them that they should never let their animal hear the click without being rewarded. Why not? Because this can result in some degree of extinction of the clicker–food association. Having said that, when using a clicker for training at a distance, it is normally difficult to maintain such consistency or avoid a long delay between the click and the primary reinforcer. A technological solution is to use some remote-controlled device for delivering reinforcers.

There are other ways to train animals at a distance. One technique is to plant reinforcers at places where the animal will find them shortly after an improved approximation of the desired behaviour (see Teela, the tracking dog in Case 42). To train a 'send away' in an obedience dog, the trainer might place a food reward less than a metre away from the dog and then mark the spot with an even more obvious visual signal such as a traffic cone. Given the signal *away*, the dog travels towards the food (i.e. it performs the desired behaviour) and is rewarded as soon as it completes the trip to the cone. Then the dog must be returned to the starting point and the food and cone placed further away. With gradual extension of the trip, the dog learns to rely on the cone as a useful target. Many dogs' enthusiasm for the send away comes to depend on having first seen the trainer travel to the cone target and appear to drop an item of food. In these cases it is up to the cunning trainer to break down this contingency. One way is to enlist the help of a third party who can behave in the same way as a steward might at an obedience trial, to ensure that reinforcement can be delivered to the target without the dog or the trainer having visited it. However, many well-trained dogs complete such tasks impeccably without reliance on such cues because they have already learned to run straight on command.

The training of sled dogs (see Case 39) also relies on the provision of rewards found away from the trainer and the den. The adventure and the possibility of spotting other animals that can be chased rewards them every time they negotiate a turn and begin charging off in a new direction. Similarly, the reliable sighting of a potential prey item is what teaches racing greyhounds their single most important lesson in life: to leave the traps as fast as possible.

Extinction of instrumental behaviour

We have seen that classically conditioned responses become progressively weaker if repeated presentations of the conditioned stimulus are no longer followed by the unconditioned stimulus. A similar process of extinction takes place when a response learned via instrumental conditioning is no longer followed by any reinforcer. The response will be performed progressively less frequently and less energetically. A dog that begs at the dinner table will stop begging if never rewarded. Often during extinction of instrumental behaviour the disappearance of the learned response is accompanied by a reversion to innate or previously learned behaviours.

There are some intriguing outcomes associated with extinction of a previously positively reinforced response. Early in extinction it is common for a *frustration effect* to occur, so that for a short while the instrumental response is made more vigorously than when reinforced (see Fig. 2.18). Like the hearty glow of a candle flame before it dies out, a burst of responding is often found early in extinction. A horse that has learned to break the rope that tethers it by being reinforced with liberty will pull much harder when it is first tethered by a chain. To avoid concluding prematurely that an extinction-based behaviour

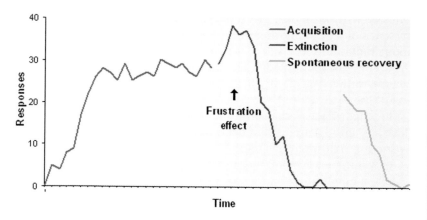

Fig. 2.18 If a rat in a Skinner box is continuously reinforced for responding on a lever during an initial acquisition phase, the number of responses per minute will increase up to some steady level. When reinforcement is no longer available during a subsequent extinction phase, there may be a burst of responding – the *frustration effect* – before responding becomes less and less frequent. If after a day or two the rat is returned to the Skinner box, it may start responding once more – *spontaneous recovery* – but this will quickly die away if reinforcement is still not available. Reproduced with permission from Danielle Karazinov.

modification programme is a failure, it is important for trainers to be aware of this effect; things may get worse before they get better.

A variant of the standard extinction procedure that is far less likely to produce frustration is one in which a reinforcer is still regularly delivered but is no longer dependent on the instrumental response. Thus, the response–reinforcer contingency has been removed, but not the reinforcer. If a rat has been pressing a lever to obtain food, but now food is delivered at about the same rate whether it responds or not, its rate of lever-pressing will slow down. This is usually not as effective a method for reducing the frequency of a response as the standard procedure of simply withholding the reinforcer. It is perhaps more usefully seen as a way in which training can fall off in effectiveness if a close link between the instrumental response and the reinforcer is not maintained.

A much more effective way of eliminating an unwanted response is to reinforce all other behaviours in the situation where the unwanted response tends to occur most strongly. This is called *omission* training: reinforcement is omitted if the target response is made, and thus is contingent on the target response *not* being made. An omission schedule can be used to change unwelcome behaviour. While this schedule withholds reinforcement of the problem behaviour, it still allows reinforcement to be delivered. Withdrawing reinforcement completely may not always be advisable, since this runs the danger of removing all incentive to respond in any way. Just as it is important to avoid confusion and promote creativity when training a new behaviour, it is imperative that, when training an animal to stop performing some problem behaviour, it is simultaneously given the opportunity to perform a more acceptable behaviour with a similar motivation. A dog that chases joggers can most easily be trained to stop and look at the handler if it associates the sight of a jogger with an owner-centred ball game into which it can channel its motivation to chase.

Stimuli present during omission training or extinction can exert considerable control over behaviour. A dog that begs at the dinner table and scavenges food from poorly trained or mischievous children will extinguish this response if no further titbits arrive. If the presence of a grandmother at the family table, laying down the rules about table manners and less than messy eating, is associated with the absence of reinforcement, then extinction will occur most quickly when Granny is at home. Begging may return, at least temporarily, when Granny is not present. Such a *renewal* effect provides an example of the importance of the context in which learning occurs. A response that has disappeared after being unrewarded may reappear if the extinction treatment has taken place only in a highly specific setting.

In a similar way an extinguished response may also recover briefly if, after a long interval since the last extinction trial, cues for responding are again present. This rebound in response strength after a 'rest' following extinction is called *spontaneous recovery*. It is sometimes overlooked as a possible outcome of behaviour therapy programmes designed to eliminate unwelcome behaviours by extinction. Furthermore, if an undesirable behaviour makes a return, trainers may forget the original response strength when they compare current behaviour with previous behaviour. So, when the response recurs after a long absence, the trainer's conclusion may be slightly damning with remarks like 'the removal of rewards hasn't helped' or 'the animal has regressed'. Spontaneous recovery can also occur after habituation of an innate response to some stimulus. For example, if over a short period of time an animal is repeatedly exposed to some initially frightening event until the fear response disappears, reappearance of the event some time later may frighten the animal once again. To prevent this happening, the trainer must continue to expose the animal to the relevant stimuli from time to time.

Partial reinforcement

So far our examples of instrumental conditioning using positive reinforcement have been ones where reward is delivered after each response. This is known as a *continuous reinforcement* (CRF) schedule. It produces faster learning of a response than when *partial reinforcement* (PRF) is used; that is, when only some proportion of correct responses are rewarded. On the other hand partial reinforcement can produce high resistance to extinction. This *partial reinforcement extinction effect* (PREE) can seem paradoxical. If the first 20 responses an animal makes are all followed by reward (CRF) and then no more reward is forthcoming, the response is likely to extinguish very rapidly. On the other hand, if only 10 of the first 20 responses are followed by reward (PRF) before all rewards are withheld, then the response is likely to continue to be repeated for a long time. The PREE is a highly pervasive feature of instrumental conditioning. It can be a great boon when a trainer wishes to ensure that some behaviour persists under conditions where continuous reinforcement cannot be guaranteed. But it can create major problems in training if some undesired response is reinforced occasionally, either inadvertently or by someone else.

Dogs that have *sometimes* been given titbits for begging at tables take longer to give up when owners learn never to reward the behaviour than those that have had constant reinforcement. Horses that have intermittently refused fences and discovered the benefits of such evasion rarely go on to perform consistently enough for their riders to trust them completely.

Partial reinforcement can be arranged in a variety of ways. Thus, reinforcement can be scheduled on the basis of the number of responses made, as in the above example where only 10 out of 20 responses were reinforced. This is called a *ratio schedule of reinforcement*. Alternatively, reinforcement can be scheduled to occur according to the time since the last reinforcement. Such schedules are called *interval schedules of reinforcement*. Study of such schedules in the laboratory has shown that they produce different temporal patterns of behaviour and different degrees of resistance to extinction. A *fixed interval* (FI) schedule is one in which reinforcement only becomes available again after some specified time has elapsed. Thus, a pigeon reinforced for pecking on an FI one-minute schedule has to wait one minute after the last delivery of grain before a peck will produce a second delivery; it will probably peck at an increasing rate during this one-minute period, but none of these pecks will have any effect.

A *variable interval* (VI) schedule is similar, except that the time from the last reinforcer until the next one becomes available is varied. Thus, if pecking is reinforced on a VI one-minute schedule, a peck just a second or so since the last grain delivery will sometimes be reinforced, but on other occasions the pigeon may find that only after several minutes is its peck reinforced; the average interval between available reinforcers will be one minute in this example. Imagine checking your voice mail when there is no signal to indicate whether any message has arrived since the last time you checked; except that here the average interval between messages is going to be a lot longer than one minute. Variable interval schedules have been found to produce slow, but very steady, rates of responding and high resistance to extinction. Three general principles of reinforcement schedules appear to hold across all species and all kinds of instrumental behaviour: first, ratio schedules tend to produce higher rates of responding, but less resistance to extinction, than interval schedules; second, fixed schedules tend to produce more pausing after a reinforcement is delivered and less resistance to extinction than variable schedules; and finally, whether interval or ratio, fixed or variable, the 'leaner' the schedule – that is, the lower the rate of reinforcement – the less vigorous the response during training, but the greater its resistance to extinction after extensive reinforcement. Trained behaviours can even persist when the benefits of performing no longer outweigh the costs. For example, Skinner trained an extreme example of a rat on ratio schedule so lean that the energy received from the food was less than the energy expended in obtaining the food. If the balance is right, animals will continue to perform behaviours even if doing so causes them some discomfort (see Fig. 2.19).

Fig. 2.19 Positive and negative reinforcement have been used to train this elephant to lie on its side while having a blood sample taken from a vein in its ear. As a result, no sedation or tranquilisers are needed to perform this important veterinary procedure.

Context dependence, stimulus control and stimulus generalisation

Pavlov's dogs may have had their movements closely restrained for experiments, but they knew that the lab was where they received meat powder. The straps that held them in place may well have caused great resentment in a different context such as a park. Their effect was context-specific in the same way that white coats represent danger to some cats, but only at the veterinary clinic; household visitors can wear white coats and interact with the same animals without provoking a panic response. The dependence of learned behaviour on a specific context is also shown by a puppy that gives appropriate responses to cues in a training school and yet apparently forgets everything when out on a walk. Good trainers do their best to reduce context specificity by varying the setting in which training takes place. One of the most time consuming elements of guide dog training, after a dog such as Robyn (see Case 47) has been taken through basic training with artificial obstacles, is the process of repetition in other contexts to eliminate any dependence on the training ground's environmental cues.

The aim of most training is to ensure that the animal makes exactly the required response when a specific signal is given and not at any other time or to any other signal. In learning theory such a signal is called a *discriminative stimulus* or S^D (pronounced 'ess dee'). As Skinner first suggested, any form of instrumental conditioning involves a three-term relationship, or contingency: the discriminative stimulus, the response and the reinforcer. If this contingency is such that the reinforcer follows the response only when the response occurs in the presence of the discriminative stimulus, then the latter will normally gain *stimulus control* over the instrumental response. In a Skinner box used for pigeons a researcher might arrange that the response key is occasionally lit, for example, by a pure green light, and only then is pecking at the key followed by the delivery of grain. Within a relatively short time the pigeon will peck only when the key turns green; the instrumental response has come under control of this key colour.

Such control is often far from precise. If a *stimulus generalisation test* is carried out in which the response key is lit by a series of other colours, the pigeon will probably peck when the key is yellow-green or blue-green, but more slowly than when the key is pure green. In other words the response has *generalised* to similar stimuli. Such generalisation may be limited. In the present example, the pigeon would rarely peck at the key when this was red. Exactly the same phenomenon is seen in classical conditioning. Indeed, the very first generalisation tests were carried out in Pavlov's laboratory. After his dogs had learned to associate a metronome ticking at a certain rate, as the CS, with the arrival of food, they were tested with the metronome set at various other frequencies. How many drops of saliva a dog produced when

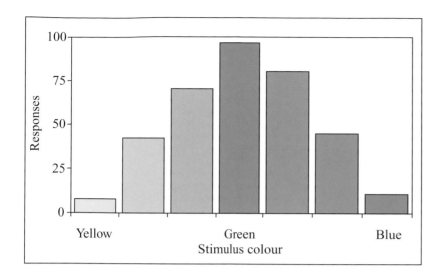

the metronome started to tick turned out to be a function of the difference between its frequency and that of the training frequency. So that the closer the frequency came to the training frequency, the more saliva was produced. Such a function is known as a *generalisation gradient*.

In some kinds of training it is not important that the response is made to signals that are to some degree similar to the training signal. Indeed, this may sometimes be an advantage. For example, a trainer may want a verbal command to be effective when other people use this command, even though the actual sound is likely to vary a great deal from speaker to speaker. However, more precise stimulus control is often required. For this some form of discrimination training is needed (see Case 41).

Fig. 2.20 A bird is first trained to peck at a response key when this is lit with a green light. It is then given a *generalisation test* in which the key is lit in succession by a variety of colours. This generalisation gradient illustrates a decline in responding as test colours become more distant from the original training colour. Reproduced with permission from Danielle Karazinov.

Discrimination training

There are two main ways to train a discrimination using positive reinforcement. As its name indicates, in *simultaneous discrimination* training the animal is given access to two or more stimuli at the same time and is rewarded if it responds only to the target, or positive, stimulus. For example, establishing precise control by a pure green colour over pecking by the pigeon described in the previous section could be achieved by providing an array of three response keys – one lit by pure green light, one by blue-green and one by yellow-green – and arranging that only pecking to the pure green is ever reinforced. In this example, as in all forms of simultaneous discrimination training, it is important that the position of the stimuli is varied very frequently. That is, of the three response keys, the pure green light may appear on the left, then on the right and then in the middle. Otherwise an animal will almost always learn about *where* to respond

Fig. 2.21 In simultaneous discrimination training on each trial a choice is offered between two or more responses. In this example a horse is being trained to discriminate between a yellow and white panel for a food reward. Half the time the yellow panel is on the left, as shown, and half on the right. In such training it is essential to prevent cueing by the trainer of the kind discovered in the case of Clever Hans (see Chapter 4). Floor plan showing location of horse in the photos.

A) Reward box
B) The horse is led to the reward boxes and learns to depress the hinged lid to obtain the reward within the box;
C) Walking at the level of the horse's shoulder, the handler accompanies it to the panels;
D) The handler is now walking at the level of the horse's hindquarters as the horse approaches the panels;
E) The unaccompanied horse now makes a choice;
F) The horse has made a correct choice and is now consuming the reward.

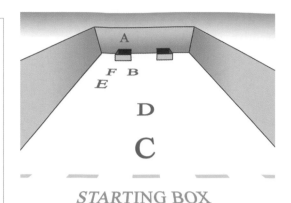

STARTING BOX

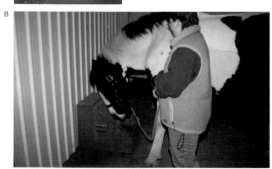

rather than *what* to respond to. In other words, it tends to develop a position preference that overshadows learning about the visual cue.

This is not a problem for *successive discrimination* training, since here the stimuli are normally presented to the animal in the same place, but at different times. Thus, using this method to train our pigeon to peck only at pure green would need a single response key. Reinforcement would be available for pecking during periods when the key was this colour, but not during other times when it is switched to blue-green or yellow-green. Sniffer dogs are trained using successive training (see Cases 41, 43 and 44). Such training commonly arranges for responses to the positive stimuli to be reinforced and responses to all other stimuli not reinforced (extinguished). However, if the discrimination is a difficult one, such a training schedule may fail to reduce responding to the negative stimuli to an acceptable level. The animal may continue indefinitely to make frequent false positive responses, even if at a rate considerably below responding to the positive stimulus. Many real-life situations require that an animal's discrimination performance approaches perfection. For example, airport managers could not cope with more than the rare innocent passenger being targeted by a dog trained to pick out narcotics or explosives. One possible solution to the problem of an animal settling for just a moderate level of discrimination performance is to reward it for *not* making the target response to negative stimuli. This is an example of an *omission schedule* of reinforcement, as discussed earlier. For some unknown reason, such schedules do not seem to be widely used outside a laboratory setting.

Another, much more commonly used, way of getting good performance on a difficult discrimination is to exploit the *easy-to-hard transfer* effect. An example is based on a recent study of discrimination learning in an increasingly rare and rarely studied Australian marsupial, the quagga, which resembles a small wallaby. Finding both a suitable response and suitable stimuli to use in the study of discrimination learning in these animals proved very difficult. The researchers eventually settled on a task that required the animal to pull with its forepaws on a cord of a certain thickness, but to ignore a cord of a slightly different thickness. If they had started with this relatively fine discrimination, the animal would never have learned to perform at all well. Instead, it was started on a very easy discrimination between a very fat and a very thin cord. Once this was learned to a high level, a second discrimination was introduced that involved a somewhat smaller difference in thickness between two cords. And so on. In general, such easy-to-hard procedures make it possible to achieve within a relatively short time far higher levels of performance on a difficult discrimination than can be obtained when this discrimination is introduced from the beginning of training.

An interesting application of discrimination learning appears in the laboratories of sensory physiologists, because there are limits to which microscopic examination of the retina can elucidate the mysteries of colour vision in animals. One of the best ways of determining what an animal can detect in its environment is to ask it. To do this we must train them to associate certain colours with rewards when they occur in the presence of other unrewarding colours. Representatives of many species have been trained to discriminate between visual stimuli for food rewards. The extent to which visual cues are selected is tested by giving conditioned animals visual stimuli that are increasingly similar. When the animals are no better in their selection than one would expect by chance we can assume that they can no longer tell the cues apart.

A similar approach to discrimination training is called *fading*. The aim of this technique is to reduce the number of errors an animal makes; that is, it is designed to ensure that few, if any, responses are made to any stimulus other than the S^D (see Case 38). If successful, it is called *errorless learning*. It can produce rapid learning of a discrimination. The basics of the fading technique are to start with thorough training for responding to the S^D in the absence of other stimuli and then to introduce very gradually in terms of time and intensity – to 'fade in' – the similar stimulus, or stimuli, that the animal is being taught *not* to respond to. In the example of the pigeon to be trained to peck only at pure green, errorless training would start with only this colour displayed on the key throughout a session and pecking reinforced on some partial reinforcement schedule. Then short periods are introduced when the lighting in the chamber is dimmed and the response key goes black. The pigeon is very unlikely to peck under these conditions. From this point the duration of these negative periods when pecking is never followed by reinforcement is progressively increased, houselight dimming is decreased and increasingly bright blue-green or yellow-green lights appear on the response key during these negative periods.

If the technique is successful, the pigeon will end up making a near perfect discrimination between the colours without having made more than a few pecks to the incorrect – or negative – stimuli during the course of training. It has been claimed that such errorless – or, at least, relatively error free – discrimination learning is superior in some ways to more conventional training. For example, the absence of frustration during training might lead to more stable performance and the absence of any spontaneous recovery of responding to the negative stimuli. However, there is little strong evidence for such claims, even though errorless learning techniques are popular among many trainers.

Verbal commands and other signals

By training animals to respond to signals reliably and then making the signals more and more subtle, a trainer can elicit behaviours without an audience perceiving the effective discriminative stimulus. Once the animal is trained to respond only to the tiniest of cues, the trainer can introduce a spurious 'command' that is given without subtlety. The animal will appear to respond to that command and even to understand the nuances of human language. As long as it is distinct, the auditory cue can be any noise. Take for example, the poacher's dog who is trained to run away whenever coaxed to approach with traditionally inviting words. Since to seize the poacher's dog is to identify the poacher, gamekeepers who have stumbled across a shifty looking man-and-dog team are keen to catch one, if not both, players at the scene. By using novel words to recall his dog, the poacher can remain slightly ahead of the game, as it were. Interestingly, when a shepherd works a brace of sheepdogs he has to teach dog A that any cue prefixed by dog B's name is a command to keep performing its current behaviour.

All of these examples are of intended effects of training. Often similar effects can occur that are unintended and may be unnoticed. The most famous historical example is that of the horse, Clever Hans. As described more fully in Chapter 4, both his trainer and the specialists that came to test this horse believed that Hans was responding to words and numbers displayed on a blackboard. In the end it was discovered that the horse was actually responding to slight movements made by his interrogators that they did not intend to make. In other words, the horse was sensitive to human body language of which the humans were for a long time unaware.

The clarity of signals can be preserved by using them only in certain circumstances. The best example of this must be the release command used by handlers of police siege dogs when they send their dogs to attack. Because, in training, everything is pitched in favour of the dog being able to seize the human identified as a suspect, confidence is built up so that the release command is a virtual guarantee for the dog of his ability to acquire a prized possession (see Kruger, Case 46).

It seems that the inclusion of a verbal command can come at any point in the training process. There is an argument for using it only when the final behaviour is being offered, as in traditional clicker training (see Topper, the clicker trained pony, Case 11). An alternative approach is to rely on classical conditioning of the association between the cue and the response by using the same word at the time of all approximations of the behaviour, as in the training of sled dogs (see Kodiak, Case 39). On the one hand, the sparing of the command until the final stage of training implies that the reserved cue will not be confusing and will prompt only exact executions of the desired response. If one has used a specific cue early in training and rewarded the animal for substandard approximations of the desired behaviour, then it has to learn to work harder for the final shaped behaviour by a process of extinction; learning that poorer responses are no longer rewarded. Meanwhile, the use of the same signal throughout training may help to ensure the animal does what is required. For example, a dog that is to be trained to *stay* for 10 minutes with the owner out of sight must first be taught to *stay* for 30 seconds in the presence of the owner.

The trained animal's task includes being able to discriminate not only between general conversation and the trained commands, but also between one command and the next. Isolating animals from their trainers, when trained responses are not required, can be an effective means of reducing *generalisation*, that is, animals eliciting trained responses to cues similar to the cue used in training. Such isolation can ensure consistency in the effectiveness of verbal cues. For example, it is undesirable for a championship candidate to hear, say, the last syllable of bis*cuit* – perhaps during a teatime conversation between humans – and respond with an immediate and impeccable *sit* response, only to go unpraised and eventually stop offering the trained behaviour. By segregating their dogs, trainers can better avoid one of their most feared of possible outcomes, the extinction of the response to *sit* in a competition. The same is usually true of numerous sheepdogs that spend most of their days chained up or in small, but possibly quite cosy, boxes. On emerging from confinement, they are very keen to work and can be certain that any auditory signals are for their ears only. Domestic cats take this point to the extreme in the opposite direction, in that they learn to ignore almost all human vocalisation.

In advanced dog obedience competitions the use of the voice attracts penalties in demonstrations of control at a distance. Consequently, trainers instead use hand signals that have been paired with vocalised commands earlier in the dog's training. The same principle is used in the training of marine mammals that respond to subtle visual cues, and to particular combinations of such cues, both in public performances that appear seamless and in research settings. Often visual signals are used from the outset of training. One example is the training of deaf dogs that can be trained to sit when they see the owner's hand being raised.

Chaining

Once a discriminative stimulus gains control of a positively reinforced response it normally acquires a further property. As a stimulus that has become a good predictor of reinforcement, a discriminative stimulus starts to function as a secondary reinforcer. As such, it can now reinforce whatever response precedes it. Thus, once stimulus z is trained as an S^D for response Z, it can be used to reinforce response Y in the presence of stimulus y. This results in a *chain* of stimuli and responses: *stimulus y* $\rightarrow$ *response Y* $\rightarrow$ reinforcer/S^D z $\rightarrow$ *response* Z. Once two links in such a chain are well trained, a third can be added, and so forth. This makes it possible to train an animal to perform a long sequence of behaviours where there may be several minutes or even longer between the initial response and the positive reinforcement that follows the last link in the chain. An example is a circus dog that was trained to perform the following sequence: find carton of six eggs, undo the lid, remove each egg individually, drop them into a bowl and then close the carton lid before returning to the bowl to consume its delicious contents. A simpler example is the discovery by Dynamite, the falcon hybrid (Case 40), that hunting forays are likely to be successful when launched from her handler's fist. This marked a turning point in her training and meant that food rewards no longer had to be delivered every time she returned to the fist. Instead, the fist functioned both as a secondary reinforcer for returning and as a discriminative stimulus for a future hunt.

Chaining can be very important for travelling along complicated routes where landmarks - visual cues, smells or other stimuli, depending on the species - can serve as the discriminative stimuli for each part of the journey (see Case 47). The most important point about any kind of training that aims to produce a chain of behaviours is the need to start with the last step and build up the chain backwards. Thus, if the aim is to train an animal to negotiate a complex maze with many choice points, making few errors during training, the trick is to begin training at the last choice point. As shown in Fig. 2.20, once the right choice at E - followed by the primary reward - is learned, the animal can be trained to get from D to E, and so on. This approach was used to train wartime messenger dogs to race back to their handlers over gradually increased distances. The final goal, a piece of liver from the trainer at the home base, was always the same, but on each training session the first part of the mission was novel and therefore challenging. Once they were on their familiar home track everything was plain sailing.

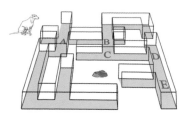

Fig. 2.22 An animal faced with finding a reward in a maze has to learn which way to turn at each choice point it meets. In this example the most effective training is to start with from D to E to food, followed by from C to D to E to food, and so on. Reproduced with permission from Sandro Nocentini.

Misbehaviour: interactions between classical and instrumental learning

Defining two types of conditioning might suggest that it is easy to decide whether a particular example of a change in behaviour produced by the use of positive reinforcement is based on classical or on instrumental conditioning. However, even under the well-controlled conditions of a behavioural laboratory this can be difficult. Imagine that your goal is to train a rat to push at a translucent plastic flap in the corner of a small, darkened chamber whenever a light is switched on behind the flap. An effective training procedure is to arrange that at irregular long intervals - averaging, say, one or two minutes - the light is switched on for ten seconds and, as it is switched off, a pellet of food is dropped into a tray behind the flap which the rat can now collect. You may be able to have the rat pressing the flap consistently within 20 trials or so. But is classical or instrumental conditioning responsible for successful training of this kind? From one point of view the procedure is a classical one: the arrival of food behind the flap is independent of the rat's behaviour, just as for Pavlov's dogs the arrival of food did not depend on whether they had salivated or not. Consequently, a possible conclusion is that pressing the flap is part of a conditioned response - approach to the light - that is elicited by the light as a CS paired with food. On the other hand the rat cannot reach the food without pushing the flap, so perhaps this response is better seen as an instrumental response under the control of the light as a discriminative stimulus?

Resolving such a question can sometimes be important for a theorist. It turns out that fairly subtle tests are needed and that the answer is often that a mixture of both kinds of conditioning are involved (see Case 41). For someone concerned with the practical task of training some particular response the question of whether an effective technique is based on classical or instrumental conditioning is rarely an important one. There are, however, some situations where it pays to look at possible interactions between the two types of conditioning. The most famous examples are those provided by the Brelands who, as we have already seen, were the first to apply the principles of instrumental conditioning to animal training in a consistent and commercially successful way. A decade after publishing a triumphant account of their successes, they wrote a paper detailing some of their failures. The title they gave to this 1962 paper was 'The Misbehavior of Organisms'.

Many of the problems they described as misbehaviour arose after training had been progressing smoothly. One example was intended as a television commercial for a savings bank. The aim was to train a pig to pick up a coin-like disc or token, carry this over to a pig-shaped receptacle with a slot in the top and then release the disc into this piggy bank. The pig was rewarded with food for each successful performance. Although the early stages of training went well, after a while the pig's performance began to deteriorate; once it had obtained a disc, it became reluctant to let go of it and instead started to root it around in the dirt of its enclosure. The same thing happened when a raccoon was trained in a similar manner, except that in this case the raccoon started to knead the disc and dunk it in its water bowl as if to wash it. The Brelands described such cases as resulting from 'instinctive drift'. They noted that the unwanted responses to the

Fig. 2.23 An orphaned African elephant appears to be playing with a stick. A good trainer would be able to divine the animal's motivation and thus devise an appropriate game. With permission from Lisa Ruben.

tokens were those that pigs and raccoons made towards food objects in more natural settings.

Subsequent research has shown that declines in performance of some trained behaviour are better understood in terms of competition between classically and instrumentally conditioned responses. In both examples above, there is a chain of instrumental responses that produces the reinforcer: obtain disc, carry disc and then relinquish disc into the correct receptacle. As performance improves, there is also an increasingly consistent relationship between a stimulus, the disc, and the food; the disc becomes a CS that reliably signals the arrival of food as the US. As a result of the classical conditioning this CS–US relationship produces, the disc acquires the properties of a surrogate food object and a hungry pig or raccoon will tend to hang on to such an object rather than let it drop irretrievably into a piggy bank or box. Responding to the disc as a food object now competes with the instrumental response of releasing the disc, so that this trained response is performed more slowly and less reliably. What may be a familiar example to many readers is that of a dog that is reluctant to let go of a stick even though it enjoys chasing after the stick when it is thrown. Effective trainers know not just when to use toys as reinforcers but also *how* to use them.

Effective ways of preventing misbehaviour from occurring vary with the situation. In an experiment based on the Brelands' experience with their pig and raccoon, laboratory rats were trained to collect a ball bearing from one corner of a chamber and then carry it to the opposite corner where they dropped the ball down a hole. When hungry and given a food pellet for letting go of the ball, the rats' performance started to deteriorate in the way that the Brelands had described. However, when thirsty and reinforced with water, their performance remained smooth and rapid. Presumably this was because under these conditions the ball did not become a surrogate food object that was difficult to relinquish.

The above examples of misbehaviour can be contrasted with the earlier example of the rat pushing a flap when a light comes on and obtaining the food that arrives when the light goes off. In this case classical and instrumental conditioning act in the same direction rather than compete. The implication for trainers is the need to ensure that these two most powerful ways of changing behaviour do not conflict.

Box 2.1 | Top training tips

- Train one response at a time (pages 54–6).
- Train one response for one stimulus (page 52).
- A reinforcer makes an event more likely in the future (page 40).
- Shaping relies on the reserving of reinforcement until an improved response appears (pages 40–1).
- Secondary reinforcers can be used to shape behaviours without the distraction that a primary reinforcer may create and at a distance (pages 45–7).
- Secondary reinforcers are most effectively established when presented before or up until the presentation of a primary reinforcer.
- Classical and instrumental conditioning sometimes conflict, but good trainers often combine them with excellent results (page 64).

Chapter 3

Fear, punishment and avoidance training

In Chapter 2 we looked at the various ways in which training can be based on the use of positive reinforcement or rewards. Here we look at the impact of negative, or *aversive*, events on behaviour. The short take-home message from this chapter is that the use of a stick – both literally and metaphorically – can produce rapid results. At first glance the use of aversive events in training may seem to have advantages. Some of the changes in behaviour it can produce can be difficult to obtain with positive reinforcement. However, they can sometimes be short lived and have undesirable side effects. In Chapter 2 we discussed the distinction made by learning theorists between classical and instrumental conditioning using positive reinforcement. The same distinction has been made between learning about relationships involving unpleasant events that are independent of an animal's behaviour - as in the classical conditioning of fear reactions - and various kinds of instrumental learning in which an animal has control over whether an aversive event occurs. The latter include punishment and avoidance training.

Classical conditioning involving aversive events

If animals learn to associate training sessions with bad experiences, this can be highly disruptive. A single bad experience can be sufficient to overwhelm previously conditioned pleasant associations. So even in the absence of *repeated* exposure to aversive stimuli (see sensitisation, Chapter 1) animals can learn to avoid those stimuli or their telltale warning signs. Anticipation of trouble when animals are being trained can save a great deal of time. Good preparation before training sessions can pay tremendous dividends if it means that we can prevent the occurrence of unwelcome aversive stimuli. For example, by taking a pup off its lead when introducing it to unfamiliar dogs in a park we can reduce the chances of it associating pain with the appearance of other dogs. Many pups recoil from unfamiliar conspecifics before playing and submitting; if this natural response is met with neck pain, then the pup may develop prevalent antisocial tendencies.

The first systematic experiments on aversive learning were carried out early in the twentieth century by a Russian contemporary of Ivan Pavlov. Although as famous as Pavlov when both were alive, Vladimir Bekhterev was soon almost forgotten. Like Pavlov, Bekhterev used dogs as subjects in experiments using an initially meaningless and neutral stimulus, such as a buzzer, that became a conditioned stimulus (CS) because it consistently signalled the arrival of a more important event, the unconditioned stimulus (US). While in Pavlov's laboratory food was almost always used as the US, for the dogs in Bekhterev's experiments the US was a brief electric shock to one of the rear paws. This elicited a reflex lifting of the dog's leg. If a CS such as a buzzer was repeatedly presented just before the shock was delivered, this too would come to elicit leg lifting.

Electric shock has continued to be used as an aversive event in behavioural research, although mainly with rodents as subjects. Most experiments of this kind give the animal a limited number of brief shocks set at a low intensity. Researchers continue to use electric shocks despite the connotations of torture they can evoke and the disastrous consequences for their public relations. This is because an electric shock is an aversive event that is resistant to habituation even at the low levels that are most commonly employed. Many other events are aversive to animals. For example, a flash of light or the smell of a cat may produce greater fear in a rat than a mild shock. However, the aversiveness of such events declines because of habituation, so that something that earlier produced an extreme reaction, such as a sudden loud sound, may soon be almost ignored. This change can sometimes take place after surprisingly few exposures to the aversive event. Consequently, experiments on fear conditioning using events other than electric shock can be confounded by habituation.

Rather than measuring a specific response like leg lifting, most research on shock-based learning has used more general responses. One way to assess how much fear a particular stimulus evokes is to test how much it disrupts some conditioned response. For example, a rat might be first trained to press a lever for food until a steady baseline rate of responding is maintained by a variable interval schedule of reinforcement, as described in Chapter 2. Then, a 30-second light is switched on occasionally and a shock delivered as the light goes off. The shock is delivered regardless of the rat's response, resulting in a classically conditioned association between the light and pain. The standard outcome of such a *conditioned suppression* procedure is that, each time the light comes on, the rat responds less and less frequently, and may stop altogether. However, it will continue to press the lever for food when the light is absent. When first described in 1940 by Bill Estes, a student of Skinner at Harvard University, this phenomenon was called *conditioned anxiety*. It is also sometimes called the *conditioned emotional response*.

Fig. 3.1 Tonic immobility as an innate fear response in a chicken presented with a stuffed bird of prey. After being placed on its back, the length of time a chicken will remain in that position is related to its current anxiety. This phenomenon, known as tonic immobility, has been erroneously described as a form of hypnotism for the purposes of popular entertainment. Reproduced with permission from Sandro Nocentini (after *Introduction to Animal Behaviour* by Manning and Dawkins).

Rats display a very distinctive transient *freezing* response to an unexpected sound, visual event or odour; as the term suggests, they adopt an alert, motionless standing position. This provides another way of measuring conditioned fear. Normally this freezing response rapidly disappears if no significant event follows the repeated stimulus. However, if a noise, for example, is followed by shock a few times, then this will produce a steady increase in the time the rat maintains its freezing posture when the noise is present. A similar result is obtained if the rat is placed in a context in which it has previously been shocked.

Conditioned suppression and freezing have been used in studies of fear conditioning in animals in order to understand the brain processes underlying fear reactions, or the effects of various drugs that affect fear and anxiety. These issues are not ones we are concerned with in this book. However, for animal trainers the purely behavioural results obtained from this kind of research are of tremendous importance. These have shown that the acquisition of fear is governed by the same set of principles as those governing classical conditioning with positive reinforcement. Among the most important of these is again *temporal contiguity*: thus, for example, the longer the delay between a noise and the arrival of a shock, the weaker the rat's fear response to the noise.

The important principle of stimulus competition has also emerged from these fear and anxiety studies. Leon Kamin was studying the properties of conditioned suppression in the 1960s when he came across the phenomenon of *blocking*. Using first a light to signal the arrival of shock and then, as a signal for the same shock, a compound stimulus consisting of the light and a noise, Kamin noted that his

Fig. 3.2 Shock delivered by an electric fence is used to restrict the movements of cattle because this is one of the few aversive events to which animals rarely become habituated.

rats acquired little fear of the noise. Even though the noise (accompanied by the light) had been paired with the shock many times, when presented on its own it did not affect the rate at which the rats pressed a lever for food. This occurred because prior learning about the light–shock relationship had blocked acquisition of fear to the noise. Essentially, animals learn to fear stimuli that most reliably predict an aversive event. In the above example of blocking, this information is already fully provided by the light, so the noise does not add any new information.

Other important principles of fear conditioning are also identical to those for classical conditioning with positive reinforcement. These include *latent inhibition*. This refers to the way that fear is acquired more rapidly to a novel stimulus paired with an aversive event than to a stimulus that is already familiar. *Stimulus generalisation* also applies. Once an animal has learned to fear a particular stimulus, it will also show fear of other similar stimuli. Our final example of a general principle is *extinction*. If a conditioned stimulus previously paired with a shock is presented repeatedly without any shock, it will lose its ability to evoke fear. Farmers who use electric fences to retain stock can switch the power off occasionally, but they cannot dispense with it completely or the animals will lose their fear of it.

Extinction of fear in real life usually differs from extinction in the laboratory in that the laboratory rat is normally given no opportunity to display the *flight* response that is a normal component of fear for almost all animals. In non-laboratory environments there is usually an escape route for an animal confronted by an object, scent or noise that represents danger. By removing itself from confrontation with the feared stimulus an animal also removes itself from the opportunity of learning that this stimulus is no longer dangerous. In clinical psychology a key ingredient of standard treatments for specific phobias, such as animal or social phobias, is *exposure* to the feared object. People with a pronounced fear of travelling in an elevator will usually spend energy and ingenuity to make sure they never have to confront this fear. This thwarts adaptive learning. Only when the therapist is successful in persuading the client to enter an elevator a number of times will this fear start to extinguish. Along exactly the same lines, trainers relying on extinction to get their animals to lose their fear of some object need to make sure the animal is unable to flee from it. The term *flooding* is sometimes used to describe treatments – for people as well as animals – that impose sustained contact with the object or situation that the individual has learned to fear with the aim of accelerating extinction of the fear. However, this technique is not recommended because of the distress associated with it.

Learned food aversions

Similar principles apply in another form of classical conditioning that involves aversive events. A *conditioned taste aversion* (CTA) is formed when experience of a taste – particularly a novel one – is followed by nausea. In the laboratory nausea is normally induced by injection of an otherwise harmless salt, lithium chloride. CTA, or food aversion learning, is not the only form of nausea-based conditioning. Animals can learn to avoid a place that has been paired with nausea. However, taste-nausea associations are learned a great deal more readily – often in a single trial – than associations between other kinds of events and nausea. By contrast, associations between tastes and shock are acquired only with great difficulty, whereas most animals can learn very readily to associate places, sounds or visual events with shock.

Food aversion learning provides an example of associations that can form between events separated by long intervals. Many animals, including humans, can learn to avoid foods that cause nausea even when the noxious effects take hours to develop. Rats are particularly good at learning to avoid baits that contain slow-acting poison, as long as the baits have a reasonably novel flavour and assuming the rats are not dead from their first taste. As opportunistic omnivores, rats regularly encounter novel foods. No surprise then that they are world leaders in food aversion learning. Indeed, as we saw in Chapter 2, they even have strategies to learn from their conspecifics' experience of new flavours. An arms race exists in pest control between pesticide manufacturers who must constantly develop new flavours to camouflage their products and the rats that must learn to avoid consuming them.

Food aversion learning has practical applications in other areas of pest control. One example is applying a pesticide called methiocarb to crops to prevent birds eating them. Interestingly, to maximise the effectiveness of this strategy, manufacturers have paid attention to the sensors birds use when selecting food. Whereas rats readily develop an aversion to the smell of a toxic substance, birds tend to select or reject food on the basis of its appearance. There is a narrow margin

Fig. 3.3 When a rat returns to its colony, other rats will sniff its breath and sample olfactory cues about what it might have been eating. Reproduced with permission from Darek Figa.

between repellent and lethal doses of methiocarb. When it is mixed with colourants to warn the birds of its presence, the amount of toxin can be reduced to a level below the lethal dose. The amount of methiocarb used can be further reduced by treating only part of the crop with the coloured formulation, the remainder being treated with colourant alone. This approach relies on the birds sampling the aversive portion and extrapolating their learned colour aversion to the whole field.

Food aversion learning has also been used to reduce predation on sheep by coyotes. By baiting a sheep carcase with lithium chloride that causes nausea but no lasting harm, farmers can teach a coyote to associate sheep with sickness. Such learning can have a major impact on an animal's behaviour. One dramatic example comes from a study in which two wolves were given lamb meat wrapped in fresh sheepskin and laced with lithium. This produced an acquired aversion to the smell of sheep. Afterwards, when a live sheep was introduced into their pen, the wolves backed away from it as soon as they detected its scent. Within a short time the sheep was chasing the wolves around the pen.

Food aversion learning has also been used by scientists interested in the impact of road transport on animal welfare, and for investigating the role of motion sickness in animals, such as chickens, that are incapable of vomiting. Hens are taught that food of a certain colour predicts the transport and presumably a feeling of motion sickness. The aversiveness of this feeling can be calibrated by the degree to which food is subsequently avoided.

As already noted, food aversion learning differs from other kinds of classical conditioning in its stimulus selectivity - nausea is much more easily associated with tastes than with sights or sounds - and

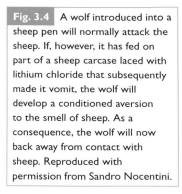

Fig. 3.4 A wolf introduced into a sheep pen will normally attack the sheep. If, however, it has fed on part of a sheep carcase laced with lithium chloride that subsequently made it vomit, the wolf will develop a conditioned aversion to the smell of sheep. As a consequence, the wolf will now back away from contact with sheep. Reproduced with permission from Sandro Nocentini.

its tolerance of longer inter-stimulus intervals. In other respects food aversion learning follows the same principles as any other form of classical conditioning. This brings us back to extinction. Under natural conditions learned food aversions can be highly persistent. Once people have acquired a strong aversion to a particular food, they may avoid it for the rest of their lives. Similarly, animals in a natural environment appear not to lose a learned food aversion. In the laboratory, similar persistence is found if a thirsty rat is tested for its preference between a bottle of unflavoured water and a bottle containing a solution of the averted taste. It will drink the plain water almost exclusively and will continue to do so even if such two-bottle choice tests are repeated many times. Such a finding can make it seem that food aversion learning is unusually resistant to extinction. However, if the thirsty rat is given no choice, but can drink only from a single bottle that contains the averted taste, it will drink more and more each time it is given this solution – so long as no alternative is available. Such an extinction treatment is analogous to the use of flooding to decrease an animal's fear.

Instrumental conditioning involving aversive events

Negative instrumental conditioning (escape training)

In Chapter 2 instrumental reinforcement was defined as an event that strengthens – in the sense of making more likely to recur – any behaviour that preceded it. The chapter included various examples of instrumental conditioning based on the use of positive reinforcement. Instrumental conditioning based on *negative reinforcement* refers to an increase in the strength of a response that has terminated or reduced some unpleasant state of affairs. Operating a switch that turns off some persistent loud noise is an example. Negative reinforcement has been central to the traditional training of horses, where removal of an unpleasant sensation is often made to follow the desired behaviour. As with positive reinforcement, negative reinforcement needs to be immediate in order to be fully effective. For example, tapping the flank with a whip to prompt sidewards movement can work as long as the tapping ceases when the horse moves laterally.

Whips provide a graphic example, but they are far from the most common source of aversive stimulation in equitation. The bits with which horses are controlled work because they cause discomfort. Although we are all used to seeing horses with bits in their mouths, we should not assume that horses tolerate them inherently. During grazing horses may take tiny bits of grit into their mouths, but they detect and expel this material and thus demonstrate tremendous oral sensitivity. This sensitivity means that young horses have to be

Fig. 3.5 This heavy-handed rider is using excessively strong rein contact, as shown by the horse's gaping mouth which is its response to pain. Reproduced with permission from Sandy Hannan.

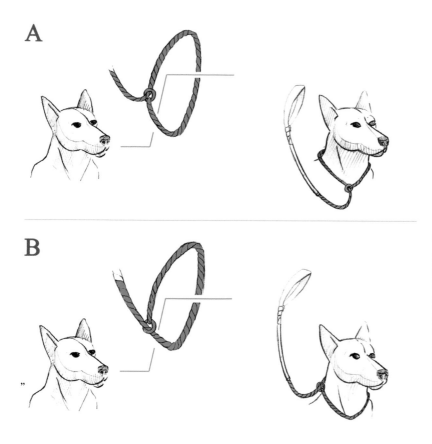

A

B

Fig. 3.6 Choke chains are ineffective and dangerous if fitted incorrectly and depend on the dog remaining on the left of the handler at all times.

a) when the chain is fitted correctly, the large end-link comes from under the dog's neck and opens up the noose to provides relief (negative reinforcement) as soon as tension on the lead is reduced;

b) when fitted incorrectly, the large end-link rests on the back of the dog's neck and acts as a ratchet, remaining tight regardless of the handler's use of the lead and giving no relief (negative reinforcement) when the dog is walking 'to heel'. Reproduced with permission from Sandro Nocentini.

'mouthed' i.e. habituated to the presence of the bit in their mouths. In the right hands, pressure on the mouth is so mild as to be almost benign.

Equestrian interventions that use aversive stimuli from the rein, leg or whip tend to include an inherent subtle cue, i.e. an initial light increase in pressure. This precedes the immediate increase in pressure to a higher level when there is a lack of response from the horse. The pressure is subsequently released immediately when the horse gives the desired response. The light increase is the cue part of each intervention. Later on through repetition of the uniformity of this structure, the horse responds through classical conditioning to additional cues, including slight changes in the position of the rider.

Outstanding equitation should revolve around subtle use of these aversive stimuli. In 1761, Henry, Earl of Pembroke, wrote a treatise on breaking horses and teaching soldiers to ride. He advised that 'that hand, which by giving and taking properly, gains its point with the least force, is best; and the horse's mouth under this same hand's directions will consequently be the best'. Unfortunately, there is a trend for heavy handedness in elite dressage competitions that is legitimising the use of excessive force. Riders need to be reminded that, as long as force is used, force will be required. The use of too much 'contact' with the horse's mouth does not just mean that the horse has to tolerate unnecessary discomfort. It makes the horse less sensitive, because failure to release the tension on the reins eventually causes the horse to habituate to the aversive stimulation. Ultimately the horse becomes 'hard-mouthed' (unresponsive), precisely what Pembroke was trying to avoid.

In a similar way, the use in dog training of choke chains can only be humane if their characteristic sound acts as a warning to the dog. If the dog ignores the warning, then pain will usually follow. Sadly, few people use these dangerous devices properly, namely by releasing the tension on the leads as soon as their dogs respond appropriately by no longer pulling. Instead owners tend to hang on and launch into the first bouts of a tug-of-war tournament that is endless for both parties, frustrating for the humans and worst of all painful for the dogs. Meanwhile, many more owners fit choke chains incorrectly, forming a unidirectional ratchet device that eliminates any possibility of reinforcement by relief from neck pain.

Punishment

What is the best way to change a persistent bad habit that, say, a companion animal has acquired? Take as an example a cat that often scratches vigorously at the upholstery. One thing to try is to have a can containing some coins nearby and rattle this loudly whenever the cat starts to scratch. For a cat such a sudden loud noise is a very unpleasant event. If scratching the furniture becomes less frequent, then this provides an example of an effective punishment procedure. In everyday usage 'punishment' is usually delivered by one individual to another. In learning theory terms its meaning is more general; it refers to any procedure which reduces the frequency of a response by making an aversive event contingent on performance of that response. To keep dogs in gardens without real fences, invisible fences can be used whereby underground wires trigger a shock from the dog's collar whenever it starts to cross the boundary. In this example, the response of 'crossing the boundary' is punished by the delivery of shock, even though no person is directly involved.

Punishment can be highly effective, but it can go wrong. Like positively reinforced behaviour, punished behaviour can come under stimulus control. The cat may no longer scratch when its owner is nearby, but the furniture may still be at its mercy when it is on its own in the room. The most effective way to avoid this problem, and generally to increase the effectiveness of a punishment procedure, is to provide an alternative response. If scratching the upholstery immediately produces a loud noise, while scratching at a post nearby does not, then the cat will quickly develop a preference for the scratching post, a preference that is likely to persist whether or not the owner is in the room.

This helps to explain the importance in animal behaviour therapy of identifying the motivation that prompts animals to perform

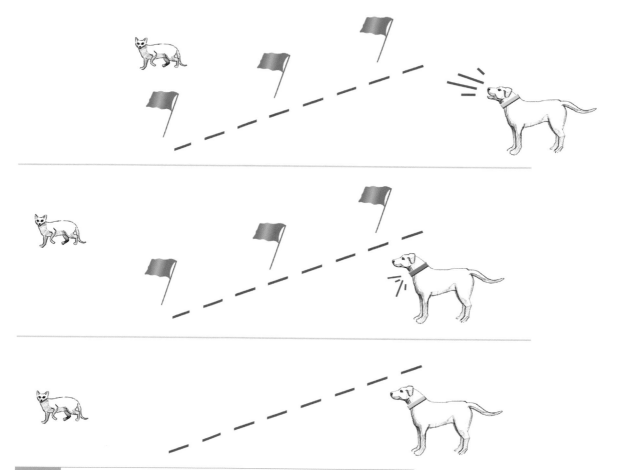

Fig. 3.7 For a so-called invisible fence to function, a dog has to wear a shock-collar with a matched receiver. When it comes close to the buried wire, the collar makes a sound before emitting a shock (US). Both the flags and the sound may become CS and therefore warning signals. In principle, very few shocks are needed before the dog learns not to approach the line even when the flags are no longer present. In parts of the world, this apparatus is illegal. Reproduced with permission from Sandro Nocentini.

unwelcome behaviours. By doing so therapists can suggest alternative behavioural responses that provide outlets through which the animals can express their behavioural needs. Some of the worst uses of punishment are those in which the punishing event tends to elicit just the response that it is intended to prevent. Whipping a horse for bolting will usually serve to rocket it forth once more. More generally, punishment of behaviour related to anxiety – such as some kinds of barking by a dog – is likely to be counterproductive, since the punishment can produce an unwelcome and inhumane escalation of distress.

If there are no alternative treatments, there may be ways of maximising the effectiveness of punishment. For instance, by using an aversive sound such as a high-pitched alarm it may be possible to

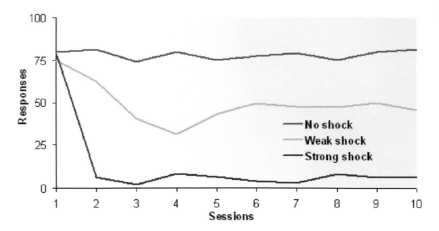

In this hypothetical example an animal trained to respond in a Skinner box on an intermittent schedule of reinforcement will normally continue responding at a steady rate. If a punishment contingency is now introduced so that some responses are immediately followed by a weak shock, some immediate suppression of responding will follow. However, responding is then likely to recover and may even return to the original level. In contrast the introduction of punishment by a strong shock will produce almost complete suppression of the behaviour that may last indefinitely. Reproduced with permission from Danielle Karazinov.

distract, as well as punish, the perpetrator. This is likely to be particularly effective if the alarming stimulus is presented at the beginning of the unwelcome behaviour sequence. It is much easier to distract an early link in a behavioural chain since this is most remote in time from the eventual reinforcement. This may be important in the use by trainers of marine animals of what they commonly refer to as the *least reinforcing stimulus* (LRS). If, for example, a dolphin starts to make a mess of a training session it may be sent back into its quarters; this can be seen as a punishment procedure involving a 'sin bin'. Another term used to denote removal of the animal from the training opportunity, or just removal of attention from the trainer, is *time out*. This also can be used very effectively as a mild punisher to reduce unwanted behaviour.

As suggested in Chapter 2, the owner who sees in the distance his dog behaving badly, calls the dog back and then beats the dog is unlikely to have any effect on the dog's bad behaviour. Instead, the dog is likely to associate responding appropriately to a call with the beating and to learn to fear its owner. This illustrates another poor use of punishment in training, that of allowing a delay between the targeted behaviour and the aversive event. More generally, a pervasive problem with punishment procedures is that the negative emotion produced by the aversive event - whether it be an electric shock, a loud noise, a sharp pain or a blow from a stick - can become associated either with the immediate source of the punishment, human or otherwise, or even the particular place where it happened. As with classical conditioning, these various kinds of event compete for association with

Table 3.1	Effect of the treatment	
Response becomes more likely in future	Response becomes less likely in future
Positive reinforcement – titbit reinforces begging.	Positive punishment – applying tension on the lead increases choking action and neck pain.
Negative reinforcement – easing tension on the lead reduces choking action and neck pain.	Negative punishment – complete removal of food extinguishes begging.

the emotion. Such competition was seen in the *blocking effect* discussed earlier in the context of fear conditioning and in the *overshadowing* of one stimulus by another, discussed in Chapter 2. Success in this competition between responses, agents, places and other stimuli depends on a number of factors, including their relative novelty and their perceptual salience.

Even under laboratory conditions, it is not always clear whether the use of a punishment procedure has resulted in the animal learning to associate a specific response with the aversive outcome; for example, that scratching the upholstery is followed by a loud noise. Instead it may produce general fearfulness that results in conditioned suppression of all behaviour in the particular context. Provision of an alternative response helps to ensure that only the punished response is reduced. Furthermore, this will make it less likely that the undesired behaviour will return if the punishment procedure is no longer applied. The suppressive effects of punishment can extinguish, just like any other learned change in behaviour, when the contingency that produced the change no longer holds.

Finally, laboratory research has shown two more ways in which the effectiveness of punishment can be undermined. The first is when the intensity of the aversive event is at first low and then gradually increased each time it is repeated. This results in the behaviour becoming very persistent. An instance of this is the use, when unwanted behaviour occurs, of a scolding cry that starts quite softly but becomes sharp and strong after the behaviour has been repeated many times. The second way punishment can be undermined is by inconsistency. If the behaviour is sometimes followed by an aversive outcome and sometimes not, it is likely to persist.

Negative reinforcement versus punishment

Let us suppose that after our begging dog has been taken away from the table, he is taken to the park and trained to walk to heel using a choke chain. Now we have an opportunity to consider, in the Table 3.1 above, how both reinforcement (a titbit of food) and punishment (a yank on the choke chain) can be positive and negative. Be it positive or negative, reinforcement will always make a response more likely in future. Conversely, positive or negative punishment will always make a response less likely in future.

Both punishment and negative reinforcement are consequences of behaviour and, as such, can be powerful agents for changing behaviour. Many trainers claim not to use negative reinforcement, but often are instead simply avoiding the use of a term that seems to have unpleasant connotations. It is almost politically incorrect. Unfortunately, this seems to have muddied the waters of animal training. In this context, negative refers to the removal of something from the animal's world, while positive refers to an addition. So, when trainers reinforce a behaviour with the removal of something unpleasant, they make the behaviour more likely in the future. The response has been negatively reinforced. Punishment and negative reinforcement are interrelated. By definition, a stimulus must be aversive in order for its removal to be reinforcing. So, in order to use negative reinforcement a trainer has to have used positive punishment as well.

Negative punishment, or omission, often forms an important part of attempts to improve or modify responses. Animals being trained in some new behaviour will first attempt to use an established response. The absence of reinforcement at that point makes repetition of this now unwanted response less likely. Reinforcement has been omitted and therefore the animal has been negatively punished. This makes it more likely to respond in new ways. The trial-and-error process continues.

The use in dogs of training discs, as developed by the late John Fisher, relies on omission or what can be regarded as a secondary punisher. These training discs make a characteristic sound when rattled or thrown to the ground. They are introduced to the dog in association with the removal of food that the dog is expecting to consume. This is done three or four times so that the discs become strongly associated with frustration. Once the association is established the discs can be presented when unwelcome behaviour, such as barking in the car, occurs. Throwing the discs can stop the response for a brief period and give the trainer an opportunity to reward the dog for stopping. In a similar and much more general way the command 'No!' can function as a secondary punisher that has gained its effectiveness by association with omission of some positive event – if only praise or attention – that the animal would normally expect.

'Punishment' is not in itself a dirty word. Nor is 'negative'. Both negative punishment and positive punishment can be extremely mild. The degree to which one relies on either reinforcers or punishers and the consistency with which one applies them are what matters to the animal.

Avoidance learning

A leading trainer of trick horses is able to get horses to gallop to her almost wherever she may be. They will even plunge into the surf in dramatic style simply to be close to her. Any reader who has had

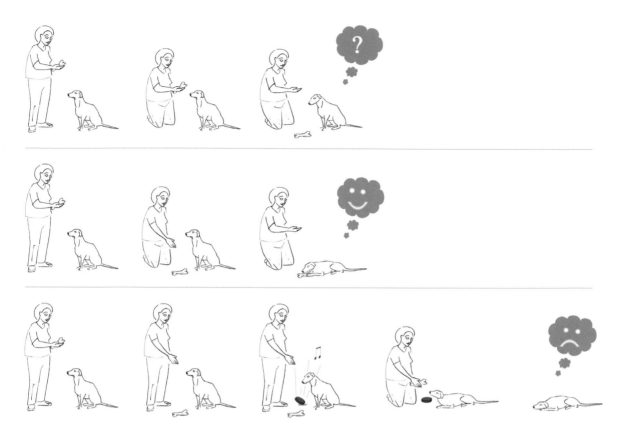

Fig. 3.9 Training discs can be used as secondary punishers for dogs. The discs acquire this property by being paired with the frustrating removal of food. As shown here, steps in the introduction of training discs, include:

- Dog sitting and having food placed on ground
- Dog being told to 'take it' and eating food
- Dog sitting and having food placed on ground, then discs thrown down just before food is removed.

Reproduced with permission from Sandro Nocentini.

trouble catching a horse or pony may be puzzled as to how this is achieved. The trainer's solution has been to use avoidance training. To explain best what this term means in learning theory we need to go back to research that started in mid-twentieth-century America.

The difference between experiments in Bekhterev's laboratory and most of those run in Pavlov's laboratory did not just lie in the use of shock by Bekhterev and of food by Pavlov. Another important difference was that - possibly for ethical reasons - the behaviour of Bekhterev's dogs could usually affect what happened on a trial. When the buzzer was sounded and then the shock started, if the leg was lifted, then the shock was terminated. Thus, the animal could *escape* the shock. Hobart Mowrer was an American psychologist who followed up on this kind of research. He noted the distinction between

Fig. 3.10 Shuttle boxes have been widely used with dogs and rats in the study of avoidance learning. In 2-way shuttle training an animal can prevent the delivery of shock by moving from one compartment to the other as soon as a warning signal such as a sound is presented. Reproduced with permission from Sandro Nocentini.

such escape learning and the procedures used with Pavlov's dogs, who could do nothing to affect whether, when or how much food arrived on each trial. In 1939, Mowrer became one of the first theorists to draw a clear distinction between classical and instrumental conditioning procedures based on whether or not the animal's behaviour affects the outcome. So far we have discussed two kinds of instrumental conditioning involving aversive events: *punishment*, where a response is likely to produce an aversive event, and *negative reinforcement* – or escape learning – where a response is likely to terminate some aversive event. Mowrer and others introduced the idea of a third kind of aversion-based instrumental conditioning: *avoidance learning*. Their ideas on avoidance were based on experiments using animals in a shuttle box.

As shown in Fig. 3.10, a shuttle box is divided into two compartments separated by a barrier. In a typical shuttle box for rats, the barrier has a central opening that allows a rat to pass from one compartment to the other. When used with dogs, the barrier is one that a dog can jump over to get from one side to the other. The metal grid floors make it possible to deliver shock to either or both compartments. A standard avoidance learning procedure using discrete trials is one where each trial starts with a warning signal (WS). Some fixed time later – say, ten seconds – the shock starts. It is arranged to terminate as soon as the animal, such as a rat, moves to the other compartment. Normally rats learn such (negatively reinforced) *escape* behaviour within a few trials. The additional *avoidance* contingency is the rule that, if the animal makes this response before the shock is due to arrive – i.e. less than ten seconds after the WS starts, in the present example – no shock is delivered. Thus, making the avoidance response *prevents* the shock from occurring on that trial. Under the right conditions animals learn such an avoidance response very rapidly and continue to perform in a highly effective way so that the shock is rarely delivered after the initial learning phase.

We can now see how avoidance training can be used to get horses to plunge through the surf. In the example above, the horses wear an

Fig. 3.11 A horse-training device called Smartrein™, being developed (by Paul McGreevy and Amanda Warren-Smith) to issue a warning signal before the bit pressure increases. This provides the horse with a chance to respond appropriately to light pressure before the bit becomes painful. This functions in an analogous way to the use of verbal 'left' or 'right' commands to plough horses. Reproduced with permission from Greg Jones.

electric shock collar around their necks. The trainer fires a cap gun as the warning signal that the shock is coming. Starting in a small paddock, she applies the shock until the horse moves towards her. The horse is shaped to come very close to the trainer to escape or avoid the shock. The sooner it comes, the sooner the shock abates. And, if it comes quickly enough when the gun is fired, no shock is delivered. The process is then repeated in larger areas, graduating from small paddocks to large fields, until the horse will find his trainer even when she is in the next valley. This technique allows her to travel in the back of a pick-up truck and call the horse that can then be filmed at full gallop again and again.

Most studies of avoidance learning using shuttle boxes have used warning signals, as in the example above. However, it is also possible to train avoidance behaviour without using a warning signal. Thus, rats can learn to press a lever under conditions in which no shock is delivered as long as lever-pressing occurs with a certain frequency, but a shock is given as soon as some specified amount of time has elapsed since the last response. Avoidance learning under such conditions is typically slower than when an imminent aversive event is preceded by a warning signal.

Given that more effective learning occurs when there is a warning signal that some aversive event is on its way, it is interesting to speculate why a system of warning signals is not used more frequently in equitation. One example is the 'half-halt check', an increase in the 'contact' between the hand and the bit, a transient tightening of the reins. Unfortunately, many riders struggle to deliver half-halts with sufficient distinction from regular increases in rein pressure as applied in reducing speed or turning. When they fail to give distinctive half-halt signals, they end up confusing their horses. It may be

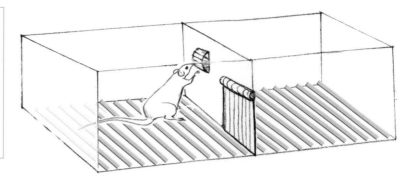

Fig. 3.12 After the rat has experienced an electric shock or two in the left-hand compartment, escape into the other compartment can serve as *negative reinforcement* for turning the wheel that opens the door between the two compartments. Reproduced with permission from Sandro Nocentini.

time to apply technology and design reins that are fitted with auditory warning devices that consistently alert the horse to increases in pressure from the bit. This could work in the same way that the sound of a choke chain does in dog training.

Mowrer provided a possible reason for the effectiveness of procedures employing warning signals. His two-process theory of avoidance learning claimed that this starts with classical conditioning of fear to the warning signal. Because the warning signal precedes the shock, it functions as a classically conditioned stimulus just as it would in an experiment designed explicitly to study fear conditioning. The second stage is an instrumental one: the consequence of making the avoidance response is that fear is decreased. In a typical shuttle box experiment from Mowrer's era the warning signal was switched off, along with the shock, when the animal made the avoidance response. Thus, according to this theory avoidance behaviour is motivated by fear and negatively reinforced by *escape* from fear.

There is no doubt that animals can learn to escape from stimuli, like a warning signal, or places that they have learned to fear. In a classic experiment, related to Mowrer's theory, rats in the first stage of training received some shocks in one compartment of a shuttle box from which they could not escape. For the next stage a wheel was placed in this compartment that, when turned, opened the door into the other compartment of the shuttle box. No shock was employed in this stage. The rats readily learned to turn the wheel so that they could escape into the other compartment. This is highly significant because the only consequence of this response was to terminate the threatening cues of the first compartment. It provides a further demonstration that animals can learn new behaviours in the absence of primary reinforcement, just as shown in Chapter 2 by the use of secondary positive reinforcers such as a clicker in training and earlier in this chapter by Fisher's use of training discs that function as a secondary punisher.

Evidence that animals can learn a new response to escape from a stimulus they have come to fear does not prove, as claimed by Mowrer, that this is all there is to avoidance learning. His theory has problems in explaining how free operant avoidance behaviour is learned in the absence of any warning signal. Furthermore, an animal

a

b

c

> **Fig. 3.13** The Federation Equestre Internationale has banned the use of the so-called 'rapping' technique. This is a form of avoidance training whereby the horse can prevent being whipped or hit by the 'rapping' pole if it clears a jump at a greater height than is really necessary. The red dot in these diagrams represents a rapping pole that is controlled by a trainer standing by the side of a jump. The sequence shows what can happen early in such training:
>
> a) The horse approaches the fence as normal
> b) The horse takes off, having committed itself to jump at a seemingly adequate height
> c) The rapping pole is raised so that the horse hits it.
>
> Reproduced with permission from Sandro Nocentini.

that has had extensive training on an avoidance response often shows no signs of fear, but instead performs in a smooth and highly effective way. For these and other reasons most theorists have concluded that, although Mowrer's two-process theory gives a good account of how an avoidance response is first acquired, long-term performance depends on more than escape from fear. This other source of reinforcement is what common sense might have seemed to suggest all along: namely, prevention of the aversive event itself. However, although it is natural to assume that this is what is sustaining a particular example of avoidance behaviour, this may not always be correct. In many cases avoidance responding may indeed be reinforced by termination of a signal for the aversive event, as described by Mowrer.

Avoidance learning shares the same properties as other kinds of instrumental conditioning. For example, discrete trial avoidance learning is sensitive to the temporal contiguity between the response and termination of a warning signal. Also, like any other kind of instrumental response, free operant avoidance behaviour can come under stimulus control; thus, for example, a rat might be trained to press a lever to avoid shock only when a light is on, just as lever-pressing for food can be controlled by such a discriminative stimulus. A notable feature of avoidance behaviour can be its persistence. In experiments using a shuttle box, dogs were first given extensive training to avoid shock by jumping from one side to the other whenever the warning signal was given. Once they were performing at a high level the shock generator was switched off, but still the warning signal was repeatedly sounded. The dogs continued to jump to this signal for a very large number of trials.

Such persistence of avoidance behaviour makes sense, of course, since until an animal occasionally fails to make the response when the warning signal arrives it has no way of knowing that the threat of shock is no longer a real one. One way of achieving rapid extinction of avoidance behaviour is to prevent the response from occurring. In a shuttle box this can be done by confining the dog or rat to one compartment and presenting the warning signal a number of times. Such a *response blocking* procedure can lead to a reappearance of strong fear that then declines; when the opportunity to make the avoidance response is returned - i.e. the animal can again get to the other compartment when the warning signal is presented - the behaviour is much weaker and soon may stop altogether.

One final point about avoidance learning needs to be made for readers who may consult other books or scientific journals on this topic. What we have described here is sometimes called *active avoidance*. Such training should be distinguished from what is - in our view - sometimes confusingly called *passive avoidance*. The latter has been used to refer to training in which an animal receives a shock or some other aversive event if it makes a particular response, but no shock is delivered if it remains 'passive', i.e. does *not* make the response. For example, many experiments have used a 'step down' test where a rat is placed on a small platform above a grid floor and it quickly learns that, if it steps down onto the floor, it will receive a shock through its paws. In everyday terms we might describe it as learning to 'avoid' stepping on the grid floor. A similar example is where monkeys used as 'helping hands' for quadriplegics are trained not to touch - and thus to 'passively avoid' - parts of their environment marked with distinctive dots. However, these are both examples of what we described earlier in this chapter as a *punishment* procedure. To avoid confusion the common practice of learning theorists has been to reserve the term *avoidance* to training that requires a specific response to prevent something aversive happening and *punishment* to training in which only performance of a specific response produces an aversive outcome.

Interactions between different forms of aversively motivated behaviour

The relationships between the different forms of aversively motivated behaviour discussed in this chapter are shown in Fig. 3.14. The major divide is between classically conditioned behaviour - where the

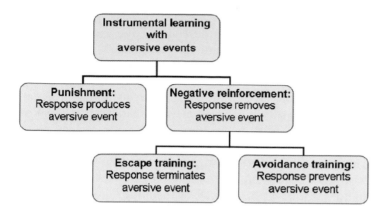

Fig. 3.14 Aversive events can be used in a variety of ways in training. Thus, behaviour can be suppressed using *punishment*, where the aversive event follows a response, or increased using some form of *negative reinforcement*, as in escape training and avoidance training. Reproduced with permission from Danielle Karazinov.

animal has no control over whether or when some aversive event will occur - and instrumentally conditioned behaviour that does give the animal some control. In human terms this corresponds closely to the difference between involuntary behaviour - such as blushing with embarrassment or feeling strong anxiety when these reactions are ones we would like not to happen - and voluntary behaviour - as when pushing the mute button for the TV is negatively reinforced by removal of a loud and irritating ad. Although neat distinctions of the kind shown in Fig. 3.14 can be made at a theoretical level, in reality most training schemes produce a mixture of different kinds of learning. Sometimes classical conditioning can make instrumental learning easier, as suggested, for example, by Mowrer's two-process theory of avoidance learning. But sometimes classical conditioning can interfere with aversively based instrumental learning, just as in the cases of positively reinforced behaviour described as *misbehaviour* in Chapter 2. We have already seen that punishing behaviour that resembles a classically conditioned response to fear may be entirely counterproductive.

A comparable example of an interaction between classical and instrumental processes is the dependence of avoidance learning on the nature of the response. An animal will show rapid avoidance learning if the response corresponds to or is highly consistent with one of its *species-specific defence reactions*. For the rat, as for most other species, fleeing is one such reaction. Consequently, the shuttle box is particularly effective for promoting rapid avoidance learning, since the avoidance response is completely compatible, if not identical, to a classically conditioned fear response of a rat or dog. In contrast, pressing a lever is not something that the average rat does when afraid and it can prove difficult, although by no means impossible, to train rats to perform this response to avoid shock. Free operant avoidance behaviour by a rat in a Skinner box is much more easily obtained if a wheel is mounted on the wall of the box instead of a lever. The lesson for trainers is that avoidance learning is an effective method only if the target behaviour is consistent with one of the animal's natural responses to fear.

The other kind of interaction between classically conditioned behaviour and avoidance learning depends on the spatial relationship between a warning signal and the animal. As predicted by Mowrer's theory and demonstrated by a very large number of shuttle box experiments, it is very easy to train an avoidance response that consists of moving away from a fear-inducing warning signal. The corollary was first documented from avoidance learning research with cats: it can be almost impossible for an animal to acquire an avoidance response that involves approach *towards* a warning signal. The description of avoidance training in horses given earlier might seem to provide a counterexample to this principle, in that the trainer fired a cap gun as the warning signal for the horses to move towards her. However, this was not a maintained signal and so not one that was terminated only when the horse began to make the avoidance response. We can only speculate that training might have been much more rapid with two trainers at a distance from each other and with the horses in between. In this hypothetical situation the horses should rapidly learn to move towards trainer A when trainer B fired the gun.

Some of the most important tests of the two-process theory of avoidance learning were carried out in the 1960s by Richard Solomon and his students at the University of Pennsylvania. In one of these experiments a dramatic discovery was made that has had a far-reaching impact on human psychology as well as on learning theory based on animal research. A group of dogs was exposed to a series of inescapable shocks the day before they started standard shuttle-box avoidance training. In the shuttle box they showed no sign of learning to make even an escape response when the shock was delivered, whereas a control group that on the previous day had been restrained in the same way, but had not been shocked, learned rapidly to escape in the normal way. In 1967 two of Solomon's students, Martin Seligman and Steve Maier, followed up the initial discovery and found that to produce this interference effect prior exposure to shock per se was not enough; the shock had to be inescapable. They demonstrated this by including a group of dogs that during the pretreatment session were able to make a response - pushing a panel with their heads - to escape from a shock once it started. The next day dogs from this 'escape' group were placed in the shuttle box and learned just as readily as dogs that had not been shocked at all before. In contrast, dogs that during the pretreatment session were given exactly the same experience of shocks as the escape group, but with no opportunity to escape, displayed signs of helplessness and failed to show any learning in the shuttle box. This key experiment, and the many since that have used this kind of experimental design, show that it is lack of control over aversive events that produces the interference effect.

Seligman and Maier noted that dogs given uncontrollable shock seemed emotionally disturbed, not just profoundly impaired in learning to make an escape response in a shuttle box. They proposed the *learned helplessness* hypothesis; this claims that exposure to uncontrollable aversive events produces both an emotional and a cognitive deficit. The emotional deficit refers to the listlessness – the low level of activity and of general responsiveness – displayed by a dog that has been exposed to this experience. The cognitive deficit refers to impairment in its ability to associate its responses with their outcome; for example, even when such a dog did make an escape response in the shuttle box, it seemed to learn very little from its success.

Researchers subsequently found that similar effects could be found in other species. From the 1970s onwards most experiments on learned helplessness have used rats. The effects of uncontrollable shock are not as dramatic in rats as in dogs. The effects are also found in mice, but it turns out that this can depend on what strain of mouse is used. Also, there is some evidence that lack of control over positive events can also produce helplessness-like effects. A developmental study found that, if infant rhesus monkeys were given control over access to food, water and toys, they grew up to be less fearful than fellow monkeys that, as infants, had been denied any control over the positive events in their lives. Research of this kind illustrates the benefits of providing animals with enriched environments. Further examples are studies in which giving young mice and rats access to a running wheel or highly varied living spaces has produced lifelong benefits.

Many learned helplessness experiments with rats and mice have aimed at gaining a better understanding of the neurochemical changes that might be taking place. This research has contributed to the development of antidepressant medications for humans. It has also been suggested that learned helplessness provides an animal model of the human condition that was originally called 'shell shock', but is currently known as *post-traumatic stress disorder*. This suggestion has been supported by a recent study by Maier of how the otherwise transient impact on rats of a series of inescapable shocks can be prolonged. It turned out that giving the rats a 'reminder' of this stressful experience by placing them in the chamber where the shocks had been delivered would almost double the length of time that they remained in a helpless condition. Giving a series of occasional reminders extended this time almost indefinitely. The implication for the trainer is that an animal will normally show spontaneous recovery from the effects of a single traumatising event, as long as it is not exposed within a day or two to stimuli that are associated with the event. Maier also found that reminders had to remain brief to retain their effectiveness. If, instead of ten minutes in the chamber where its ten-minute shock session had been given, a rat was placed there for 90 minutes, this served as a *flooding* treatment producing extinction of the association with shock so that subsequent placement in the chamber no longer had any reminder effect.

There is still considerable controversy over how best to characterise learned helplessness effects. Some research has suggested that uncontrollable aversive events produce generalised anxiety or shifts in an animal's attention; i.e. in the classes of stimuli it focuses on or learns about more readily. For the trainer, however, the important lessons to be drawn are that: exposure to uncontrollable aversive events can make an animal unresponsive and hard to train; the extent of this deficit can vary very widely from species to species; the duration of this deficit can also vary widely, from a day or two to much longer periods, especially if the animal is reminded of the traumatic experience; animals with prior training involving *controllable* aversive events are unlikely to show this deficit when later exposed to uncontrollable aversive events; and – although there is no direct evidence for this – it seems likely that young animals are more vulnerable to learned helplessness than older animals.

Box 3.1 | Top training tips

- A punisher makes an event less likely in the future (page 75).
- Punishment can be effective when the punishing agent is only mildly aversive (page 74).
- Aversive stimuli should only be used in training with great care (pages 77–8).
- Removal of aversive stimuli is reinforcing (pages 74–5).
- Once an animal has learned to fear a particular stimulus, it will also show fear of other similar stimuli (pages 69–70).
- Fear often disrupts conditioned responses (page 74).

Chapter 4

Animal intelligence

Animal consciousness and animal needs

When interacting with animals, it is natural to wonder what they are thinking about and experiencing. Any number of questions of this kind can arise. Are animals conscious in the way that humans are conscious? Does an animal ever know why a particular event happened? Do animals feel pain or experience happiness as humans do? Do birds and bees see the colour green in the way we do? Given that bees are also sensitive to ultraviolet light, what does this seem like to them? Bats, although mammals, have such a different lifestyle from humans, as well as different sensory mechanisms such as sonar; so what is it like to be a bat?

Unfortunately, no kind of evidence can tell us what the conscious experience of an animal is like. To believe that any animal experiences similar feelings and perceptual experiences to those of fellow human beings is an act of faith. It is a belief that is widespread in urbanised Western societies where an increasing proportion of the population have little contact with animals other than companion animals. Perhaps that is why there is now more generosity towards animals than in the past. However, while it can be easy to empathise with a fellow mammal such as a cat, dog or horse, this is not as easy towards a cockroach, let alone some creature that we can hardly see with the naked eye.

Even though we cannot tell what the conscious experience of an animal is like, we can find out what it likes or dislikes and what needs it has. Choice measurements offer a way of determining, for example, what kind of floor a battery hen prefers to stand on. In this particular case it turned out that the floor that humans had predicted would be most comfortable for a hen - a heavy-gauge wire - was not what hens preferred; they preferred a thin-gauge wire floor that researchers incorrectly assumed to be painful. Even though we may not know what an electric shock feels like to a rat, we can observe its effects in terms of fear-related behaviour, and perhaps ultrasonic distress cries in the context where the shock had been delivered. By observing the facial reactions of a rat, or by measuring how much it drinks, when given a particular taste, we can find out whether the taste is unpleasant, pleasant or neutral to the rat. To a surprisingly large extent rats like and dislike the same tastes as humans. Nevertheless, there are some marked differences. For example, while rats show as strong a preference for sugar as people, they are indifferent to the chemical aspartame. This is the artificial sweetener that the food industry uses on a huge scale because people generally find it an acceptable substitute for sugar.

Another way to find out about an animal's needs is to provide it with a manipulandum (see Chapter 2) that gives it instrumental control over some aspect of its environment. Thus, pigs have been trained to operate cold showers when the ambient temperature increases, hens to control infra-red lights according to their thermal preferences and mice to switch their cage lighting on or off according to when they need to sleep. Arranging that a single response will, say, turn on a shower or switch off a light provides little indication of the relative reinforcing values of such resources. The strength of a reinforcer or preference can be assessed using techniques to estimate what is known as *consumer demand*. Essentially, these measure what 'price' an animal will pay in order to obtain some object or outcome. In the 1930s experimenters measured what shock level a rat would accept from an electrified grid floor it had to cross in order to reach a particular resource on the other side. Not surprisingly, when the resource was food, the acceptable shock level increased as time went by since a rat had last fed. Perhaps more enlightening was the discovery that the highest levels were tolerated by mother rats whose pups were on the other side of the grid.

The more humane methods of recent decades for assessing an animal's demand count the number of responses it will make to obtain some outcome; that is, how much work it is prepared to invest. This relies on the animal being motivated to acquire the resource, that is, to find it reinforcing. In a commonly used procedure an animal is initially required to make only a few responses to obtain a particular reinforcer, but each time a reinforcer is obtained the requirement is increased by some fixed amount. The 'break point' at which the animal stops responding reflects the strength of a reinforcer. When used in experiments on addictions in animals, this break point can be very high. For some reinforcers an animal may be prepared to pay any price. In the language of economic theory such demands are 'inelastic'. For example, it turns out that the demand of hens for a nest at the time of laying is inelastic.

Two notes of caution are needed about such preference measures. The first is that they measure the immediate appeal of some object, situation or substance. They may not always reflect wise choices. As with people, animals may well prefer something that in the long run is harmful. Sweet foods and addictive drugs are important examples. An early-twentieth-century physiologist, Walter Cannon, introduced the phrase, 'the wisdom of the body', to capture his belief that animals are even more likely than people to regulate their lives in a way that is optimal for healthy survival. This phrase may well express some general truth - a species with a foolish body would soon become extinct - but, since Cannon's time, many limits to the 'body's wisdom' have been documented.

The second note of caution is that measures of preference are always relative. This is obvious when an animal is faced with a choice between A and B, as with a hen given two types of floor or a rat given a bottle of sugar water next to a bottle of plain water. It is less obvious when, for example, we test how many lever presses a rat will make to open a door to enter a running wheel. It could depend on whether the alternative is to remain in a small, featureless cage or in a large, complex and stimulating environment. More generally, preferences can often turn out to depend on an animal's current state; the choices made by a well fed and watered dog are likely to be quite different from those of a lean and hungry one.

This point about the relativity of likes and dislikes is important to the question of whether animals enjoy being trained. In most cases the combination of novelty and varied stimulation in a safe context, together with close attention from the trainer, is likely to be attractive relative to an otherwise humdrum life - unless, of course, the training procedure contains an excess of aversive treatment. In operant conditioning experiments that require an animal to make some complex discrimination it is routinely found that, even though in early stages of training the pigeon, rat or monkey may need to be highly motivated to work for food by maintaining a restricted feeding schedule, very little food deprivation is required once training has become routine. Some experiments have even found that well-trained pigeons will continue to peck a response key to obtain grain even though a full cup of the same grain is available in the conditioning chamber. However, as long as the pigeon is as familiar with eating from the cup as from the grain hopper, this effect is small and may depend on *sensory* reinforcement provided by the sound of the hopper being operated. In an otherwise monotonous environment, a sound or switching a light on or off can serve as weak reinforcement for the instrumental response that produces such a stimulus change. Some kinds of training may become enjoyable for their own sake and not just as an escape from boredom. This probably depends on the extent to which the trained behaviour becomes a form of play for the animal.

Do animals think?

Most readers are probably sure that, for example, insect behaviour is entirely instinctive and that no insect is capable of thinking, whereas mammals and possibly other vertebrates display at least some degree of thought. But what does it mean when we claim that an animal is, or has been, 'thinking'? We can expect a reasonable answer if we ask someone else: 'What are you thinking about?' Obviously no animal could answer such a question because no other species shares our language. Thus, we cannot find out directly whether an animal experiences 'having thoughts' any more than we can answer any other kind of question about an animal's conscious experience. Nevertheless, it is possible to look for evidence to answer a slightly different question: do animals at least sometimes behave in ways that are more complex than instinctive reactions to particular stimuli or conditioned responses they have previously learned? More specifically, we can ask whether a particular animal or species can remember, can count, has a sense of time, or can solve a problem or otherwise show an ability we might call 'reasoning'. These are questions that *can* be addressed by experiments and this area of research - *animal cognition* - has recently become a particularly lively one. The rest of this chapter discusses some of the findings from this research.

Memory

In Chapter 2 the concept of extinction was introduced in the context of one of Pavlov's earliest experiments on classical conditioning. As a procedure, it refers to withholding the unconditioned stimulus (US), or reinforcer, that has previously been paired with the conditioned stimulus (CS). As a result, responding to the CS ceases; Pavlov's dogs stopped salivating to the sound of the metronome. We saw that extinction also applies to instrumental conditioning; if the reinforcer no longer follows the instrumental response, then the response becomes increasingly infrequent. Unlike Pavlov, for some reason the pioneer of instrumental conditioning research, Thorndike, did not study extinction. He probably took it for granted that, once extinction was introduced, his dogs or cats would soon stop operating the latch or paddle on the floor that had previously opened the door to their puzzle box. However, he did ask a different question about what his animals had learned: would they later forget what to do in a puzzle box?

To answer this question he trained them in a particular puzzle box and then let different animals stay in their home quarters for varying periods, ranging from days to weeks, before testing them in their puzzle boxes once again. He found that all the animals performed well, however long it was since their last training session. So, if the question 'Do animals have a memory?' means 'Can the effects of training persist over long periods?', then the answer Thorndike obtained - as have many researchers since - is 'Yes'. Perhaps this should be no surprise. After first learning to swim or ride a bicycle or even juggle, for some people there may be a lapse of many years before they get a chance to perform such a skill again and yet 'learning *how* to' - as opposed to 'learning *that*' - is rarely forgotten.

In general, very little forgetting occurs in animals as a result of the passage of time alone. The very simplest kind of remembering involves the process of habituation. If an animal spends some time inspecting a new object in a familiar setting, but spends less time

Fig. 4.1 In a simple T-maze an animal can rapidly learn to turn left or right in order to reach some reward at the end of an arm. However, retention of what it most recently learned can become difficult if at one time the animal has been trained to turn left and then later trained to take the right arm instead.

when finding the object again the next day, then in some sense it has remembered the object. Perhaps, if we waited a month instead of a day before introducing the object for a second time, we might find that the animal displayed more of its initial curiosity; in learning theory terminology, some spontaneous recovery from habituation might occur. However, the recovery is likely to be small and any renewed curiosity will habituate much more quickly the second time round. Similarly, the effects of classical conditioning rarely fade away with time alone. For example, there have been studies with pigeons in which shocks were paired with the appearance of a distinctive colour on the translucent response key that they were pecking to get grain. When the colour was introduced again over a year later, it still retained its ability to suppress the birds' pecking response.

The effects of both classical and instrumental conditioning are very well retained over time – that is, not forgotten – as long as nothing similar has been learned that could serve as interference. The simplest example of how such interference can produce forgetting comes from studies using simple position learning. Take a rat that has first been trained to run up the stem of a T-maze and then turn left to find the goal box containing food. At a later date it is again trained in this T-maze, but this time to find food in the goal box to the right. If we test how well this last trained habit is performed after various retention intervals, we will find that the longer the interval, the worse the performance, in that the rat will show an increasing tendency to turn left instead of right. Thus, the original training is *proactively interfering* with the most recently trained response. In any training programme that teaches an animal a series of responses there is always a risk that previously acquired behaviour will interfere with later training. Such risks can be reduced by making the contexts for different kinds of training highly distinctive. Thus, in the rat example above, it is likely that proactive interference from first being trained to turn left would have been greatly reduced if the shape, smell, appearance and location of the T-maze had been changed in the meantime.

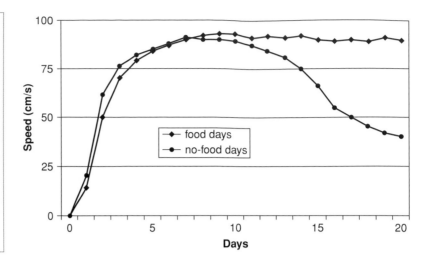

Fig. 4.2 If once a day a rat is placed in the start box of a long runway and sometimes finds food in the goal box at the other end, its running speed will increase up to some steady level. When a schedule is used in which food days alternate with no-food days, it can learn that no food yesterday means food today. In other words, recall of what happened 24 hours earlier can be associated with the current outcome. As a result, it comes to run more slowly on no food days. Reproduced with permission from Danielle Karazinov.

There is potentially a lot more to animal memory than the equivalent of humans remembering how to swim or recognising some object as familiar. This kind of *procedural* memory normally remains totally intact in people diagnosed as suffering memory loss after some kind of brain injury or disease. The first indication of human amnesia is usually a failing of what is commonly called *short-term* memory, the ability to recall events of the past few minutes or hours as distinct from events from long ago. A variant of this ability is for an individual to remember what happened the last time he or she was in a particular situation, as opposed to all the previous times. This ability has been demonstrated in rats using a very simple experiment. Once each day they were placed in the start box of a runway and the only cue as to whether they would find food in the goal box at the other end was what had happened on the previous day; for example, if there had been food on Monday, there would be none on Tuesday, but it would be there again on Wednesday. With this simple alternation schedule a rat that remembers finding food in the goal box the previous day might start to run more slowly, while the memory of no food the previous day might serve as an internal conditioned stimulus signalling the likely presence of food and thus start to elicit faster running. This is the result found from such experiments: within 20 trials – and thus within 20 days – rats run faster on the days when food is available under conditions where all possible cues other than memory for yesterday's outcome have been removed.

Clearly, whether or not it finds food is an important event for a hungry rat. Experiments on animals' short-term memory for neutral events have relied very heavily on a procedure known as *matching-to-sample*. As the name might suggest, this consists of the presentation of a sample stimulus at the start of a trial, followed by a set of comparison stimuli; the task is to select the comparison stimulus that most closely matches the sample. One of the first studies to use this procedure was carried out in Moscow with a chimpanzee called Ioni

Fig. 4.3 Ioni, the chimp, has been trained to select an object of the same shape as that held up by the trainer. This is a very early example of the matching-to-sample procedure now used for a variety of species. Reproduced from Boakes, 1984.

early in the twentieth century. The experimenter, Nadia Kohts, held up an object in her hand and gave the chimp a titbit of food if it picked up the similar object sitting in an array of objects nearby (see Fig. 4.3). Remarkably, this chimp was also able to perform well on a version of this task that tested for transfer from one sense to another. This procedure required the chimp to put its hand into a bag and select on the basis of *touch* the object that matched the sample that it could *see* being held up by the experimenter.

Decades later Skinner developed a version of the procedure for use with pigeons. A typical matching-to-sample experiment with pigeons uses a Skinner box that contains three response keys in a row. Each trial starts with a sample stimulus appearing on the middle key: a diffuse red light or a black vertical line, for example. When the pigeon pecks at the sample on this middle key, comparison stimuli then appear on the side keys, with one of them matching the sample stimulus. If the pigeon then pecks on this matching stimulus, grain is delivered; if it pecks on the wrong stimulus, then no food is delivered and often there is a brief 'time out' period when the chamber goes dark. This is illustrated in Fig. 4.5. When three distinct colours are used as the stimuli, pigeons can learn to perform at a very high level within about a thousand trials, usually at a rate of 100 trials in each daily session.

Pigeons can just as easily be trained in conditional discrimination tasks that do not involve matching. For example, when a vertical line appears on the sample key, choice of a red comparison stimulus is reinforced and, when a horizontal line appears, choice of a green stimulus is reinforced. Training given to sniffer dogs includes such conditional training, one in which the 'sample' is a verbal command

Fig. 4.4 A delayed matching-to-sample procedure can be used to test short-term memory for perceptual events. As shown here for a typical procedure used with pigeons, a trial might contain the following the sequence of events: (a) Green sample stimulus appears on the central response key while other two keys remain dark; pigeon pecks at the green sample until this disappears; (b) During a retention interval that typically may range from 1 to 60 seconds all three keys remain dark; (c) The comparison stimuli appear on the side keys, with one red and the other green. If the pigeon correctly pecks at green, a hopper delivers grain; if it chooses red, then there is a *time out* period of a few seconds when the entire chamber is dark. On other trials the red stimulus would appear as the sample at the start of a trial. Whereas the red comparison is shown on the left here, on half the trials it would be on the right, with the green on the left. Reproduced with permission from Sandro Sandro Nocentini (after Clive Wynne).

(e.g. 'truffles') and the stimulus to be selected is an odour (e.g. the smell of truffles; see Case 44). Where this differs from Ioni the chimp's ability to match the feel of an object to its visual appearance was that Ioni was never explicitly taught such equivalence. Most equivalence relationships, or conditional discriminations, require protracted training.

The simple step required to turn a matching-to-sample procedure into a method for measuring short-term recognition memory is to insert a delay between removing the sample stimulus that appears at the start of a trial and presenting the comparison stimuli. As one might expect, the longer the delay, the more likely an animal is to choose the wrong stimulus when the comparison stimuli eventually arrive. The length of time over which a pigeon can remember the stimulus that most recently appeared on the sample key depends on a range of factors. These include the kind of stimuli, how long the pigeon has to continue on each trial to peck the sample when it first appears and the interval between trials. Best performance is obtained under conditions that combine the use of a small set of simple stimuli such as distinctive colours, the requirement that the pigeon pecks on the sample stimulus for an appreciable time, e.g. 10 s, rather than making just a single peck to initiate the delay interval, and long inter-trial intervals, averaging at least several minutes.

Even under optimal conditions the pigeon's short-term memory is not impressive when measured in this way. Its performance may drop to near chance level when the delay interval is increased to around a minute. This may be because the delayed matching-to-sample procedure involves considerable proactive interference; memory for stimuli presented on preceding trials may well compete strongly with the crucial memory of what sample stimulus appeared on the current trial. Other species, including birds such as crows and primates such as rhesus monkeys, seem to be better than the pigeon at distinguishing the most recent event from all that happened previously, in that they can perform well with longer delays. Nevertheless, generally speaking short-term memory in animals, as measured by matching-to-sample procedures, is surprisingly poor.

In contrast, memory for spatial location is strikingly good in the many species that have been tested. This was first clearly shown by David Olton who reported in 1975 the results of using an ingenious, but simple, method for measuring in rats what he called their *working memory*. He constructed a radial maze with eight arms that was mounted about 70 cm above the floor of a well-illuminated room containing several distinctive landmarks – including the experimenter who remained seated in a fixed position. Before a trial began the cups at the end of each arm were baited with a small amount of food. A hungry rat was then placed in the centre of the maze and the trial ended when it had collected all eight pieces of food. The point of this design is that, when the rat returns to the centre after collecting food from the end of a particular arm and now has to choose which arm to visit next, it would help to remember which arms it has already visited and therefore no longer contain food. Olton found that after only four or five such daily trials his subjects hardly ever made the mistake of running down an arm that they had already visited on that trial. Various control procedures ruled out less interesting possibilities such as following their own scent trails or smelling the presence of food from a distance.

The only long-term information about a radial maze that a rat needs to remember is that all trials start with food at the end of all eight arms. Olton called this *reference* memory. Human memory researchers would classify such knowledge as part of semantic memory. A further result from his laboratory required the addition of a set of gates to the maze. These were set up so that, after visiting an arm and collecting the food at its end, a rat could be kept in the central area for some specified time before the gates were opened to allow it choice of the next arm to visit. Even when confined for an

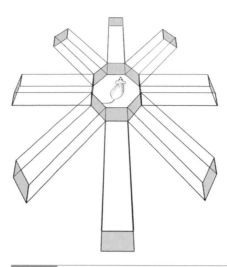

Fig. 4.5 In an 8-arm radial maze an animal can be trained to find food at the end of every arm. The challenge is to avoid re-visiting an arm that has already been emptied of food on that trial. This challenge can be increased in the version of the maze shown here, by confining the animal in the central area each time it returns from the end of an arm. If the confinement time is long enough, the animal will start to forget which arms it has visited and thus which arms must still contain food. The maze in this drawing is resting on the floor; normally it would be raised a metre or so above floor level. Reproduced with permission from Sandro Nocentini.

hour or more after visiting an arm, rats could still select an arm they had not yet visited that day over ones already visited. For this reason Olton used the term *working memory*, rather than short-term memory, to refer to the ability of rats to keep track of which arms they had visited within a trial.

Following Olton's pioneering experiments the study of spatial memory and spatial learning has expanded to encompass a variety of methods and an even wider range of species. It turns out that the ability of an animal to remember where it has visited over the past few hours is not special to rats. Pigeons also perform well in a radial maze, even though - as seen earlier - their short-term recognition performance is poor when measured using a delayed matching-to-sample procedure. The birds that have attracted particular interest in spatial memory studies are, however, not pigeons, but species that cache food. The North American chickadee, for example, is a bird that hides seeds in seasons of plenty and retrieves this food when times become hard. The suggestion from field studies that such birds are able to remember many hundreds of hiding places over many months has been tested in laboratory studies. Researchers have provided chickadees with artificial trees - wooden posts with holes drilled into them - placed in a large enclosure. When given a bowlful of seeds, a chickadee will readily deposit them in a number of different holes and have no difficulty in finding the seeds some time later when hungry - unless the experimenter has rearranged landmarks within

Fig. 4.6 Recalling a memory can be easy in one context, but difficult in another. The same in true of trained behaviour. That is why, following initial training, a sniffer dog needs further training in novel environments.

the enclosure during the intervening period. The chickadee's ability is not based simply on a good spatial reference memory; that is, remembering, for example, which holes it chose as storage sites out of the 128 provided by an experimenter. This was shown by the results of a three-day experiment that started by allowing the birds to store seeds on the first day. When made hungry and allowed into the enclosure again on the second day, the birds were given only enough time to retrieve half of the seeds. The third day was a test to see whether the birds would concentrate on the hiding places they had not been able to visit on the previous day. The chickadees passed this test. Thus, these birds can not only remember the precise locations of dozens of hiding places, but can also keep track – using working memory – of which of the sites they have recently visited.

For the trainer it is important to note that tasks relying on spatial memory may be relatively easy for an animal to acquire, while those relying on perceptual memory are likely to be very difficult. In many kinds of training special precautions must be taken to counteract the animal's bias towards learning on the basis of spatial location. An example is provided by the training given to sniffer dogs (Case 41). Tasks that require an animal to recognise a particular visual, auditory or even olfactory stimulus as being identical to one that was perceived earlier, but in a different position, can be particularly difficult to train. An example of training that takes advantage of an animal's spatial abilities is that of Bobby, the border collie (Case 44). It is possible that spatial memory abilities vary widely across species according to their ecology and evolutionary history. Thus, the rat and chickadee might be unusually good at the tests described in this section. However, there is no strong evidence for this as yet.

People report what has been called 'mental time travel', namely, going back in time to remember a specific event in such detail that it is almost like re-experiencing the event. Is a chickadee's memory of the hole from which it retrieved a seed the previous day at all like this kind of human episodic memory? While a bird cannot tell us what 'remembering' is like, a method has recently been developed for assessing whether an animal can remember a particular episode in terms of *what* occurred and *when* and *where* it happened. The subjects in this research programme belong to another North American caching bird, the scrub jay. The appeal of the scrub jay for this kind of research is that, just like the chickadee, even in a laboratory it will readily hide food when this is plentiful, but, unlike the chickadee, the scrub jay eats a wide variety of food. Thus, when given a bowl of peanuts and an ice cube tray that has been filled with sand, a scrub jay will bury peanuts in various compartments of the tray, and it will just as readily hide meal worms or dead insects such as crickets. These different kinds of food decay at different rates, with seeds and peanuts remaining essentially unchanged for weeks, while a dead worm will rapidly become inedible. Consequently, it would be useful for the scrub jay to have a memory ability more complex than any previously demonstrated in any species so that it could remember, not just *where* food was hidden, but *what* kind of food and *when*.

By allowing their jays first to learn about the different decay rates of three kinds of foods (rates that were artificially controlled), and then giving the birds the opportunity to hide the three kinds of food in different places and at different times, researchers have obtained results indicating that this species does possess something they describe as *episodic-like* memories. To date, such results have been obtained only for the scrub jay. However, it is possible that all vertebrates have this kind of ability. On the other hand it may be found only in those species for which episodic memory of this kind could have been important for survival. The challenge for those studying animal cognition is to devise tests of such episodic memory that do not have to rely on the animal being a cacher of a variety of foods.

Time and number

Almost all bodily functions, including levels of activity, vary according to daily - or *circadian* - rhythms. These are generally synchronised by the output of a 'biological clock' in the brain that is itself synchronised by external variations in light level. The natural daily rhythms of eating and drinking, of defaecating and urinating, of resting and patrolling, or of interacting socially or remaining solitary, for one species may be quite different for the next. However, they are by no means inflexible. A naturally nocturnal rodent like the rat will normally sleep mainly when there is light and, if food is readily available at all times, eat and drink mainly at the beginning and end of each night, remaining highly active throughout the period of darkness.

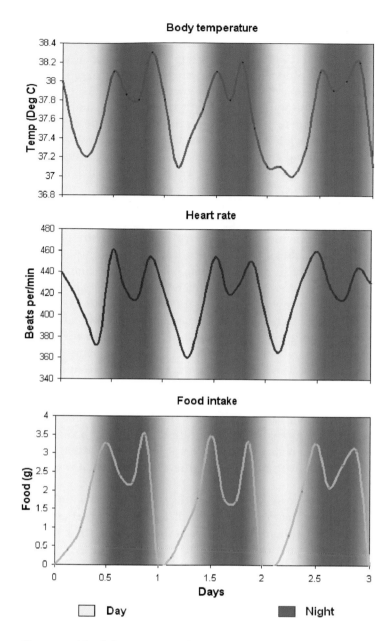

Body temperature

Heart rate

Food intake

Days

☐ Day   ■ Night

Fig. 4.7 All vertebrates show regular patterns of changes across 24 hours – *circadian rhythms* – in both physiological activity and behaviour. For a normally nocturnal animal like a rat, body temperature (a) declines during daylight hours and peaks during the night; similar patterns are shown by its heart rate (b) and, if it has unrestricted access to food, by the amount it eats (c). Such rhythms can be shifted by environmental changes such as making food only available only during daylight hours. Diurnal animals like ourselves tend to show the reverse pattern. Reproduced with permission from Danielle Karazinov.

However, if a laboratory rat is fed regularly only for a few daytime hours, over a period of about two weeks it will become increasingly active during the hours prior to feeding time, and its body temperature and other circadian rhythms will also shift. Where working animals - such as police dogs - are required to work at all hours, their training needs to be carried out at all hours.

Just as it can be responsive to the time of day indicated by signals from some internal clock, an animal's behaviour can also be highly sensitive to the exact amount of time since some event occurred. As described in Chapter 2, with a fixed-interval (FI) schedule of reinforcement a response is followed by reinforcement only if some specified time has elapsed since the last reinforcement. As training is continued on such a schedule, the animal's behaviour starts to develop a distinctive temporal pattern. For example, after a few sessions of training on a fixed-interval 30-second schedule an animal will rarely respond during the first ten seconds following the previous reinforcement, then start to respond at a gradually increasing rate until reaching its maximum rate for the final few seconds before the next reinforcement becomes available. Using a modified fixed-interval schedule researchers have found that an animal's sense of elapsed time since some event can be extremely precise. From other research we also know that time cues can be particularly effective stimuli that can overshadow perceptual cues. For this reason it can be important in training to make it difficult for an animal to predict exactly *when* some event will occur in the absence of the particular stimulus the trainer wishes to establish as the critical signal. If intermittent reinforcement is required to maintain some behaviour and induce high resistance to extinction, it is usually preferable to use a *variable-interval* rather than a fixed-interval reinforcement schedule.

Compared to their sense of time, most animals' perception of number is very poor. Ornithologists exploit birds' weakness in arithmetic by arranging that, say, four observers enter a hide near some flock of birds, but only three leave, in the hope that the birds are unable to deduce that one observer must have remained in the hide. Occasionally there have been challenges to the general belief that only humans can really understand numbers. One of the first serious challenges was made a hundred years ago by a retired German schoolmaster, Herr von Osten, who believed that horses at least might display some human-like skill in arithmetic if only they could be given the right kind of education.

The name of the horse, Clever Hans, that was trained by von Osten to prove his theory, has remained attached to a certain effect ever since. After a long period of training Hans showed evidence of having learned some mathematics by giving the correct answer - communicated by a number of foot taps - to questions that required it to add two numbers or even find the cube root of a number. When Hans' fame spread, a committee of experts including horse trainers and cavalry officers was sent to investigate. The experts were very impressed that Hans could respond appropriately to questioners other than von Osten and they were unable to detect any trickery. Herr von Osten had clearly not trained Hans with the deliberate aim of simulating intelligent performance - unlike many trainers before and since, as in the recent example of the macaw described in Case 32. Nonetheless, some of the experts remained sceptical.

After a further series of tests, it turned out that the scepticism was justified. Hans was unable to answer even the simplest question if his interrogator did not know what the answer should be. His tapping behaviour was completely under the control of his interrogator's bodily posture. After asking Hans a question, most people would lean forward very slightly, without being aware that they were doing so.

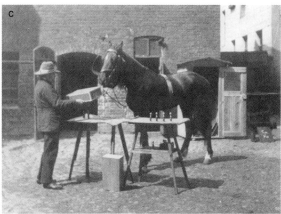
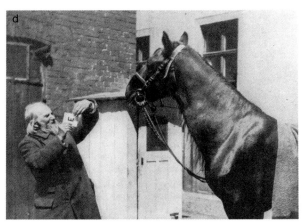

Fig. 4.8 The man with the white beard and hair, wearing a long coat, see (a) and (d), is Herr von Osten, who became famous for claiming that his horse, Clever Hans, had been successfully trained to count and to read. Herr van Osten never accepted the criticism of this claim. Instead he helped some of his admirers, shown in (b) and (c), to train and test successors to Clever Hans, as shown in this set of photographs from 1912. In (e) van Osten is on the right of the four onlookers and wearing the hat that – unknown to him – was probably critical in training Clever Hans. From Krall, 1912.

Fig. 4.9 Ai, the chimpanzee, has been trained to count using Arabic numerals. To obtain a reward she needs to pick the numerals one by one in ascending order.
Reproduced with permission from Tetsuro Matsuzawa.

Most, including von Osten, were equally unaware that they straightened themselves just very slightly when Hans reached the correct number of taps. Hans had not learned anything at all about numbers. Instead, a very slight inclination of a human being standing in front of Hans had become the discriminative stimulus for foot tapping and straightening up the discriminative stimulus for stopping. The term, *Clever Hans effect*, has since been used whenever unconscious cueing on the part of a trainer produces the misleading appearance in the animal's behaviour of some kind of intellectual skill.

Nevertheless, von Osten's theory was not entirely wrong. Subsequent studies of counting in animals have obtained positive results under conditions that make it unlikely that they have instead produced a Clever Hans effect. Several researchers using various species of birds and mammals have trained animals to make relative number judgements whereby, for example, they respond on the basis of how many dots are projected onto a response key. However, in such studies it is easy to conclude that the animal is responding to numbers when in fact it is choosing on the basis of some physical dimension such as overall brightness or the pattern made by a few dots. We noted earlier that animals are highly likely to use time as a cue instead of some physical event the trainer has set up as the critical signal. The opposite is true when numbers are involved; an animal is far less likely to learn about the numerical cue intended by the trainer than some physical cue that the trainer may have overlooked. Nevertheless some recent studies involving pigeons, rats and raccoons seem to have overcome these problems and succeeded in demonstrating that animals can make both relative and absolute number judgements.

Counting is a more complex skill than responding on the basis of the number of some set of objects or of some series of events like sounds. Counting requires some symbolic representation like the visual patterns used as Arabic numerals or the sounds used in human

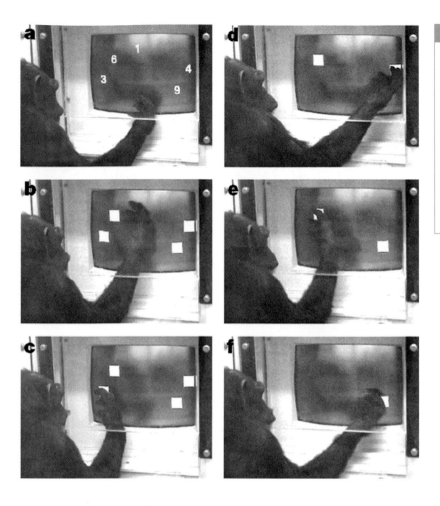

Fig. 4.10 This is a test of Ai's short-term memory after she has been trained to count (see Figure 4.9). The first nine numerals flash up briefly in arbitrary locations that change from trial to trial. They then turn into identical white squares. The task for Ai is to press the squares in ascending order of the numbers they have replaced. Adult chimps can do this as well as humans. Reproduced with permission from Tetsuro Matsuzawa.

languages: as in 'one', 'two', 'three' and so on in English. This may be why the best evidence that an animal can count comes from studies of chimpanzees, who possess human-like ability to discriminate between visual patterns, and from an African grey parrot previously given years of training to produce English words. To date there is only limited evidence that even a non-human ape can go beyond counting to simple addition and subtraction, the kind of skill that one hundred years ago von Osten believed was relatively easy to train in a horse.

Reasoning and problem solving

If we see some eye-catching performance by an animal – at a circus, zoo, aquarium for marine mammals, sheep dog trial or horse show – it is easy to applaud the animal for being so 'clever'. What we should really be appreciating is the ingenuity and dedication of the trainers and the long hours and patience required before the animal's behaviour reaches a point at which it can be made public. More

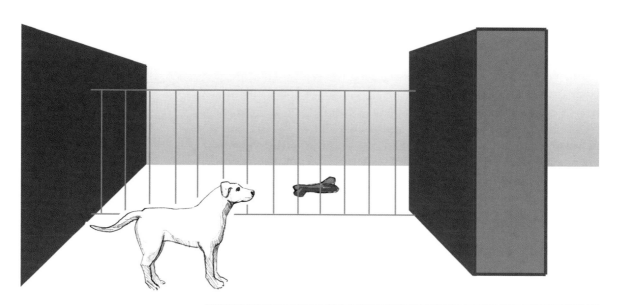

Fig. 4.11 In a detour problem the animal can see some desired object – normally food – but direct access is blocked, for example, by a fence. Given that the geography of the test setting is already familiar to the animal, the question is whether it will solve the problem by turning away from the food and taking a circuitous route. Wolfgang Koehler reported that his dog solved such problems much more impressively than his chickens; the latter seemed to rely on trial-and-error learning alone. Chimpanzees were particulary impressive. Reproduced with permission from Sandro Nocentini.

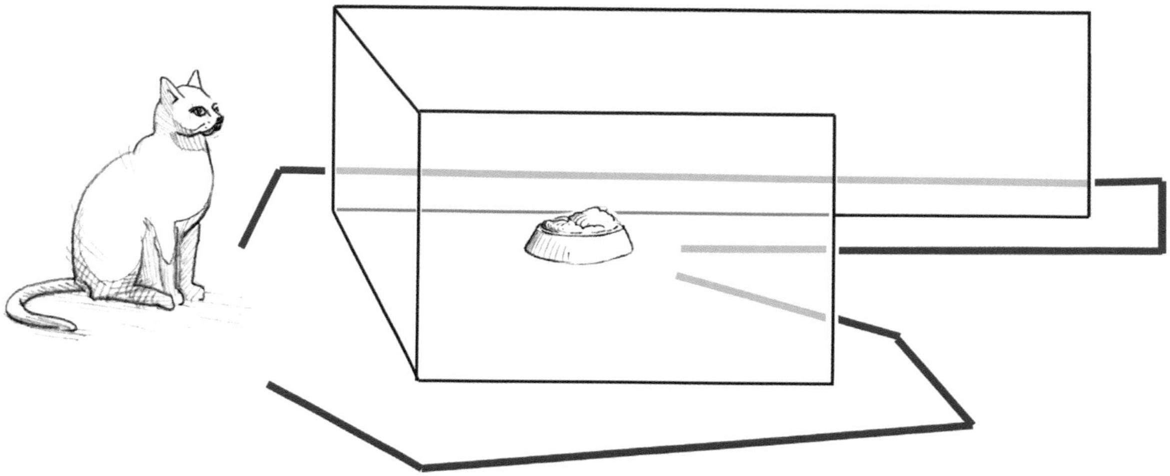

Fig. 4.12 In a more recent study that used this version of a detour problem for cats, whether the cat took the shorter path depended on the precise location of the food it could see, and probably smell, through the fence. If the food was placed somewhat towards the longer wall, the cat was likely to make the illogical choice of the longer path. Reproduced with permission from Sandro Nocentini.

generally, we tend to attribute intelligence and understanding to an animal when we see it behave in an unusual, impressively adaptive and apparently insightful way during the course of some isolated observation. It is a much less common experience to observe the course of development of some example of complex behaviour. (The case histories are included in this book partly for this reason.) When we do understand the development of some performance, it can be easier to see how the behaviour was produced by a long history of reinforcement, whether one deliberately arranged by a trainer or one that occurred incidentally during the animal's successive interactions with its natural environment. On first reporting his pioneer experiments on trial-and-error learning, Thorndike challenged his successors to disprove his claim that *all* apparent examples in animals of intelligent behaviour like problem-solving are based on instrumental conditioning without any of what in humans is called 'understanding'. (Incidentally, he later claimed that most human behaviour was also based on instrumental conditioning and lacked understanding.)

The first successful challenge to Thorndike's claim was mounted by a German contemporary of Thorndike. Wolfgang Koehler argued that the puzzle boxes used by Thorndike to test dogs and cats guaranteed that they would learn by trial-and-error since no amount of reasoning could deduce the arbitrary response required to open the door of a box. Koehler decided that spatial problems would provide a more natural test of an animal's problem-solving ability. He tested his chimpanzees, hens and a dog on *detour* problems that tested an animal's ability to choose an appropriate route to some goal, one that they may not have ever taken before, when the direct route to the goal

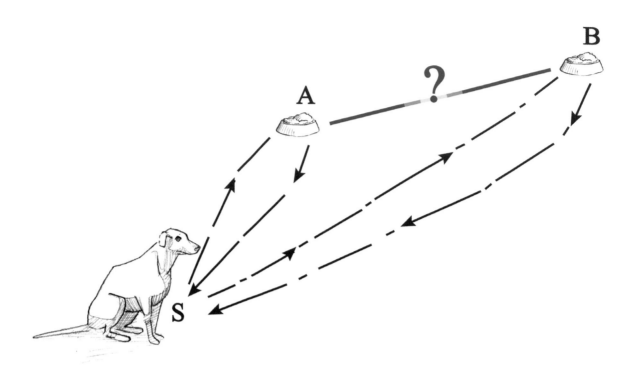

Fig. 4.13 Initially a dog is walked from Start (S) to A where it finds food and then returns; it is also trained in the same way to find food at B. On a test trial the dog is released from S but now finds no food at A. Will it return to S, as it has been trained, or for the first time take a short cut to B? Under some conditions dogs have taken the short cut in such a test of spatial reasoning. Reproduced with permission from Sandro Nocentini.

was blocked. His chimpanzees were good at solving such problems, while the hens performed poorly.

Since Koehler's time, spatial reasoning has been found in various species using a number of variations on his original detour task. One variation has been used extensively with dogs to test their ability to work out short cuts. For example, in a French study dogs were walked across a large meadow from the starting point, S, to point A, where they were shown the food placed there, but not allowed to touch it. After returning to S, they were then walked to B, where untouchable food was also displayed, and then back to S. After a short delay they were released. As shown in Fig. 4.13, the quickest way for the dogs to collect the food at A and B was to run, say, to A and then take a short cut across to B, instead of retracing the original route via S. Most of the dogs chose the appropriate short cut in such tests. Subsequently it became clear that whether an animal chooses a short cut depends on a variety of factors. These include the angle between S-A and S-B in the above example, whether A can be seen from B and whether there are obstacles that prevent a direct route from A to B and thus require a detour of the kind studied by Koehler.

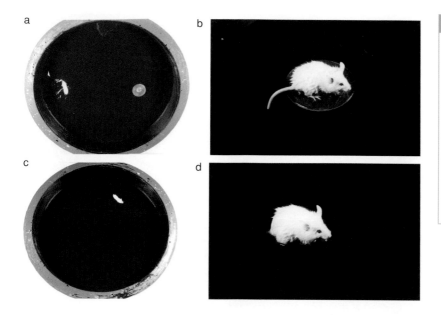

a   b   c   d

The Morris water maze (or swim maze) is a task that is used extensively to test the spatial abilities of rodents. The equipment consists of a circular swimming bath containing water and a small white-painted platform just below the surface of the water. The walls of the bath are sheer so that, once placed in the water, a rat cannot stop swimming until it discovers the underwater platform. Although there are no nearby cues to indicate the location of the hidden platform, a rat will learn very quickly to swim to the platform, as long as this remains in a fixed location in relation to visual landmarks beyond the walls of the swimming bath. If given three training trials, of which one starts from the north, one from the east and one from the south, when started from the west on the fourth training trial a rat will head in the direction of the hidden platform, even though this is an entirely new starting point.

A clouding agent is added to the water so that the researchers can be certain that the rats are not solving the problem simply by looking for the platform and swimming towards it. As part of pre-training, the naive rat is placed on the hidden platform for 15 seconds and then placed in the water for the same length of time. When first placed in water, rats show frantic paddling and attempts to escape. As part of pre-training, the handler:

1. Places the rat in water in a random starting position, facing the wall of the tank.
2. Allows the rat to explore the tank for 60 seconds.
3. Guides the rat to the platform if it failed to locate it after 60 seconds of exploration.
4. Allows the rat to climb on and remain there for 25 seconds. These four steps constitute a trial.

Fig. 4.15 Traces of an animal's movement within a Morris water maze can be used to analyse spatial learning. In these pictures the circle marks the location of the submerged platform. Track (a) shows a common error, that of searching in the opposite quadrant to the platform. Track (b) shows a random track pattern typical of early training trials. Track (c) indicates that the animal has learned the location of the platform in that it now heads straight towards it. In track (d) the animal starts in the opposite direction, but then corrects itself and finds the platform fairly quickly. Reproduced with permission from Toni Harper.

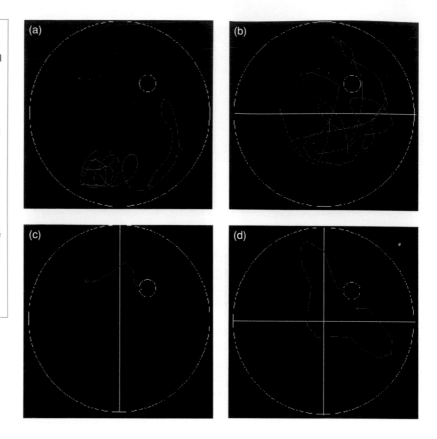

Each session comprises four trials. After four trials the rat is then towel dried and placed in a warm cage to rest for at least 20 minutes. Two sessions of swim maze training are administered each day. After several exposures to the problem, rats learn to find the escape platform using environmental cues and swim directly to the platform with a minimum of exploration.

This so-called probe trial takes place when the platform is removed completely. Repeated circling at the former site of the platform demonstrates that the rat is using environmental cues from the walls of the tank (and beyond) to form a cognitive map to locate the platform (Fig. 4.15 shows the location and size of the platform).

The abilities that animals display in spatial memory and spatial reasoning tasks may reflect a fundamental aspect of their evolutionary history. After all, what characterises an animal, as opposed to a plant, is that it moves around in search of food, and sometimes a mate, and that it needs to reach a safe shelter quickly when there is a serious threat. However, while tests like the Morris water maze have revealed that animals have some understanding of their spatial world, evidence for a similar kind of understanding of non-spatial problems remains elusive.

In the first systematic tests of the problem-solving abilities of chimpanzees, Koehler developed tests that were intended to be equivalent to the initial detour tests, but where the solution involved more than taking the best route to a goal. One test required that the chimp detach a loop of rope from a hook so that a basket of fruit would descend from above. Another was the box test, whereby in order to reach a banana suspended from the ceiling a chimpanzee needed to move a large box from a corner of the enclosure to a position immediately below the banana and climb up on it. More difficult versions required that a chimp pile two or more boxes on top of each other to reach an even higher banana. A third was the rake test; this required that the animal poke a stick through the bars of its enclosure and rake towards it a banana that was otherwise just out of reach. Koehler was at first surprised that problems such as these that seemed trivially easy to human beings proved a major challenge to his chimps. He was looking for a sudden solution that would indicate some kind of insight rather than a gradual solution by the process of trial-and-error described by Thorndike. Eventually several of the chimps solved many of the problems in a way that convinced Koehler their performance showed some level of understanding and went beyond the learning process described by Thorndike.

Since Koehler's time many studies have used his box and rake tests, or developed their own, to provide apes, monkeys or other species with an opportunity to demonstrate some form of insight when faced with some new problem. What has become clear is that even a species like the chimpanzee, with its highly developed visual system and good ability to manipulate objects, shows little insight unless all the behavioural components are already well learned. For example, chimpanzees do not solve a rake test unless they have already had experience of using sticks to move objects around - experience that can as well be acquired during play as during some purposeful behaviour. With an arduous amount of effort pigeons (with wings clipped to prevent them flying) can be trained both to move a box towards a target placed at various points in an arena and - separately - to climb up on a box that is already just below a container full of grain. Once proficient at these somewhat non-pigeon-like behaviours and presented for the first time with the box test - that is, the grain just out of reach above them and the box somewhere else in the arena - some pigeons have been observed to solve the problem by moving the box to the point immediately below the container. However, the pigeon's problem-solving ability appears to be much more context-bound than that of the chimpanzee. In an unpublished study we found that no pigeon trained to move boxes in another setting, or trained to climb on a box to drink water rather than eat grain, ever passed the test.

Chimpanzees are one of the few species known to use tools in natural settings. These include leaves to use as sponges, twigs for 'fishing' for termites and brandishing branches to threaten a rival. These appear to be techniques that the young acquire, often quite gradually, by observing their elders and by frequent practice, rather than by sudden insight. A very different species with a well-developed visual system and a natural tendency to use tools is the crow. In the wild crows have been observed to use their beaks to 'manipulate'

Fig. 4.16 This Caledonian crow demonstrates manufacture, as well as use of, a tool by fetching a piece of wire and, after bending it into a hook shape, using it to lift food out of a cylinder. Reproduced with permission from Alex Kacelnik.

objects, such as twigs used to poke out potential food items from holes. In a recent laboratory study a crow proved adept in using a piece of wire shaped with a hook at one end to retrieve items from a jar with a thin neck. Subsequently, when presented with a uselessly straight piece of wire, the crow bent this into a suitable shape before using it to retrieve a food item from the jar. As in the examples given above, this impressive and rare example of problem-solving on the part of a bird almost certainly depended on ample experience of bending wires prior to the crucial test.

Most trainers work with animals that do not have the superb visual system that we share with other primates and that have only very limited capacity for manipulating objects. Consequently, unless the problem is a spatial one, trainers should not expect their animals to arrive spontaneously at the solution to problems that adult human beings *see* as being simple.

Comparing intelligence

Few readers are likely to have been surprised to learn that the human-like chimpanzee with its 500-gram brain can sometimes solve a problem in what most people would agree was an intelligent way. It can be more confronting to learn that a crow, or even a pigeon with a one-gram brain, can solve a similar problem. It seems obvious that the chimpanzee should be more intelligent than most other species. On the other hand, as we have seen, it has very good vision and primates generally have exceptional skill in manipulating objects, so perhaps this is why the chimpanzee is better than most animals at solving the kind of problem its fellow primate, *homo sapiens*, tends to set. At various times over the past century comparative psychologists have devised tests intended to compare the intelligence of different species in a way that is not biased by differences in their sensory abilities, or in the ways in which they can interact with their physical world, or by different levels of motivation or emotional reaction to the test.

Removing these biases from a comparison between two species can be very difficult and is never complete. For example, South American monkeys have poorer colour vision than African and Asian monkeys and so a comparison between them on a task requiring discrimination between objects should not use coloured ones. Even if a difference is then found, it remains possible, for example, that the reinforcer was more effective or that the test conditions were more frightening for one species than the other. To the extent that obvious biases have been ruled out, little variation has been found in the rates at which different species learn fairly simple tasks, such as instrumental conditioning of a response suitable for a given species or learning to associate reward with one position in a maze and not with the single alternative.

In view of how difficult it has been to find differences in intelligence or learning ability between quite diverse species, paradoxically enthusiasts insist with unquestioned confidence that, for example, one breed of dog, or even one individual, is more intelligent than another. This raises two questions. What do trainers – whether professional or amateur – mean when describing an animal as 'intelligent'? And, what might trainers usefully learn from studies that have compared the learning and other abilities of different species?

The answer to the first question seems to be that everyday judgements about the intelligence of an animal are based on how easily it is trained to perform a specific task or, at most, a limited set of tasks. This means that an animal regarded as intelligent on the basis of its performance in one training regime might not seem at all intelligent in a different setting. But, of course, this is rarely tested. Instead, there is often a tacit belief that training depends on the animal understanding what the trainer intends. Thus, if an individual animal turns out to be very trainable in a particular task, this must show that it has better understanding of what is required than another individual that was difficult to train. However, as we have seen, only on rare occasions does an animal's learned behaviour seem to depend on some understanding of the task. Instead, successful training depends on the trainers' skill in using the principles we have described in these chapters, whether they are aware of these or not. Individual variations in how well animals respond to training are likely to reflect a very large number of factors, starting with differences in emotionality (or fearfulness) produced by their genes and early experience and ending with subtle differences in how reinforcement is used during the course of a particular training programme. Individual variations in trainability are very *unlikely* to result from differences in anything resembling what in humans we call intelligence.

The second question was whether studies of cross-species learning abilities have resulted in findings of use to trainers. The answer is that some interesting differences have been found in the way species learn complex tasks and that some may be of use to the trainer. These

Fig. 4.17 Harry Harlow included this sketch in one of his first reports on discrimination training in rhesus monkeys. In the Wisconsin General Test Apparatus (WGTA) the experimenter can set up a trial while a screen is lowered to prevent the animal seeing what is being prepared. For a simple object discrimination task there are two food wells in the stimulus tray and on each trial one of the wells contains a peanut or some other small tit-bit. Each well is covered by a different object (a cylinder and a cube in this sketch). The animal has to learn which object is on top of the reward. Reproduced with permission from the American Psychological Association.

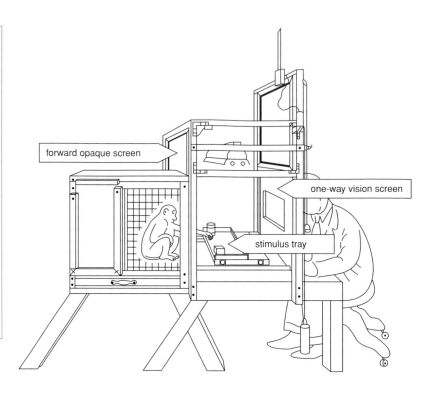

tasks do not obviously contain sensory or motor biases that favour some kinds of animal. The oldest dates from work with rhesus monkeys in the 1940s by the American comparative psychologist, Harry Harlow. He invented the *learning set* procedure in which an animal is given a series of problems that are all of the same kind. Harlow's monkeys started with object discriminations. Once they had learned to select object A, and not object B, to find the peanut hidden under A on each trial, two new objects, C and D, were introduced and, randomly, either C or D was then designated the positive stimulus that concealed the peanut. In the course of several hundred such problems the speed with which a monkey learned a new discrimination improved dramatically. Harlow called this effect *learning to learn*. Interestingly, animals from two different primate species might solve the first few problems just as quickly, but later one might show much more rapid improvement in their learning rate.

Learning to learn depends not just on the species, but also on the sensory modality that is used. Thus, dolphins can solve the kind of visual object discrimination that Harlow gave his monkeys, but show very slow improvement from problem to problem. In contrast, when the set of problems consists of discrimination between sequences of sounds, dolphins have displayed as great a learning set ability as rhesus monkeys. Rats are poor at learning visual object discriminations compared to either monkeys or dolphins, but when given a series of odour discriminations they show good learning to learn. Thus, it seems likely that, even when initial training of that other odour-sensitive mammal, the dog, takes a great deal of time (see the sniffer

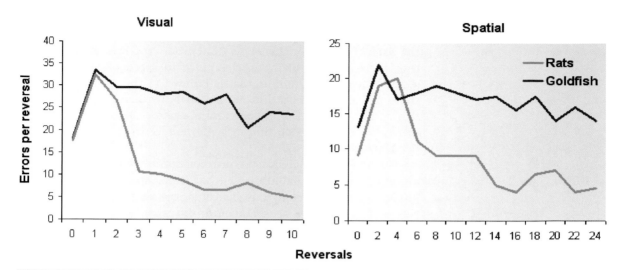

Fig. 4.18 A rat can be trained to choose a black door over a white door and, when this has been learned well, the contingency is reversed so that now the white door leads to food. When this second task is mastered, the contingency is again reversed, so that the black door is again correct. And so on. As shown in the left-hand panel, rats given such a *visual serial reversal* task soon learn to adapt to these changes, making only a few errors when a contingency is reversed. They do equally well on a *spatial* version of the task, as shown in the right-hand panel. On the other hand goldfish are very slow to adapt to a series of reversals, whether given either the visual or spatial version. Reproduced with permission from Danielle Karazinov.

dogs in Case 41), learning to discriminate new odours should become progressively less time consuming. Once trained to detect explosives a dog can be retrained relatively quickly to detect drugs.

A key element of good learning set performance is to focus on recent events. The animal needs to ignore the now irrelevant details of previous problems and concentrate entirely on the outcomes of choices on the current problem. This element is also necessary for another learning task used to compare species, the *serial reversal* task. This consists of training an animal on a two-choice discrimination – for example, something as simple as turning left, but not right, to find food – and, when this has been learned, reversing the rule, so that, to follow the example, food can now be found only by turning right. Once this first reversal has been learned, there is another reversal so that now the food is on the left once again. And so on. Over many reversals animals start to learn the current discrimination – e.g. turn left, not right – faster than they did the original problem or the early reversals.

The rate of improvement across reversals can vary widely across species. A widely accepted claim is that animals with higher ratios of brain to body weight – such as primates and dolphins – show faster serial reversal and learning set improvement and probably have more effective working memories. However, this has been disputed on the grounds that the evidence comes from testing very small groups of animals from any given species, and because of continuing doubts that the comparisons have really been bias-free. For the trainer the safe, if weak, conclusion to draw from cross-species research is that species are unlikely to vary much in speed of training for a single training programme that is tailored to the species. However, there may be wide variations in the flexibility shown by animals put through a series of training programmes where the success of a given programme depends on minimal interference from what an animal has learned previously.

This chapter concludes the introduction to general principles of animal behaviour that transcend particular species and particular kinds of training. As already indicated, the very specific case histories that follow have been chosen to illustrate these principles over as wide a range as we could find. Although it is our contention that all training follows the principles we have featured in these first four chapters, very few of the trainers in these case studies use the terminology of learning theorists. Unsurprisingly, the language used by trainers to describe their methods differs enormously from one specialisation to another. We have included some of the terms more commonly used by professional trainers in the glossary at the end of this book.

Box 4.1 | Top training tips

- Short-term memory for spatial information is generally good, while short-term perceptual memory is usually poor (pages 95–6).
- Learned skills are rarely forgotten (pages 91–2).
- To demonstrate insight in animals, trainers must be certain that their animals have not picked up cues they gave inadvertently (the Clever Hans effect) (page 102).
- Animals are unlikely to *understand* the task they are required to perform so much as they simply know how to perform it (page 100).
- Assuming cognitive powers in animals can lead trainers to attribute human intelligence to animals in ways that can compromise training (page 110).
- Animals can learn to learn (page 112).

Part II

Case studies

INTRODUCTION TO PART II

Our 50 case histories have been grouped together in terms of the purpose for which the animals have been trained. Surprising examples appear in some categories. For example, there is a sheep in the exotic animal chapter (Chapter 6), because this particular animal is neither a companion nor a working animal but is an exhibit in a display.

The way experts describe their special skills can provide invaluable insights into the nature of these skills. This is the main reason why the following case studies are closely based on the accounts given by the trainers. So, for example, we have wherever possible used the terms trainers used. However, a note of caution has to be sounded. In the few areas of expertise that have been closely examined – such as medical diagnosis – striking differences have been found between what the experts *say* that they do and what they *actually* do. Thus, it is just as likely in animal training as elsewhere that when trainers reflect on their methods in interviews, they could well emphasise features that may not be so important and likewise miss what in reality are crucial components of their approach.

The ways in which trainers describe their techniques vary widely and can often suggest that their animals have very human-like minds. To a large extent the techniques can be understood in terms of the principles discussed in the preceding four chapters. However, we have not attempted in these case histories to recast in a rigid way the trainers' accounts into the terminology used by behavioural scientists. One reason is that it does not always work.

For example, a particularly interesting exception to the usual parallels between learning theory and trainers' practice is the latter's use of what we will label here *reinforcement-to-command transfer* – this is not a term that can be found in any textbook on learning theory as we have invented it for the present purpose. A widespread training procedure (one frequently used in training dogs; see, for example, the sled dog in Case 37 and the sheep dog in Case 48) is to wait until the desired response occurs and then produce the word, phrase or signal that is intended to become the controlling, or discriminative, stimulus for that response in future. For example, a trainer might repeatedly wait till a dog started to move in a clockwise direction and then say *right*, while saying *left* after it begins an anticlockwise move. Many trainers report that under analogous conditions issuing such commands *prior to any movement* comes to control the appropriate response; thus, eventually, *right* will elicit clockwise movements and *left* anticlockwise movements.

This is a mysterious claim in terms of known conditioning principles. Waiting until a pigeon pecks at a response key or until a rat presses a lever and then presenting, say, a brief tone will not result in the tone gaining control of pecking by the pigeon or lever-pressing by the rat, no matter how many times the procedure is repeated. An equally vain hope is to present the tone or some such stimulus after presenting food (*backward conditioning* procedure) to obtain some kind of classically conditioned effect. A possible solution to this puzzle comes from noting that whereas a tone is of little interest to a pigeon or rat, a spoken word or any kind of response on the part of the trainer can be a strong positive reinforcement for a well-socialised animal. Thus, a dog's clockwise movement can be *instrumentally reinforced* by the word *right* and anticlockwise movements by the word *left* because attention from the trainer can be a positive event. It is possible that what starts as just a reinforcer for a particular response comes to acquire the function of discriminative control, a discriminative stimulus (S^D), for that response. At the same time its reinforcing function may be replaced by alternative and possibly intermittent sources of reinforcement under real-life training conditions. This suggestion could in principle be tested by laboratory experiments, but in practice this could be very difficult. This may be why the possible principle of *reinforcement-to-command transfer* has not been studied by learning theorists.

Some readers may find some of the training techniques or, for that matter, the specific use to which animals are being put unacceptable. It is therefore worth repeating that the case histories are provided purely as illustrations of training approaches that work and not as models for readers to emulate.

The table below summarises the case histories that appear in the following three chapters:

Chapter 5   Companion and performance animals

Case	Target behaviour	Animal
1	Staying still for 15 minutes	Rat
2	Standing on command	Rabbit
3	Unrolling carpet	Pig
4	Fetching stick	Pig
5	Jumping through hoop	Cat
6	Waving	Cat
7	Playing keyboard	Cat
8	Pulling carriage	Cow
9	Saluting	Cow
10	Bowing	Horse
11	Spanish walk	Horse
12	Emptying washing machine	Dog
13	Picking up objects	Cat
14	Chasing tail	Dog
15	Limping	Dog

Chapter 6   Exotic animals
Trying to create a good display by:
(a) showing off the physical abilities and natural behaviours of the animals on command

Case	Target behaviour	Animal
16	Rolling over	Sealion
17	Flipper stand	Sealion

Case	Target behaviour	Animal
18	Jumping through hoop	Sealion
19	Retrieving ball and balancing it on his nose	Seal
20	Riding a tricycle	Macaw
21	Blowing a jet of water from her trunk	Asian elephant
22	Tail-walking	Dolphin
23	Extracting food from a log using a stick	Capuchin monkey
24	Taking lid off jar	Octopus

(b) demonstrating how brave the humans are

Case	Target behaviour	Animal
25	Rearing on command	Tiger
26	Leaping from A to B on command	Leopard

(c) trying to make the animals seem more clever than they are for comic effect

Case	Target behaviour	Animal
27	Finding a specific site on podium	Sheep
28	Painting on a canvas	Asian elephant
29	Placing litter in a bin	Australian magpie
30	Stealing coins	Galah
31	Matching shapes and colours	Macaw
32	'Counting'	Macaw

(d) training for veterinary procedures and to maximise the safety of personnel

Case	Target behaviour	Animal
33	Lifting hind leg on command	White rhinoceros
34	Standing in crush cage	Giraffe
35	Holding tail of elephant in front	African elephant
36	Lying down on command	Wolf

Chapter 7 True working animals

Case	Target behaviour	Animal
37	Pulling sled left and right on cue	Reindeer
38	Walking in a yoke	Ox
39	Turning on command	Dog
40	Flying to fist	Falcon
41	Detecting explosives	Dog
42	Tracking a scent	Dog
43	Detecting termites	Dog
44	Detecting truffles	Dog
45	Control of dog for search-and-rescue work	Dog
46	Apprehending humans	Dog
47	Guiding around obstacles	Dog
48	Sendaway (gathering sheep unseen)	Dog
49	Moving the public, crowd control	Horse
50	Rearing on command	Horse

Chapter 5

Companion and performance animals

Our first set of case studies focuses on animals that have learned to perform entertaining or helpful behaviours for praise and food rewards. The studies demonstrate a spectrum of motivations and training techniques, but are linked by the pleasure and sense of achievement felt by the human trainers when their companions acquire new responses. Some of the animals in this chapter earn money for their owners in displays and as animal actors, others help to demonstrate that their owners are credible as professional train-ers. Obedience brings praise from observers, undoubtedly enhancing the trainer's sense of self-worth, while general compliance, especially when shaped with positive reinforcement, enhances a harmonious human–animal bond.

Humans from some cultures may regard training animals as cruel and unnatural, but there is some evidence that companion animals that 'work' for a living are more active and possibly more healthy than those that are simply petted and fed. Just as maintaining men-tal activity in humans may delay the onset of Alzheimer's disease, it is possible that sustained environmental complexity can be good for the mental health of pets. Although we currently have no means of measuring such a subjective response, it may be that 'working' can enhance an animal's feeling of self-worth. It may be important to ensure that the animal continues to learn throughout life as the ben-efits of learning one 'trick' as a youngster (see Fig. 5.1) and performing it in a stereotyped fashion thereafter may be limited.

Animals are likely to retain particular enthusiasm for physical activity that allows expression of a behavioural need. Experiments have shown that hens, given a perfect ready-formed nest, will con-tinue to show nest-building behaviour. Hens don't just need a nest, they need to build their own! By diverting such natural behaviours towards a novel object or material, owners can allow their companion animals to demonstrate instinctive drift (see Chapter 2), whilst at the same time producing an amusing outcome. For example, the pigs and cats in this chapter are performing behaviours that have analogues in natural foraging. In using his snout to unroll a carpet, Charlie, a Vietnamese pot-bellied pig (Case 3), is exercising an ancestral need

Fig. 5.1 Dog sitting up on its haunches in a so-called begging posture. Many dogs perform this as a default response when near people who are eating because it prompts so many of human observers to give food i.e. it is rapidly generalised.

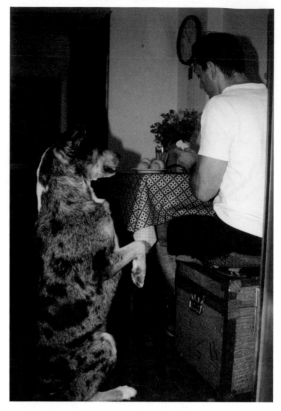

to root, whilst the keyboard skills of Simon, a domestic shorthair cat (Case 7), involve a modification of the kneading action used by kittens to stimulate milk let-down from their mothers.

Another benefit of training a companion animal is the increased control, which can make the animal safer for itself and others. Dogs taught to stop at kerbs are more likely to slow down as they approach roads than those that rely on 'road-sense'. Trained dogs can be called back from all sorts of potential danger and therefore their chances of reaching old age are probably increased.

The tasks that the animals in this chapter are required to perform range from remaining motionless to galloping along pulling a carriage, but each task presents special challenges. Hubert (Case 1), for example, is a rat and therefore a highly active, opportunistic scavenger. The foraging skills of rats have been honed by natural selection to ensure that they generally expend the minimum effort per energy unit gained when foraging, but it is unlikely that they will normally acquire food by doing absolutely nothing. Inhibition of action is therefore potentially a difficult thing for a rat to learn. However, by a process of instrumental conditioning, Hubert's trainer has reinforced him with chocolate for resisting the temptation to wander around. Remaining in one place is also required of Pumpkin the rabbit (Case 2), who has been trained to rear up on command, despite his strong tendency to keep close to the ground and his hair-trigger sensitivity to signs of possible predation.

Fig. 5.2 Dog sitting at a kerb, waiting for traffic to pass.

Fig. 5.3 Tethered Indian house calf being habituated to human activity.

Fear of the trainer, whether the trainer is perceived as a potential predator or a more dominant member of the same species, is perhaps the factor most likely to impede learning. But once they trust their trainers, animals often begin learning to learn. Susie and Ramblie (Cases 8 and 9), the two cows in this chapter, are distinguished by having been extensively handled as youngsters. This has habituated them to humans and thus prepared them to concentrate on lessons and made them very safe to handle and impressively responsive to commands. The effects of habituation to humans can result in an expansion of behavioural repertoire in normally timid animals. In India, for example, sacred street cows forage in novel and adventurous ways, browsing through inner city rubbish for remnants of cardboard on which to chew, despite the presence and activity of humans.

Manageability is, of course, a key requisite for most training tasks and the effects of early experience are exemplified by two horses in this chapter, Archie (Case 10) and Topper (Case 11). While Archie was virtually hand-reared, Topper had entrenched fear responses to humans and had become seriously aggressive before he found his current home. For this reason, Topper's training included considerably more habituation than did Archie's. In general, it would be difficult to replicate most of the feats demonstrated in this chapter with animals that have not been well handled from an early age.

Case 1 — Rat *Rattus norvegicus (Black-eyed white)*

Training profile

Target behaviour:	staying in a given spot for up to 15 minutes
Name:	Hubert
Age:	12 months
Trainer's assessment of temperament:	placid, intelligent, responsive
Trainer's name:	Ann Head

Background

Despite a general awareness that rats are used in psychology laboratories many of us expect all rats to be more or less uncontrollable. It is therefore striking that Ann Head, a renowned trainer of animal actors, trains her rats to a 100 per cent consistency because the cost per unit time of setting up a film shoot totally precludes the use of unreliable animals.

For their occasional, but nonetheless striking, film roles rats are generally required to run from A to B, a behaviour that is readily established using the sanctuary box technique outlined in Chapter 2. Beyond this, Ann has trained rats to steal items and most importantly for film work, to remain in one spot. Her rats will stay for much longer than most pet dogs.

Training programme

Number of training sessions per week   7
Duration of session   15 minutes
Time taken to learn   2 weeks

Before commencing training the animal must: be calm with humans generally as a result of being very well handled. For film work the rat must also be accustomed to travelling. Male rats may be easier to train as females are normally more active.

Changing the animal's motivation before a training session: nothing.

In the process of shaping the final behaviour, the trainer:
1. Worked from an armchair since this was a time-consuming exercise but could be accomplished while watching television. She fed rewards when Hubert was calm on the chair. By stroking Hubert along his back with conviction and gently pressing him against the cushioned surface, she convinced him that he was secure.

2. Edged away from the chair after giving the rat the stroking cue to stay, then immediately returned with a reward. This is essentially the

General processes in training

Auditory cues: constant chat assures the rat that even on a film set he can expect a reward for simply staying put.

Visual cues: the hand's characteristic position as it leaves the rat, after stroking, helps to let the rat learn that he should stay put.

Use of reinforcers

Rewards used: chocolate.

Variation in the size of a reward: no.

Variety of reward used: no.

Reinforcement schedule: continuous.

Highlights: despite rats being contraprepared to learn that food is contingent on doing nothing, it was possible to reinforce stationary behaviour (see Chapter 2).

opposite of a recall command in dog training. Instead of prompting the animal to travel to her, Ann's training was designed to teach the animal to move nowhere.

3. Increased the distance from the chair and returned immediately with a reward. Then increased the time spent away from the rat very gradually while continually talking to him.

4. Finally to break down any dependence on her first being sat beside him, Ann taught the rat to stay when placed and stroked on a variety of surfaces. She used the same cues that were established while he sat on the chair.

Stumbling blocks: If the trainer rushes any stage in the shaping process the rat will learn to move from his spot and begin exploring.

Case 2	**Rabbit** *Oryctolagus cuniculus (Orange rex)*

Training profile

Target behaviour:	standing on haunches on command
Name:	Pumpkin
Age:	8 months
Trainer's assessment of temperament:	unflappable, patient, responsive
Trainer's name:	Emma Magnus

Background

When attempting to train a rabbit the first thing to do is to suspend one's own disbelief that the species can be trained. Emma Magnus is a professional animal behaviour counsellor with a special interest in rabbit behaviour. Many members of Emma's profession train animals other than dogs as an exercise to refine their training techniques. That is what motivated Emma to train her own rabbit to rear up on command.

Training rabbits is difficult because they are so focused on flight responses that they tend to panic easily, and this can put a bar on their ability to learn. Patience is tremendously important because whenever they are awake, rabbits perform many antipredator behaviours such as surveillance and sudden darting that one would not wish to reinforce. However, as long as they are not distressed or placed in positions that compromise safety and especially their means of escape, they can be taught to sit, lie on their side and rise up on their haunches. They can even be taught to retrieve.

Training programme

Number of training sessions per week   7
Duration of session   5 minutes
Time taken to learn   2 weeks

Before commencing training the animal must: be habituated to humans.

Changing the animal's motivation before a training session: treats are withheld for an hour or so before training.

In the process of shaping the final behaviour, the trainer:
1. Identified a favourite delicacy to which Pumpkin did not have *ad libitum* access.

2. Took a regular clicker device and slightly muffled the sound it emitted by binding it in masking tape.
3. Began to associate the clicker with food by making a click and then giving food on 15 or so occasions.
4. Put Pumpkin in a corner so that the number of possible behaviours that she could perform was reduced. Then allowed him to relax.
5. Using food, lured Pumpkin into an approximation of the desired behaviour i.e. sitting up. And gave the food only after a click.
6. Waited for Pumpkin to perform a complete rise without the lure of food. Clicked and rewarded.
7. Introduced a verbal command coincident with the next repetition of the behaviour in order to develop the command as a prompt for a complete rise.

Stage 2   Stage 3   Stage 5

Stumbling blocks: offering food to rabbits by hand can cause apparent confusion because their vision does not allow them to locate food directly under their noses. Food offered by hand should be held well above nose height. Rabbits may take rather longer than dogs to clicker train perhaps because of the reduced relevance of sound in food acquisition by herbivores.

General processes in training

Clicker-training: yes.
Use of restraints: walls.
Other equipment: none.
Auditory cues: up.
Visual cues: a rabbit that has been trained only to stand up on command may use the offer of food from the hand as a cue to perform the behaviour.

Use of reinforcers

Rewards used: small pieces of oat biscuit or carrot.
Variation in the size of a reward: no.
Variety of reward used: no.
Reinforcement schedule: continuous.
Use of rewards as lures or targets: in the initial stages food is used as a lure to prompt elevation.

Highlights: the verbal cue is introduced *after* the rabbit has learned the correct response. The verbal cue becomes linked with rearing up by a process of discrimination training.

Case 3 — Pig *Sus scrofa (Vietnamese pot-bellied)*

Training profile

Target behaviour:	unrolling a carpet
Name:	Charlie
Age:	4.5 years
Trainer's assessment of temperament:	conspiratorial, quiet, nosy
Trainer's name:	Heather Powles

Background

It may seem unusual to see a pig work for food but, when it forages for roots and worms and molluscs using its snout, that is exactly what it is doing. Rolling out a piece of carpet is a simple channel for this rooting behaviour. The secretary of Britain's Pot-bellied Pig Club which boasts 570 members found training her two pigs, Charlie and Roger, surprisingly easy when they were youngsters, but has noted that their enthusiasm to learn new tasks has waned slightly as they have matured. Charlie and Roger have promoted their breed at numerous country shows and have been on television several times. They play a claxton duet which is particularly amusing.

It seems that teaching old pigs new tricks is thwarted by their having grown used to getting reinforcers in such established ways that novel foraging strategies are scarcely worth pursuing. Like many top trainers Heather has found it best to give short regular lessons that end with an established response (the oft-quoted high note) and she seeks to reduce the possibility of errors even if that involves physically placing the pig into position. Once a new response has been trained Heather integrates it into a series of behaviours using apparatus in the pig obstacle course she uses for exhibition purposes.

Training programme

Before commencing training the animal must: associate humans with fun and food.

Changing the animal's motivation before a training session: if the pigs are expected to perform on grass, it is important that they have had plenty to eat otherwise they will tend to look for food under the turf.

Number of training sessions per week   7
Duration of session   5 minutes
Time taken to learn   5 days

In the process of shaping the final behaviour, the trainer:
1. Rolled up the carpet with rewards placed regularly after each revolution, putting several food items in the centre of the roll.
2. Let Charlie see her placing a few choice rewards on the trailing edge of a rolled up carpet.
3. Allowed Charlie to investigate the carpet and gave the first command as it did so.

4. Allowed the innate snout-based foraging activity to unearth the hidden rewards.

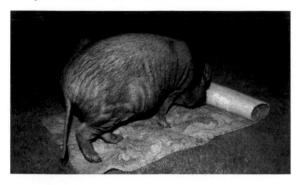

5. Repeated with fewer rewards along the way, so that Charlie learned to unroll the entire length of the carpet before feeding.

6. Withdrew all hidden items and reinforced Charlie with an extraneous reward only when he had completed the task.

Stumbling blocks: occasionally the pig may be distracted, especially if the exercise is conducted on a novel grassed area which, particularly for a mature pig, provides tremendous distraction because it demands investigation.

General processes in training

Clicker-training: no.
Use of restraints: none.
Other equipment: a rectangular piece of carpet.
Aversive stimuli: none.
Auditory cues: carpet.
Visual cues: none.

Use of reinforcers

Rewards used: pig pellets (or even messy but highly preferred foods such as sardines) can be used, but the tendency towards obesity in pot-bellied pigs indicates the use of low-calorie foods such as Weetabix and Ryvita. Rewards are given every time the carpet is unrolled until the exercise is included as part of a trained pig obstacle course.
Variation in the size of a reward: yes.
Variety of reward used: no variety is used within a single training session.
Reinforcement schedule: continuous.
Ratio of variable reinforcement: not applicable.
Use of rewards as lures or targets: food is wrapped into the carpet.

Highlights: this is a reasonably easy behaviour for pigs to learn because of the relevance of using the snout to find food.

Case 4

Pig *Sus scrofa (Chinese pot-bellied)*

Training profile

Target behaviour:	fetching a stick
Name:	Bruno
Age:	5 years
Trainer's assessment of temperament:	keen, food-focused, bubbly
Trainer's name:	Darren Beasley

Background

While Western pig farmers have selected animals for rapid ham and bacon growth and a certain tolerance of intensive housing conditions, Asian producers have kept their stock in smallholdings close to their own dwellings and therefore demand a greater degree of placidity from their pigs in the presence of humans. The temperament of the Vietnamese and Chinese pot-bellied pigs has been the secret of their success as pets in recent times. They are fond of company, preferably porcine, but human seems to suffice, and their love of food makes them reasonably easy to motivate.

Darren Beasley is a professional animal trainer at Longleat Safari Park in Wiltshire. With a strong background in parrot training, he has applied the principles of learning theory to the pot-bellied pig herd in the Pets' Corner of the park. Visitors are often surprised to see a pig performing a behaviour more usually associated with dogs, and it is fair to say that dogs are generally more enthusiastic about retrieving than most pigs. Dogs have evolved to bring food items back to the den so that they can be eaten away from competitors or fed to youngsters. Pigs do not naturally move food or, in this case, anything that has become associated with it. Keeping the animal keen is the secret; this keenness is made manifest by a quick response to the stick being thrown.

Training programme

Before commencing training the animal must: learn to associate the reinforcer (i.e., being fed or scratched) with the training context. He must also respond to a recall command and must be habituated to a variety of novel objects e.g. footballs and tyres with which he can play. The pig must be habituated to equipment, crowds and personnel.

Changing the animal's motivation before a training session: the pig is groomed for five minutes or so to help him wake up and focus on human interaction. Then he is brought out of his pen into a concrete yard that has come to represent his training ground.

Number of training sessions per week 12
Duration of session 25 minutes
Time taken to learn 4 weeks

In the process of shaping the final behaviour, the trainer:
1. Selected a stick that Bruno had encountered before but that still held some interest. Threw the stick a metre or so away. Rewarded Bruno for walking towards the stick.

2. Rewarded Bruno only for touching the stick with his nose.

3. Rewarded Bruno for moving the stick with his mouth.
4. Stood on the stick so that the pig's grip became firmer.

5. Introduced the recall. As soon as the pig put his jaws around the stick the trainer called him and retreated a little.
6. Only rewarded the pig when it had picked up the stick in its mouth and returned to the trainer.
7. Rewarded the pig for presenting the stick to the trainer for longer periods
8. Withheld rewards until Bruno walked around the trainer and sat in a 'heel' position.

Stumbling blocks: pigs that have interacted with footballs or food balls tend to move every novel object as if it were a ball. Standing on the stick can

General processes in training

Clicker-training: no.
Use of restraints: none.
Other equipment: stick.
Aversive stimuli: none.
Auditory cues: fetch.
Visual cues: none.

Use of reinforcers

Rewards used: pig pellets, apples and scratches. These are often greeted with tail wagging and snuffling noises by the pig, indicating contentment.
Variation in the size of a reward: three pig pellets offered at once are sometimes used as jackpots.
Variety of reward used: yes. Pig pellets, apples and scratches are sometimes given in combination to maintain the pig's interest.
Reinforcement schedule: continuous.
Ratio of variable reinforcement: not applicable.
Use of rewards as lures or targets: not applicable.

sometimes encourage the pig to gnaw at it rather than simply grip it. When the recall command is introduced pigs sometimes flick the stick rather than picking it up and returning, but changing to a chunkier stick can help here. Pigs that have learned to associate the trainer with food are often most reluctant to move away, as it seems to go against all natural tendencies to move away from an established food outlet.

Case 5
Cat *Felis catus (Domestic shorthair)*

Training profile

Target behaviour:	jumping through the trainer's arms
Name:	Simone
Age:	2 years
Trainer's assessment of temperament:	docile, friendly, entertaining
Trainer's name:	Alessandro Nocentini

Background

It is unusual to see a cat vaulting over anything more animate than a garden fence. Having grown up with his owner who works from home, Simone has play fights with his human every day and therefore is thoroughly habituated to robust handling. He has learned that Alessandro will never harm him.

Simone sits quietly in front of Alessandro's feet and when given the cue leaps over his arms rather like a lounge room agility dog in cat's clothing. On a good day Simone performs this behaviour within seconds of being placed in his starting position. He leaps cleanly over the human obstacle and returns to his starting position with obvious enthusiasm for the game.

Training programme

Before commencing training the animal must: learn that he cannot escape from the starting position whenever he pleases. Only when he accepts that he must sit there until released can the leap be taught.

Changing the animal's motivation before a training session: if Simone has been dozing, he is woken up with a retrieving game involving a ball of scrunched up paper. The wake-up play sessions

should last no longer than five minutes because the motivation to exert energy rapidly wanes in felidae.

Number of training sessions per week 4
Duration of session 5 minutes
Time taken to learn 2 weeks

In the process of shaping the final behaviour, the trainer:

1. Picked up Simone before his meal. Crouched down, placing the cat between his feet.

2. Put his arms ahead of the cat so that Simone had to run through the hands to move away towards the bowl. Then allowed Simone to feed.
3. Gradually brought his hands together so that

the cat had to jump over them to reach the food.

4. Over ten days or so, by gradually raising his linked arms - shaped the behaviour until the leap was impressively high. To avoid the cat

'banking', i.e. using his arms as a launch pad, he dropped them sharply if the cat touched them as he jumped. This taught him to jump cleanly.

Stumbling blocks: the cat can be disinclined to leap and seems prepared to stay put at the starting position for much longer than the human can be bothered to wait.

General processes in training

Clicker-training: no.

Use of restraints: Simone is restrained by hand until he has learned that he should not leave the starting position until given his cue.

Other equipment: none.

Aversive stimuli: none.

Auditory cues: get over.

Visual cues: arms linked in front of the cat at any level cue jumping over them.

Use of reinforcers

Rewards used: cat food in its usual receptacle.

Variation in the size of a reward: yes.

Variety of reward used: yes. The flavour of cat food used is not the same at all times but changes are gradual because, when it comes to food, cats are neophobic (see Chapter 1) and so generally take time to enjoy novel flavours.

Reinforcement schedule: variable.

Ratio of variable reinforcement: 1:5.

Use of rewards as lures or targets: food is placed away from the cat to prompt forward movement.

Case 6

Cat *Felis catus (British silver tabby)*

Training profile

Target behaviour:	sitting up on haunches and waving
Name:	Rimet
Age:	15 months
Trainer's assessment of temperament:	aloof, ladylike, pensive
Trainer's name:	Debbie Yates

Background

It is interesting to see cats performing learned behaviours on command in the way dogs usually do. After patient training, cats offer maximal fore-leg extension and demonstrate a responsive attitude.

The cats at the Waltham Centre for Pet Nutrition, UK, take part in studies designed to increase our understanding of their nutritional and behavioural needs. They live in social groups in an enriched environment but also receive extensive human contact from their carers. In addition to petting and grooming their cats, the carers have found that they can improve the value of their social contact by training the cats to 'play' in certain ways to receive rewards. Although learning in cats happens all the time in a domestic context (e.g. cats developing strong associations between the sound of a tin-opener and food), few owners

seem to be able to structure this learning. Cats at the centre are trained by a number of carers using a uniform method. This ensures that the cats respond to a variety of people and do not become overattached to an individual carer.

Training programme

Before commencing training the animal must: be well socialised to people. Before a specific behaviour can be taught, the cats must be trained that the sound of a click from a clicker is a reliable prelude to food i.e. the click must become a secondary reinforcer. Approximately 50 click repetitions, paired closely with food, are usually required to establish this association. The latency of the food reward should initially be less than one second. Later the time between click and reward can be gradually increased to as much as ten seconds.

Changing the animal's motivation before a training session: as a model of what goes on in so many domestic contexts these cats are fed *ad libitum*. They know that their training sessions come at a certain stage in their daily routine. Therefore the cleaning of their quarters serves as a prelude to an invitation to accompany staff into the training room adjacent to their play facility. Just as the arrival of an owner in a family home alerts cats to the possibility of food, all of these cues prime the cats to know that clicking is about to commence. To focus the cats, primary reinforcement (i.e. food) is given in association with the clicker at the beginning of each training session.

Number of training sessions per week 5
Duration of session   2–3 minutes
Time taken to learn   20 minutes

In the process of shaping the final behaviour, the trainer:
1. Initially put Rimet in a sitting position and reinforced any movement by either foot. This helped

to identify which of its feet the cat was keener to use in pursuit of a food reward.

2. Withheld further reinforcement and thus created a puzzle.

3. Reinforced (with a click-plus-food) all improved approximations i.e. greater elevations with

single foot became the way to solve the puzzle.

4. Introduced the verbal cue ('*wave*') and a supporting visual cue (a raised left or right index finger) fractionally before click-plus-food. The cat then learned to discriminate the commands from the regular chat that they have with their staff. Then they learned to discriminate between an inadequate and an improved performance of the behaviour.

5. Repeated steps 2 and 3 with 10–15 cycles until the final behaviour was shaped.
6. Used the verbal and visual cues in isolation as stimulants of the desired behaviour.

Stumbling blocks: cats become distracted easily and try to use their paws to obtain the food as soon as they see it.

General processes in training

Clicker-training: yes.
Use of restraints: none.
Other equipment: none.
Aversive stimuli: none.
Auditory cues: wave.
Visual cues: if the cat chooses to raise its left paw, the trainer standing in front of it raises her right index finger (or vice versa) as a visual cue.

Use of reinforcers

Rewards used: part of the daily ration. If the cat gives a poor performance, the food is returned to its bowl to be consumed later. Human interaction constitutes an important reinforcer for these cats.
Variation in the size of a reward: yes, anywhere between one and ten kibbled food rewards can be given.
Variety of rewards used: yes.
Reinforcement schedule: continuous reinforcement is used until the response is established. One hundred per cent of correct performances by these cats are reinforced with a click, whereas only 60 per cent of these are contiguously reinforced with pieces of kibble. This represents something of a departure from traditional clicker training in which the clicker never 'lies'.
Ratio of variable reinforcement: ultimately 1:10.
Use of rewards as lures or targets: to focus the cat when establishing the behaviour, food is placed in the hand with the raised finger.

Case 7   Cat *Felis catus (Domestic shorthair)*

Training profile

Target behaviour:	playing an electric keyboard
Name:	Simon
Age:	15 months
Trainer's assessment of temperament:	bold, friendly, outgoing
Trainer's name:	Ann Head

Background

It is rather unusual to see a cat operating a machine or indeed do anything out of the ordinary especially without being touched or prompted. A well-trained cat, however, will show no hesitation with a keyboard; on seeing it he plays as an immediate response. Unlike dogs that will perform behaviours for a variety of secondary reinforcers, cats are more likely to require a direct and reliable primary reward. Ann Head, the trainer of all the Arthur cats, famed for eating branded tinned food direct from the can using their paws, suggests that, if the reward is insufficient, cats will rarely oblige.

By selecting cats from rescue centres on the basis of their temperament and to some extent their good looks, Ann is able to stock her stable of feline actors with a remarkably low attrition rate. While most of her cats are taught keyboard skills, all of them are taught to use their paws for some form of food prehension. She explains that the best way to teach a cat is to let him 'believe' that everything was his idea in the first place i.e. to discover the solution to any food-based puzzle without physical help from a human. It is best to avoid touching a cat when training it in this way, since most enjoy physical contact; they push back and therefore often travel away from the spot in which they are supposed to be stationed. In the interests of taste and good temper, the output volume of the electric keyboard should be switched off when training cats to use a keyboard. Their skills as musicians are equal and opposite to their excellence as hunters.

Training programme

Before commencing training the animal must: sit on command and be clicker trained.

Changing the animal's motivation before a training session: about half of the cat's daily ration can be given before a training session. Withholding any more than this will tend to make him overexcited about rewards and unable to persist in a single behaviour. As a reminder, the cat must be clicker trained with one or two rewards at the start of the first training session.

Number of training sessions per week   2
Duration of session   15 minutes
Time taken to learn   2 days

In the process of shaping the final behaviour, the trainer:

1. Presented Simon with a keyboard at an appropriate height. By placing the keyboard between the cat and the treats, the trainer engineered

the arrangement of the cat and the keyboard so that he was likely to bump into it. As soon as he did so, she rewarded him with a clicker.

2. Asked him to *sit* in front of the keyboard.

3. Waited for his forepaws to touch the keys. Rewarded as soon as he did so.

4. Allowed Simon to develop his own style and rewarded him for moving both paws around the keys as much as possible.

Stumbling blocks: persuading the cat to remain in one spot with his hindlegs in a sitting portion takes approximately half one's time during training. The time taken to train this behaviour depends largely on the patience of the trainer.

General processes in training

Clicker-training: yes.
Use of restraints: no.
Other equipment: keyboard.
Aversive stimuli: no.
Auditory cues: none.
Visual cues: the keyboard certainly acts as a visual cue. Also the trainer holds the treats on the far side of the keyboard in a hand that is raised to keep the cat's attention.

Use of reinforcers

Rewards used: dried cat food.
Variation in the size of a reward: yes, the clicker can be used several times in rapid succession to deliver a jackpot.

Variety of rewards used: occasionally on a film set, raw meat or a fresh prawn may be used to renew the cat's interest.
Reinforcement schedule: continuous.
Ratio of variable reinforcement: not applicable.
Use of rewards as lures or targets: not applicable.

Highlights: the kneading action of Simon's forepaws can be readily shaped because it is so similar to the kneading action kittens use when suckling and adult domestic cats use as a form of social bonding behaviour e.g. with owners. It is a response to which cats readily default as a result of what has been labelled instinctive drift (see Chapter 2).

Case 8

Cow *Bos taurus (Belted Galloway × Friesian)*

Training profile
Target behaviour: pulling a carriage
Name: Susie
Age: 4 years
Trainer's assessment of temperament: feisty, affectionate, adventurous
Trainer's name: Amanda Saville

Background

Although they provide a much less comfortable ride, cattle can be ridden as readily as horses. They can also be driven and it seems that Susie is a particularly good example. She is a novelty member of a driving team, *Chariots of Fire*, that thrills crowds all over the UK with displays that would make Ben Hur shudder. Amanda Saville is an unusual carriage driver in that her ponies jump fences at speed while in harness (if it engages on the ramps provided, the carriage flies over the fence in pursuit) and so does her cow, Susie. The remarkable thing about all of the animals in this display team is the trust they demonstrate in the humans who handle them. Even without being on their backs, the drivers give them the confidence to crash through water hazards, ascend ramps and scurry down greasy hillsides. Many of the ponies have been trained to charge through barricades ablaze with flames (see Fig. 1.12a in Chapter 1), and it seems only a matter of time before Susie will do this too. Because she demonstrates plenty of enthusiasm as she pulls her carriage, Susie builds up an impressive head of steam so her training focuses on establishing good control.

Training programme

Before commencing training the animal must: be well handled i.e. habituated to humans and halter broken.

Changing the animal's motivation before a training session: getting harnessed seems to serve as a context cue reminding Susie what to do.

Number of training sessions per week 5
Duration of session 30 minutes
Time taken to learn 4 weeks

In the process of shaping the final behaviour, the trainer:

1. Accustomed Susie to having a bit in her mouth by leaving her with a bit in place for two hours at a time in a stable without food. This took approximately two weeks.

2. Dressed the cow in full harness and led her around while instilling the commands: *walk on, Susie trot, Susie canter, whoa* (or a specific high-pitched trill), *come* (left) and *get* (right). While wearing blinkers, Susie had to learn to

encounter visual stimuli ahead of her and to ignore to some extent auditory stimuli other than commands from her driver. The potential for a flight response is therefore increased unless she is habituated to noises from behind. Chains can be jangled and buckets rattled until they fail to elicit a flight response.

3. Introduced the carriage while leading the cow.

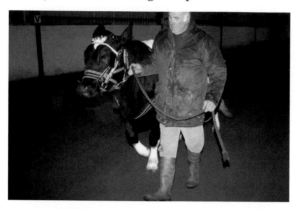

4. Introduced the cow to the weight of a driver on board the carriage. Steering from the groom (who is on foot) fostered the correct responses to vocal commands issued by the driver.

5. Gradually dispensed with the groom for moving in a straight line and later for cornering.

Stumbling blocks: assuming that she has learned more than is the case, especially in terms of sensitivity to the bit and responsiveness when being directed. Cows differ from horses in that, without falling over, they can flex their neck whilst moving at speed in a straight line. This accounts for cows presenting problems when being led in the show ring where it is usual for them to have their heads raised in a bid to maximise control.

General processes in training

Clicker-training: no.

Use of restraints: a driving bit fitted in the diastema (the toothless part of a herbivore's mouth between the canines and the molars) as it is in a horse.

Other equipment: regular breastplate harness including blinkers which help to guide the animal in a straight line and minimise peripheral distractions that can cause wandering (towards a tasty meal) or panic and bolting (away from a threatening stimulus).

Aversive stimuli: the noise of a riding whip striking the outside of the harness is used to send her forward. Bit pressure also becomes something that the cow learns to avoid.

Auditory cues: walk on, Susie trot, Susie canter, whoa, come and get.

Visual cues: Susie jumps small obstacles as part of her display.

Use of reinforcers

Rewards used: pats, scratches and verbal praise. Removal of pressure from bit or harness.

Variation in the size of a reward: yes.

Variety of rewards used: yes.

Reinforcement schedule: positive reinforcement.

Ratio of variable reinforcement: not applicable.

Use of rewards as lures or targets: not applicable.

Case 9 — Cow *Bos taurus (South Devon × Jersey)*

Training profile

Target behaviour:	lifting front legs on command
Name:	Ramblie
Age:	6 years
Trainer's assessment of temperament:	placid, co-operative, sociable
Trainer's name:	Hayley Randle

Background

Even when trained for showing purposes, cattle are rarely handled sufficiently for them to learn anything more interesting than being quiet to lead in a head-collar. Ramblie, on the other hand, was born on a research facility, Little Eco-Ash Farm, that produces some fascinating data on animal behaviour.

Hayley Randle lectures in animal behaviour at the Duchy College in Cornwall and was awarded a Ph.D. for her work on bovine cognition. Ramblie is owned by Hayley and was one of the research animals she used in her doctoral studies. Ramblie is a member of a multispecies ballet troupe that has been featured a number of times on television. Each animal in the troupe is accompanied by a human. Both members of each pair mirror the actions of one another. When set to music, the leg flexion response featured in the current case study forms an integral part of Ramblie's performance.

Training programme

Before commencing training the animal must: be habituated to humans to the extent that she has learned to take food from the hand. Verbal praise must have been established as a secondary reinforcer and the word 'No' must have been established as a punisher i.e. as a signal that no reinforcement should be expected.

Changing the animal's motivation before a training session: nothing.

Number of training sessions per week   1
Duration of session   25 minutes
Time taken to learn   1 day

In the process of shaping the final behaviour, the trainer:

1. Stood in front of the cow and gave the voice command *Ramblie lift leg* with a simultaneous visual signal (the trainer raised her leg opposite the cow's leg). Then physically lifted the cow's leg in the same way as one might with a horse. As soon as the leg was lifted, the trainer rewarded her with verbal praise swiftly followed by a food reward or a scratch preferably on the head of her tail.

2. Repeated step 1 with a reduced physical prompt; simply touching the front of the cow's leg became sufficient stimulation.

any flexion of this joint produces the desired effect.

3. Repeated verbal command up to three times. If no response was forthcoming, the trainer reminded the cow using a physical prompt but continually aimed to reduce the signal so that the movement of the trainer towards the cow's leg was recognised as a prelude to the signal and was therefore acted upon. There was no need to shape a higher leg lifting response since cows have such short bones below the knee that

Stumbling blocks: unlike horses who often resort to established activities 'as if any response will do', cows that have yet to perfect a response tend to simply stand still. Sometimes a cow that has learned to lift her leg may begin to lift the wrong leg. This leaves the trainer with a potential dilemma since to omit rewards for such a response could transiently extinguish all lifting.

General processes in training

Clicker-training: no.
Use of restraints: halter.
Other equipment: none.
Aversive stimuli: the cow's foot is tickled by the human.
Auditory cues: Ramblie, lift left leg and *Ramblie, lift right leg.*
Visual cues: the trainer raises her own leg as a visual prompt.

Use of reinforcers

Rewards used: verbal praise, rolled barley, scratching, particularly at tail.
Variation in the size of a reward: no.
Variety of rewards used: yes. Some form of reinforcement is given every time the behaviour appears, but generally during training verbal praise is used first and then later in the session, if responses are shaping appropriately, this is replaced with food. The ratio of verbal reinforcement to food is approximately 2:1.
Reinforcement schedule: continuous.
Ratio of variable reinforcement: not applicable.
Use of rewards as lures or targets: not applicable.

Case 10

Horse *Equus caballus (Arab)*

Training profile

Target behaviour:	bowing head down to the ground
Name:	Archie
Age:	8 years
Trainer's assessment of temperament:	friendly, inquisitive, trusting
Trainer's name:	Cecilia Lindberg

Background

Archie has been shaped to perform in-hand behaviours beyond the normal repertoire of horses when mounted. When humans are on the ground, rather than in the saddle, a new range of possibilities opens up because the horses can see the humans with whom they are interacting. Training a horse to strike an unusual and impressive pose can be achieved by a form of target training in which the horse learns to touch the trainer's fist to reveal the treat within. However, to persuade a horse to lower his head and shoulders into the rather compromising position of a bow depends entirely on first convincing him that you are safe to be around. The establishment of a close bond between the horse and trainer goes beyond the animal simply recognising the human as a reliable source of food. The horse must have sufficient experience of that human to have learned that she does little to threaten him and that she is a reliable companion that will never react unex-

pectedly. Generally speaking, the ability to work with horses without alarming them is a critical attribute of good horsefolk. It is part of what is meant by the oft-quoted but poorly defined term 'horse sense'.

Although horses occasionally scratch themselves using an analogue of this posture, a deep stationary bow is not a normal behaviour in horses. It looks dramatic with the added anthropomorphic inference that Archie is saying 'Thank you'. A keen endurance competitor, Cecilia Lindberg is decided to train Archie, one of her endurance horses, to bow as an exercise in training technique and also because it is believed that the bow is a useful stretch exercise for equine athletes.

Training programme

Before commencing training the animal must: stand completely still on command. Remain calm; in other words not get too excited, despite the prospect of an imminent titbit. Lift legs in desired direction on command.

Changing the animal's motivation before a training session: nothing; although training is conducted before normal time of concentrated feed.

Number of training sessions per week 2
Duration of session 10 minutes
Time taken to learn 8 weeks

In the process of shaping the final behaviour, the trainer:
1. Told Archie to stand still, lifted his forelegs forward a little at a time and used the verbal command to *stand* (with which the horse was familiar from other more traditional training). At this stage, the horse's natural tendency was to return his legs to their original place to support his bodyweight.

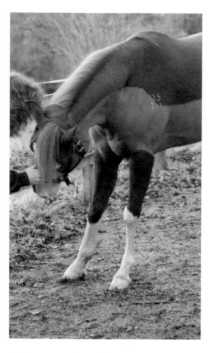

2. Placed the two legs far enough apart for the head to pass between them i.e. further apart than most horses would naturally choose to place them.

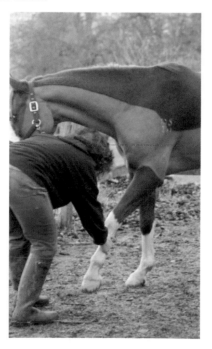

3. Rewarded Archie for remaining in the new position and then cued to end the movement rather than waiting for him to get tired.

4. Encouraged Archie to move his hind legs back a little at a time either manually or by tapping with a whip. Cecilia issued the *stand* command and rewarded him for maintaining this position for a short time before she ended the movement.

5. With the horse in an extended position as described above, began to prompt him to lower his head by offering food at around fetlock height. Keeping residual tension on the lead-rope helped to convince him that he could not simply move his legs to reach the food.

6. Gradually offered the food nearer the ground between the legs and then nearer to his brisket to bring his head into a deep bow.

7. Ultimately rewarded only when the horse extended his forehead fully towards the ground to complete a deep bow.

Stumbling blocks: refusal to stand still once the front legs have been moved forward. This was overcome by placing a short plank behind Archie's front feet. This temporary measure helped Archie accept the novel placement of his feet because it is was easier for him to keep his feet in the advanced position than lift them back into a normal position over the plank.

General processes in training

Clicker-training: no.

Use of restraints: headcollar is used only to keep the horse still.

Other equipment: a plank, placed on the ground behind the fore feet, is used in early training to discourage movement.

Aversive stimuli: a schooling whip is very gently used to tap the legs to encourage them to move into position. A stern voice is used to correct unwanted behaviour and a tug on the headcollar can help to discourage unwelcome raising of the head.

Auditory cues: none.

Visual cues: the hand being lowered to the ground prompts the behaviour.

Use of reinforcers

Rewards used: apples, carrots and proprietary pelleted horse food. Removal of pressure exerted during stretching.

Variation in the size of a reward: yes, jackpots are given for exceptional responses towards the end of a training session.

Variety of rewards used: yes.

Reinforcement schedule: continuous.

Ratio of variable reinforcement: not applicable.

Use of rewards as lures or targets: food is held between the horse's front legs to encourage him to bow to reach it.

Case 11 — Pony *Equus caballus (Shetland cross)*

Training profile

Target behaviour:	Spanish walk (an extravagant display gait sometimes seen as an haute-école movement in top level equitation)
Name:	Topper
Age:	14 years
Trainer's assessment of temperament:	nervous, jumpy, suspicious
Trainer's name:	Katie Rourke

Background

Some members of the equine family have to be taught exclusively from the ground because they are too small to be ridden. One such pony is Topper who had a troublesome life before arriving at his new home. Left entire, i.e. ungelded, he had developed many unwelcome behaviours to defend his herd from perceived threats. For these he had been beaten and as a result became fearful and very dangerous to humans. He did not know that they could be pleasant, companionable sources of carrots. He had to learn to trust them. As a measure of the fear humans evoked in him, Topper's first associations with the clicker were made with the most rewarding outcome - the departure of humans from his stable. Only when he had learned to take treats from humans could the clicker be associated with food.

These days, though still easily spooked, Topper is very fond of humans he knows. He walks to heel - like an obedience dog - without a lead. He happily approaches people who enter his field. Indeed he regularly marches up to them offering his display gait - the Spanish walk. Among his many tricks, this is the one we will examine in detail. One does not expect to see so small a pony, especially one that has not been ridden, performing this 'high school' movement. A clear lift of the leg above its normal arc and defined extension of the shoulder is what an experienced judge might look for in an excellent execution of the desired behaviour.

Katie Rourke is a professional dog trainer who decided to train Topper to perform this impressive gait simply because she wanted to see what was possible with clicker training in horses.

Training programme

Before commencing training the animal must: want the reward you are offering and must have learned to trust humans enough to take a food reward offered by hand.

Changing the animal's motivation before a training session: nothing.

Number of training sessions per week   7
Duration of session   10 minutes
Time taken to learn   24 weeks

* Much of this time was spent building up Topper's confidence in the first instance and polishing his response in the later stages.

In the process of shaping the final behaviour, the trainer:
1. Established the click as a treat. In Topper's case this initially involved linking the click with

the departure of humans (on approximately 15 occasions) and then the appearance of food (on approximately 25 occasions). It helped to have another pony in close proximity when offering rewards during training. The element of competition seemed to increase the value of the resource.

2. Rewarded Topper for shifting his weight from one foreleg to the other but without walking forward. Then withheld the click and reward until alternate legs were being lifted well off the ground.

3. Established a visual cue by standing in front of Topper and indicating with the right hand to get the left foreleg to lift and vice versa.

4. To encourage a walk, only rewarded Topper when his lifted foreleg was replaced forward of its original position. Walking backwards, Katie then cued one leg then the other.

5. Variable reinforcement was used to encourage increasing numbers of steps, with the cue *big steps*, while *too bad* was introduced to alert Topper that unimproved responses would not be rewarded.

6. Katie gradually shifted her own position so that, instead of standing in front of Topper, she was at his side.

7. To establish immediate responses, taught the pony that after the verbal cue there was only a limited time during which a reward could be expected to appear.

Stumbling blocks: persistence in lifting one leg is a common sticking point. Also the establishment of a link between hands being waved

General processes in training

Clicker-training: yes.

Use of restraints: a headcollar is used only to lead the pony in and out of the training area.

Other equipment: treat bag.

Aversive stimuli: a verbal cue *too bad* marks the loss of an opportunity to earn a treat.

Auditory cues: 'big steps'.

Visual cues: waving is gradually faded.

Use of reinforcers

Rewards used: mint confectionery, apples, carrots and breakfast cereals.

Variation in the size of a reward: yes, jackpots are given for exceptional responses.

Variety of rewards used: yes, a variety helps to keep the pony interested during a training session.

Reinforcement schedule: continuous. A reward is given every time a click is given. The clicker never lies. Once the response is established reinforcement is transiently withheld to increase the duration of responses.

Ratio of variable reinforcement: not applicable.

Use of rewards as lures or targets: not applicable.

Highlights: in teaching the pony that responses have to be offered within a certain period after the cue, Katie is indicating that there is a finite opportunity to be reinforced for a given behaviour in the same way that an indicator light can function as a discriminative stimulus for a rat in a Skinner box.

and a cue being given. Topper had to overcome his fear of being struck to make this association. The movement of the forelegs beyond their original position relies on the pony spontaneously bringing his hind-limbs with him. Topper had to be reminded of this technicality. The introduction of a verbal cue is a challenge because most horses have come to regard the continuous chat of humans around them as being irrelevant.

Case 12

Dog *Canis familiaris (German shepherd dog × Airedale terrier)*

Training profile

Target behaviour:	empty the washing machine and give the items of clothing to owner
Name:	Scamp
Age:	7 years
Trainer's assessment of temperament:	happy, even-tempered, docile
Trainer's name:	Jose Goodinson

Background

Inasmuch as they have been used for pulling bath-chairs, dogs have been used for assisting physically disabled people for centuries. The use of dogs in therapy is flourishing, and often their very presence as companions can enrich the lives of institutionalised people.

Dog Aid is a UK charity that aims to enable physically disadvantaged dog owners to use their own dogs as assistants rather than just companions. Trainers facilitate the process of teaching dogs new responses while the bulk of training is conducted by the owners themselves. Scamp and Jose represent one such owner–dog team. He picks up dropped items for her, pulls her out of her chair when she presents him with a specially designated tug toy and will open and close doors on request. Central to many of his tasks is the ability to retrieve. Among the named items he has learned to identify and bring to his owner are the TV remote control device, the mobile phone, magazines and Jose's walking stick. When emptying the washing machine once it has been opened by hand, Scamp is especially highly praised for clean manoeuvres that involve no dropping of or playing with the items.

Training programme

Before commencing training the animal must: pay attention to the owner, hold items in its mouth and come to call. Additionally, he must be clicker trained, i.e. he must have learned that a given sound can be reinforcing. This can be established by giving a valued food reward contiguous with the sound on as few as ten occasions. A central theme in clicker training is to foster creativity. Therefore it is important to 'click' the dog when it does something appropriate of its own volition. Furthermore, it is useful to click no more than three iterations of a single behaviour. This seems to stop the dog becoming fixated on a single behaviour and prompts it to attempt the modifications of the behaviour that are essential for shaping a refined response.

Changing the animal's motivation before a training session: nothing, although some trainers find it helpful to isolate dogs briefly to increase their motivation to focus their attention on the trainer.

Number of training sessions per week 7 (one with a facilitator)
Duration of session 20 minutes
Time taken to learn 8 weeks

In the process of shaping the final behaviour, the trainer:
1. Clicked and rewarded when the dog looked at a given attractive mouthable object such as a squeaky toy.
2. Clicked and rewarded only when the dog turned his head towards the object.

3. Clicked and rewarded only when the dog's head interacted with the object, e.g. when he nosed it.
4. Using food on the object encouraged the dog to use his mouth on the object. Clicked and rewarded when he mouthed the object.
5. Very gradually shaped holding the object for increasing periods of time by withholding the click and reward until longer periods had elapsed with the dog holding the object.
6. Placed hand under the dog's mouth. Clicked and rewarded when the dog dropped the object.
7. Refined this release until the dog dropped the object only into the hand.

8. Introduced the command only when the dog appeared 100 per cent competent and con-

fident that he knew what was required of him.
9. To establish confidence in his being around the washing machine, placed a titbit of food on the rim of its opening.

10. To establish confidence in his putting his head inside the washing machine, placed a favourite toy inside it.

11. Put the toy inside a sock then clicked and rewarded when dog retrieved the paired items.

12. Replaced paired items with the sock alone then clicked and rewarded when dog retrieved it.
13. Introduced a new command (*washing machine*) then clicked and rewarded when dog retrieved an item of clothing from the washing machine.

14. Gradually introduced a series of novel items of clothing.

Stumbling blocks: poor timing on the part of the trainer who occasionally missed the opportunity to reinforce significant improvements in performance. Additionally, there was some initial reluctance on the dog's part to put his head in the machine.

General processes in training

Clicker-training: yes.
Use of restraints: a regular collar and lead can sometimes help in training by controlling the radius within which the dog can work.
Other equipment: none.
Aversive stimuli: none.
Auditory cues: washing machine means go to the laundry and *pull them* means remove the clothing.
Visual cues: none.

Use of reinforcers

Rewards used: click, food (sweet biscuits), toys, verbal praise, smiles and strokes.

Variation in the size of a reward: yes.
Variety of rewards used: yes.
Reinforcement schedule: click and reward usually arrive in tandem for two weeks. After that verbal praise is continuous.
Ratio of variable reinforcement: some form of reward is given every time the dog performs the correct behaviour or approximation thereof.
Use of rewards as lures or targets: food is used on the rim of the washing machine then the toy (with or without the sock) is used inside the washing machine.

Case 13 — Cat *Felis catus (Domestic shorthair)*

Training profile

Target behaviour:	picking up objects
Name:	Moses
Age:	1.5 years
Trainer's assessment of temperament:	relaxed, inquisitive, normal
Trainer's name:	Lindy Coote

Background

At six months of age, Moses was a 'free-to-good-home' kitten in a veterinary clinic. His juvenile appeal was waning and there was a serious risk of his being euthanased unless he found a home. Happily he was adopted by Lindy Coote to join her animal family of three dogs and one cat. He developed an immediate rapport with the dogs and joined them and Lindy on their daily trips to work at *Animal House*, an agency supplying animals for film and television.

As a professional trainer, Lindy was keen to explore the challenges of training a cat to pick up an object but recognised the critical importance of understanding a species' biology before commencing training. Picking up objects is a response that dogs generally find very easy, presumably because their ancestors regularly carried objects in their mouths, e.g. food back to the den. It is considerably less common in wild felidae that tend to eat where they kill their prey. As members of predatory species, both dogs and cats can be encouraged to chase moving objects, but Lindy set herself the goal of training Moses to pick up items that were lying stationary beside him. She used a pencil because it was a suitable size and commonplace (and so was easily replaced) and could be exchanged with other similar sized objects in later training.

Training programme

Before commencing training the animal must: be clicker trained and relaxed in the training area. The cat must also be trained to expect rewards on the training table and remain on it rather than jumping off to explore the room.

Changing the animal's motivation before a training session: never give *ad libitum* food and always leave a gap of at least three hours between previous meal and training.

Number of training sessions per week 14
Duration of session 10 minutes
Time taken to learn 2 weeks

In the process of shaping the final behaviour, the trainer:
1. Held the pencil near Moses' face and reinforced him for looking at it.

2. Clicked and rewarded for turning neck towards the pencil.

3. Clicked and rewarded for touching the pencil with his nose.

5. Placed the pencil on the table top and repeated steps 2 and 3.

4. Clicked and rewarded for mouthing the pencil.

6. Clicked and rewarded for picking up the pencil.

Stumbling blocks: distractions. Because he associated it directly with the delivery of food, the cat tended to follow the trainer's hand first and foremost.

General processes in training

Clicker-training: yes.
Use of restraints: no.
Other equipment: clicker.
Aversive stimuli: none.
Auditory cues: none.
Visual cues: pencil.

Use of reinforcers

Rewards used: cat biscuits, liver treats and roast chicken.
Variation in the size of a reward: no.
Variety of rewards used: yes.
Reinforcement schedule: continuous.
Ratio of variable reinforcement: not applicable.
Use of rewards as lures or targets: no.

Case 14   Dog *Canis familiaris (Cairn terrier cross)*

Training profile
Target behaviour: chasing tail on command
Name: Cricket
Age: 3 years
Trainer's assessment of temperament: naughty, easily distracted, comedic
Trainer's name: Lindy Coote

Background

Cricket was rescued from a local pound at seven months of age. Although she was far from easy to manage because of separation-related distress, she soon began to show star quality. This delighted her new owner, Lindy, who is head trainer with *Animal House*, Australia's largest animal talent agency. Within two weeks of her adoption, Cricket had landed a lead role in a short film, playing the part of the devoted companion of an elderly lady. The many responses required of Cricket by the script included having to go to her place on set, bark, put her paw on the woman's hand, jump onto beds and generally tear around like a lunatic - all on cue. The variety of responses she learned and the speed with which she did so confirmed her suitability for film work. Being relaxed and spontaneous on set, Cricket is more natural than strictly obedience trained dogs, a characteristic directors find invaluable.

One of the more unusual responses requested of Cricket by scripts has been to chase her tail (on cue). This response is sometimes seen excessively in certain breeds (e.g. English bull terriers) and is considered a behavioural abnormality if it cannot be controlled. Unfortunately for Lindy, Cricket was not innately afflicted with a tail-chasing tendency so the behaviour had to be shaped from first principles.

Training programme

Before commencing training the animal must: know the commands to *stay* (standing) and *get it* (hold object in mouth). Be clicker-trained and keen to develop new responses as a type of game.

Changing the animal's motivation before a training session: the trainer alerted the dog to the start of each training session by removing the other dogs from the training facility and focusing attention on her.

Number of training sessions per week 20
Duration of session 10 minutes
Time taken to learn 1 week

In the process of shaping the final behaviour, the trainer:
1. Rewarded slight turns of the head.

2. Shaped turning of the head and shoulders.

3. Shaped looking round at her tail.

4. Increased the dog's interest in her tail by playing with it and giving the command *get it*.

5. Rewarded the dog for a complete revolution before chaining a series of eight revolutions together (as stipulated by the script at the time).

Stumbling blocks: the dog tended to sit down to look at or grasp her tail. The other challenge was training Cricket to perform this response while at a distance from the trainer (who needed to be at least two metres away from her to be out of shot).

General processes in training

Clicker-training: yes.
Use of restraints: no.
Other equipment: none.
Aversive stimuli: none.
Auditory cues: get it and *that's not it* (the least reinforcing stimulus).
Visual cues: the trainer's hand moves in the direction of intended travel.

Use of reinforcers

Rewards used: cat biscuits, liver treats and roast chicken.
Variation in the size of a reward: yes – jackpots were given when Cricket actively engaged eye contact with her tail and when she first completed a revolution.
Reinforcement schedule: continuous then variable.
Ratio of variable reinforcement: eventually 1:8.
Use of rewards as lures or targets: no.

Case 15
Dog *Canis familiaris (Australian shepherd dog)*

Training profile
Target behaviour:	limping on command
Name:	Boo
Age:	8 years
Trainer's assessment of temperament:	territorial, keen-to-please, devoted
Trainer's name:	Lindy Coote

Background

Purchased from a breeder at 13 weeks of age, Boo has always shown the sort of trainability you would expect from a working breed. Lindy has trained him successfully for the show ring as well as for obedience and agility trials and a variety of demonstration displays.

Boo has worked with Lindy in her capacity as a trainer of animal talent on a variety of television programmes. The list of novel behaviours he has learned to perform on cue include: digging, sneezing, saluting and even limping.

Training programme

Before commencing training the animal must: be trained to shake hands, stay, stand (from a sitting position) and come to call.

Changing the animal's motivation before a training session: nothing.

Number of training sessions per week 14
Duration of session 15 minutes
Time taken to learn 1 week

In the process of shaping the final behaviour, the trainer:

1. Reinforced the dog for touching her hand with his paw on the cue *sore paw* while he remained standing (i.e. rather than while sitting as one finds with most dogs that have been trained to shake hands).

2. Shaped the dog to stay still with one paw raised while she stood a few steps away from him.

3. Stepped back and raised her hand to encourage the dog to touch her hand without putting his paw to the ground i.e. to reach for her.

4. Reinforced a single hop towards her.

5. Shaped several hops together.
6. Shaped several hops together interspersed with a halt, again with a raised paw.

Stumbling blocks: dogs that have been trained to shake hands have usually learned to do so while sitting and therefore take some time to learn to raise a forepaw while standing. In a similar vein, many dogs respond to the recall command by default and so travel towards the handler without raising a forepaw i.e. using normal locomotion.

General processes in training

Clicker-training: no.
Use of restraints: no.
Other equipment: none.
Aversive stimuli: none.
Auditory cues: sore paw.
Visual cues: trainer's hand.

Use of reinforcers

Rewards used: chicken loaf and verbal praise.
Variation in the size of a reward: no.
Variety of rewards used: yes.
Reinforcement schedule: variable.
Ratio of variable reinforcement: 1:2.
Use of rewards as lures or targets: no.

Highlights: this case includes the combination of several learned responses meshed together and also shows how the trainer's hand can be used in target training (see Chapter 2). The dog learns that to touch the hand is a response that brings rewards. As soon as possible, Lindy trains her dogs to work at a distance from her so that they will reliably produce their trained responses when they are on set and she has to be out of 'shot'.

Chapter 6

Exotic animals

There are a number of reasons why exotic animals are trained. In a zoological exhibit, being able to demonstrate some of the behavioural and physical attributes of a species can help to educate the visiting public (*see* Section a, below). Meanwhile, with crowd appeal in mind, some trainers try to make the animals seem cleverer than they are, for comic effect (*see* Section b, below). Additionally, dangerous exotic animals are sometimes conditioned to be handled by humans specifically for film, television or display purposes (*see* Section c, below). A further group embraces animals that are trained primarily for veterinary procedures and to enhance the safety of personnel (*see* Section d, below).

Displays involving trained animals in zoological collections are designed to attract crowds and certainly do turnstile figures no harm. For this reason some argue that there is a grey area between these and circus performances. Zoo environments may suit some animals very well, and their training may truly be a good way of improving their welfare. In other cases, this is very suspect.

a. Training to show off the physical abilities and natural behaviours of the animals

Although they often employ simple techniques, trainers of exotic animals can refine the behaviour of their animals to demonstrate the biological traits of a wide variety of species for educational purposes. Zoo and aquarium trainers have traditionally used seals to entertain crowds with their astonishing feats of skill, speed, agility and balance. These traits are intrinsic in the nature of these naturally social, inquisitive and playful marine mammals. However, the animals rarely show these traits spontaneously in the confines of captivity, or at least not when the visiting public is around. Of the known seal species (pinnipeds), Californian sealions and Australian fur seals are regarded as the most easily trained. Interestingly, some trainers feel that South African fur seals appear less focused on food and therefore slower to respond to secondary reinforcers than Californian sealions are. Others argue that species, gender and age are irrelevant and that individual differences in ability and motivation will have the most significant effect on ultimate performance. Sealions differ from seals in that they have external ear flaps, they walk on all four flippers and they use their front flippers to swim. Patient trainers can successfully modify the natural behaviours of seals and sealions such as prehension, control of objects and balancing on uneven slippery surfaces to perform tasks for the entertainment of the audience. For example, Magellan (Case 16) the sealion was taught to roll in the same way as a dog.

Many sealion trainers remark on the similarities between their professional training subjects and their canine pets. The social nature of both species and the need for athleticism and co-operation during hunting account for many of the similarities. However, a key difference would be that many more sealion trainers get bitten than do dog trainers. Food for sealions is generally rationed to prevent obesity in a captive environment. Thus, each morsel is zealously earned, and if any food is not delivered when expected the sealions can become fractious. They show little of the 'will to please' that dog owners find so endearing. Another key difference of course is that sealions do not wear collars. Dogs can be restrained physically until one has their attention; sealions cannot. Keeping the sealions in one place at the outset of training is one of the most helpful ways in which to control them and avoid being bitten. As for many species, exotic and otherwise, once the animal knows that its 'station' is the place where it must be in order to get fed, its behaviour can be modified more safely (see place-training and feeding stations, Chapter 2). The extent to which behaviours performed at the feeding station can be refined is extremely impressive in exotic species.

Once the rules about where the animal can expect food have been established, more elaborate behaviours can be shaped at an increasing distance from the feeding station. Locomotory displays such as jumping through hoops (Case 18) and retrieving balls (Case 19) rely on the use of a secondary reinforcer as a bridging stimulus (see Chapter 2). The importance of the secondary reinforcer is that it liberates the animal from the station, and facilitates the shaping of acrobatics and chains of complex behaviours that can contribute to the maintenance of athletic and mental fitness in captive animals. The sealions are target-trained to touch the trainer's hand before they learn to follow the direction of the pointed hand (for instance, when sent to the far side of the tank). Other important cues for the sealions include the position of the trainer, the presence of key items of training apparatus, the order of the behaviour during the show and the release command that allows them to move on to the next behaviour in the chain.

Some of the behaviours in this chapter are only obliquely related to physical abilities and natural behaviours of the animals. When Romario (Case 20) the macaw rides his custom-built tricycle he is not illustrating tremendous balance or accurate steering. Instead, he is using the power in his legs that allows all members of his species

Fig. 6.1 New Zealand fur seal targeting trainer's hand with an open mouth giving sufficient room for a rudimentary dental inspection.

to scale branches and grip boughs while foraging for fruits and nuts. Some zoo visitors have suggested that they would like to see birds use their wings as well as their legs. With appropriate training and the use of radio-tracking devices to retrieve errant members of display teams, zoos are responding to this demand by developing free-flight shows.

Fig. 6.2 White-bellied Sea Eagle from Taronga Zoo, an injured bird who now plays an exciting role in a free-flight display.

In a similar vein, there is a current debate about the extent to which elephants should be trained. It is argued that the animals' mental and physical fitness can be enhanced if they are biddable enough to be taken out of their home compound. Trained elephants can be taken out of their pens for daily exercise, a form of environ-mental enrichment denied to many other species and a feature of management that helps a great deal in justifying the use of aversive stimuli. The training of elephants in zoological collections has many supporters, not least the public, who are entertained by the animals performing certain behaviours and taught how useful the animals can be as workers in their native habitat.

However, the role of training in captive elephant husbandry is not without controversy. Elephants are unusually sensitive to tactile stimuli. This largely governs the methods used to educate them. The threat of cutaneous pain can be used to guide elephants. As we will see in the case studies on trained elephants, the judicious use of painful stimuli can become as subtle as that employed by a Grand Prix dressage rider. Archive accounts from elephant training schools speak of inhumane practices including tying up wild young elephants for over a week to 'break their spirit' (see 'learned helplessness' in Chapter 3). The hooks (or *ankus*) used to train them were large and rough compared with the modern equivalent (see Figure 1.13) but, just as the humane horse rider uses spurs with either extreme reluctance or tact, so the potential aversiveness of either ancient or modern hook remains in the hands of its user. Subtle elephant training is based on the premise that, if an entire elephant can be moved, so can parts of an elephant, and thus very delicate manoeuvres can be trained.

Captive elephants need specialist staff to care for and manage them. The time taken to train an elephant to be safe to handle is sufficient to dissuade many zoological parks from keeping elephants altogether. However, elephant keeper training camps are now a reg-ular feature of the zoo calendar, and it is hoped that the increased dissemination of humane handling and management skills will be beneficial for elephant welfare.

The value of training as a form of environmental enrichment is under scrutiny from animal welfare scientists, as more zoos the world over consider whether to embark on training programmes for many of the animals in their collections. The bottom line is whether the benefits of training outweigh the costs in terms of animal welfare. Studies that examine the impact of such conditioning on behaviour as well as reproductive and physiological variables will help us find the best way forward in exotic animal husbandry. But the controversy will not end there. Regardless of whether one supports training pro-grammes per se, decisions still have to be made about whether to use purely positive reinforcement or a blend of positive and aversive stimuli. At Woburn, home to Chandrika (Case 21) and Raja (Case 28), the latter mix is applied because it is felt that using positive stimuli alone can foster a lack of 'respect'.

It is interesting to note that not all elephants are safe to train. Young females are generally the most amenable to training, while adult males can be very difficult especially when in musth (i.e. dur-ing the breeding season). When dealing with animals that can crush humans simply by failing to respect their personal space, one can appreciate the critical importance of being able to repel the animals rapidly. Trainers point out that their safety is assured as a result of repeated disciplining of the elephants. But should training continue beyond the point where the animals can be handled and led safely? Should they be taught to paint or stand on one leg? Is there a point at which elephants suffer compromised dignity? Even if the animals themselves do not have the sort of self-consciousness that could allow them to feel embarrassed or humiliated, people's perception of animals is undoubtedly affected by seeing them perform these types of tricks. Whilst some people may develop an admiration for the animals' learning abilities, others may develop a degraded perception of the animal, seeing it as the 'dumb' victim of the trainer.

In terms of the ethical debate that surrounds the training of exotic animals, elephants may be a special case, not least because of the use of negative reinforcement. Many of the other animals in this chapter have learned new responses simply as a means of acquiring food. Just as the capuchin monkey (Case 23) and the octopus (Case 24) behave with their operant devices as if they were enriching their environments, many of them become excited when the opportunity to work for food arises. It is important to note that for an individual animal the alternative, presentation of food in a bowl, may be as far removed from a natural foraging context as riding a tricycle or balancing a ball on its nose.

Fig. 6.3 Octopus 'playing' inside an upturned jar. With permission from Michael Jaruis-Chaston.

Case 16   Californian sealion *Zalophus californianus*

Training profile
Target behaviour: roll over
Name: Magellan
Age: 6 years
Trainer's assessment of temperament: relaxed, steady, imperturbable
Trainer's name: Jenny Evans

Background

Many sealion trainers find it easiest to explain their approach to training to a lay audience in the language of dog owners. This is exemplified by a behaviour such as rolling over that can be performed by both dogs and seals. Unlike many sealions, Magellan rarely responds to subtle cues. Effective instructions need to be clear and simple. It is almost as if Magellan demands as good a performance on the part of his trainer as vice versa. The sealion should both start and stop rolling on command. The entire rollover should be performed at a speed dictated by the trainer who acts alongside the sealions in their show. The 'roll over' forms a critical part of the themed performance – in this case a short, comic Western story in which Magellan uses this response to feign death when shot in a mock gunfight.

In early training the sealions must be habituated to equipment, crowds and personnel. Then they must learn to discriminate between good and mediocre responses and between the various commands used in the show. Because training sessions and shows provide the main opportunity for the sealions to receive most of their ration during the summer, performances are at their best at this time of the year. During winter, free food becomes available and rigorous training is withdrawn.

Training programme

Before commencing training the animal must: be target-trained to touch the trainer's hand and must be clicker-trained to respond to the sound of a whistle as a secondary reinforcer. This association is established with approximately 150 pieces of fishy reward over a three- or four-day period.

Changing the animal's motivation before a training session: the sealions are alerted to the imminent start of each training session by hearing the preparatory noises (such as the filling of the fish bucket) that tell them food is about to become available. By placing his or her hand in the fish bucket the trainer primes the sealions to work. They can soon lose interest in performing their trained behaviour if the trainer forgets to issue this promise of food to come.

Number of training sessions per week   14
Duration of session   15 minutes
Time taken to learn   3 weeks

In the process of shaping the final behaviour, the trainer:
1. Allowed Magellan to climb down from the stand and sit in front of the trainer. The sealion could be kept in one place just because it was target-trained to place its nose close to the trainer's hand.

2. Lowered her hand to bring Magellan into a lying position in combination with the command 'lie down'.

3. Introduced Magellan to the concept of a second target (the trainer's other hand) which prompted the sound of the whistle only when the near-side flipper touched it.

4. Moved this second target slowly over Magellan's back to bring the flipper off the ground and begin the roll.

5. Shaped this behaviour to form an arc over the back in five or six steps.

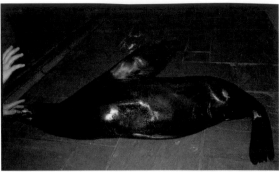

6. Introduced the visual cue (a rotating index finger) in front of Magellan and then began to slow the roll down so that its pace was set by the trainer not the sealion.

Stumbling blocks: getting the sealion to shuffle his offside flipper under his body to allow the roll to take place is crucial. In the absence of this prerequisite, Magellan would default to performing a front flipper stand.

General processes in training

Clicker training: yes.

Use of restraints: none.

Other equipment: bucket.

Aversive stimuli: being ignored and occasionally even returned to their quarters.

Auditory cues: 'OK' and 'good' are used to finish the behaviours.

Visual cues: the sealions follow pointed hands much of the time (for instance, when sent to the far side of the tank) and are target-trained to touch the trainer's hand. Other visual cues the sealions rely on include the position of the trainer, the order of the behaviour during the show, the presence of the hoop and the release command that allows them to move onto the next behaviour in the chain.

Use of reinforcers

Rewards used: whistle, fish.

Variation in the size of a reward: yes.

Variety of rewards used: yes – whistles, fish (herring, mackerel and sprats).

Reinforcement schedule: continuous then variable. Whistle/bridge training can be achieved over three to four days. After that, the whistle is used whenever the animal performs a correct behaviour but is phased out for shows (because the theme show approach does not lend itself to whistled interruptions).

Ratio of variable reinforcement: 1:3. Once trained behaviours become chained together a primary reinforcer can be delivered at variable points in the chain.

Use of rewards as lures or targets: a single fish may be used as a lure in early training.

Highlights: this case and the way in which it fits into a series of responses provides a useful illustration of chaining (Chapter 2). By standing in certain places, the trainer can cue the next behaviour in the chain. Having seen the cue the sealion knows which response is required and must simply look for the release command so that it is performed at an appropriate time in the show.

Case 17

Californian sealion *Zalophus californianus*

Training profile

Target behaviour:	front flipper stand
Name:	Max
Age:	3 years
Trainer's assessment of temperament:	calm, agreeable, doglike
Trainer's name:	Peter Bloom

Background

Of the six Californian sealions at Yorkshire's Flamingoland, Max is the young apprentice. His role model Benson, at 13 years of age, responds to more than 50 verbal and hand commands. The sealions put on two shows a day and receive part of their ration during performances. This makes the behaviours required of them rather analogous to a hunting exercise. The sealions anticipate shows with displays of excitement and agitation. Some sealions seem to find the wait prior to a performance quite frustrating and even perform stereotypies when their arousal reaches fever pitch. Despite their cute appearance and appealing tricks, sealions retain the ability to deliver a nasty bite with little warning when presented with a threat. During training of a new behaviour, confusion and frustration can prompt potentially dangerous responses in sealions, there-fore it is imperative during this time never to stand between the animal and its escape route (i.e. the water or its den). The sealions have to habit-uate to the training environment and to humans, so that they can eventually find human contact and the associated stroking rewarding.

When supporting his weight on his forelimbs and curving his spine to raise his tail, Max is said to perform a front flipper stand. It is a good demonstration of upper body strength and is easy to equate with human gymnastics. Peter is shap-ing a smooth U-shaped posture that is held until the '*stop*' cue is issued.

Training programme

Before commencing training the animal must: know that unless he is penned, he is most likely to receive fish when he is on the stand. This must be established as his place of work – his feeding sta-tion. He must also be clicker-trained by receiving at least 100 fish in close temporal association with the sound of a whistle, and then target-trained so that he knows that stretching for and reaching the blue zone on a target stick is a sure way of receiv-ing a reward.

Changing the animal's motivation before a training session: the sealions are separated for approxi-mately 30 minutes from the trainer and other sealions prior to all training sessions.

Number of training sessions per week 21
Duration of session 20 minutes
Time taken to learn 4 weeks

In the process of shaping the final behaviour, the trainer:
1. Rewarded Max for leaning forward towards the target.

2. Encouraged Max to take less and less weight on his hind limbs.

4. Shaped the curve of the back by rewarding Max for lifting his torso off the stand.

3. Rewarded Max for lifting his back flippers off the stand.

5. Further shaped the desired posture by rewarding Max when his hind flippers engaged with the trainer's hand as a target.

6. Achieved the final posture by rewarding Max only when a smooth U-shape was offered.

Stumbling blocks: the belly very easily comes to rest on the stand often without the trainer spotting it. This can lead to accidental shaping of a less than perfect response.

General processes in training

Clicker-training: yes.

Use of restraints: none.

Other equipment: bucket, toys.

Aversive stimuli: a shouted '*no*' with direct eye contact and a crouching posture at sealion level is the best response a human can make if the animals become aggressive.

Auditory cues: up means assume the front flipper stand position.

Visual cues: raised hand in front of the sealion.

Use of reinforcers

Rewards used: whistle, fish, stroking (the latter is a secondary reinforcer).

Variation in the size of a reward: yes. Although sealions receive a pound of sprats individually in an average training session they can also hit jackpots. The biggest reward Max gets is three big mackerel plus vocal praise.

Variety of rewards used: yes.

Reinforcement schedule: continuous for three months then variable.

Ratio of variable reinforcement: 1:2.

Use of rewards as lures or targets: food is used as a lure only in the first week of training to establish the correct association with the feeding station.

Highlights: the target-training (Chapter 2) of the pelvic flippers in this case provides a helpful reminder that it is possible to target-train virtually any body part. When training an animal one is not confined to train the nose or a forelimb to touch the target for a reward.

Case 18   Californian sealion *Zalophus californianus*

Training profile

Target behaviour:	jump through hoop held above the water
Name:	Monica
Age:	3.5 years
Trainer's assessment of temperament:	eager, inquisitive, excitable
Trainer's name:	Ricky Newton

Training programme

Before commencing training the animal must: be target-trained to touch the red end of a staff and must be clicker-trained.

Changing the animal's motivation before a training session: the clanking of the feed bucket seems to arouse the sealions.

Number of training sessions per week   14
Duration of session   15 minutes
Time taken to learn   7 weeks

Background

Of the four Californian sealions at Woburn in Bedfordshire, Monica is the most biddable. She responds appropriately to the following list of commands: walk (like a dog doing heel work); wave; applaud; front flipper stand; front flipper walk; gurgle when held around the neck as if being strangled; leap off a ten-foot-high tower; follow humans; cover her face with her flippers; roll over; kiss; open mouth; retrieve a ring; slide across stage; peer into the water from the side of the tank; jump up and down; shake head; jump for a ball suspended from the ceiling; raise both flippers; push human into the water; spin; look over barriers; lie down; place a toy in a barrel; drink from a cup; slap her hindquarters; scratch her hindquarters; and creep along like a caterpillar.

Jumping out of the water through a hoop is a popular behaviour. It involves members of the public, because ultimately it is they who hold the hoops aloft. Training aims to shape a clean jump (i.e. not touching the hoop itself). Although most behaviours are practised daily, evidence from winter training schedules suggests that the hoop jumps can be retained for at least four weeks without reinforcement.

In the process of shaping the final behaviour, the trainer:
1. Habituated Monica to the hoop.

2. Placed the target near the hoop.

3. Placed the target through the hoop from the side furthest from the sealion.

4. Swapped hands so that the target was on the far side of the hoop.
5. After a week or so of the above procedure, placed the hoop alone in the water and bridged Monica for passing through it completely.

6. Gradually raised the hoop out of the water.

7. Moved the hoop away from the side of the tank.
8. Moved the hoop around the pool so that Monica became aware of the need to travel around in search of it.
9. Introduced the second hoop and rewarded only when Monica had passed through both hoops.

Stumbling blocks: getting the sealion to perform at a distance from the trainer is the trickiest part of the shaping process. Sometimes the sealion seems to miss the hoop as it is lifted out of the water. Also, finding the second hoop at the rim of the tank seems to challenge some animals.

General processes in training

Clicker-training: yes.

Use of restraints: none.

Other equipment: bucket and hoops.

Aversive stimuli: being ignored and occasionally even returned to their quarters.

Auditory cues: 'OK' and 'good' are used to finish the behaviours.

Visual cues: hand signals.

Use of reinforcers

Rewards used: whistles, fish including herring, mackerel and sprats.

Variation in the size of a reward: yes.

Variety of rewards used: yes.

Reinforcement schedule: continuous. Clicker-training can be achieved over three to four days. After that, the whistle is used whenever the animal performs a correct behaviour but phased out for shows because the theme show approach does not lend itself to whistled interruptions.

Ratio of variable reinforcement: 1:3. Once trained behaviours become chained together a primary reinforcer can be delivered at variable points in the chain.

Use of rewards as lures or targets: a single fish may be used as a lure in early training.

Highlights: in most cases, it is difficult to increase motivation once a training session has commenced. The length of each of Monica's training sessions is therefore tailored to suit her prevailing mood on each day. If she is co-operative, the secret is to capitalise on this by extending the session (but not to do so beyond the point at which she loses interest). This is surely something that distinguishes excellent trainers from average ones. Since rewards are more likely to be given despite indifferent responses to stimuli during a show, sealions tend to discriminate easily between shows and training sessions. This shows the importance of environmental context and unintended discrimination learning.

Training profile
Target behaviour: retrieving a ball from the water
Name: Bill
Age: 15 years
Trainer's assessment of temperament: inquisitive, happy, hard-working
Trainer's name: Paul Hare

Background

Bill was found in 1986 washed up on a Sydney beach. He had extensive injuries due to a shark attack, leaving a bone in his flipper exposed, and his back injured. He spent four months recovering in Taronga Zoo's veterinary centre. Initially, Bill was very weak, and had to be force-fed, but gradually he came to accept food willingly and then to eat on his own. After Bill had gained weight and recovered, he started being trained as a show seal. He was fed a strict diet that would keep him in condition for shows – content, yet still motivated enough to work for food. The main difficulty was that Bill was both a fussy eater and would play with his food. As with many captured seals, it was hard to make him accept that he should eat dead fish. This is obviously a problem when the central tenet of training is to reward with fish; the animal must want food and eat it immediately upon presentation.

Retrieving the ball is actually a series of behaviours, which can be initially triggered by the seal's naturally inquisitive nature. In the wild they often show unconditioned responses such as inves-

tigation, prehension and manipulation when they encounter various items in their environment, be it ocean debris or cast-off human detritus. This can help them make the first contact with a ball. In the fully trained sequence the ball is thrown into the pool, Bill comes up underneath it, balances it on his nose, carries it out of the pool and stations himself by a rock. Pet dog owners who struggle to teach retrieval in their animals could learn from this case study. Ball balancing has been associated with seals for as long as there have been seals performing in circuses. It is used in the seal show at the zoo, partly because audiences expect colour, movement and to see the seals perform 'tricks'. It is also used for educational purposes, to demonstrate the sensitive whiskers the seal uses to detect slight movement in the ball (and in catching food in the wild) and the suppleness and flexibility of the neck and back necessary to keep the ball balanced.

Members of the public are often amazed by what Bill can do, intrigued by how he is taught and how the trainer communicates with him. An excellent performance requires prompt entry into the pool, concentration on the keeper for signals and the ball to be maintained comfortably on the nose until the stop cue is issued.

Training programme

Before commencing training the animal must: have learned several other behaviours, so that it understands what training involves and so the trainer can determine how motivated the seal is. A seal will first be trained in husbandry procedures, e.g. opening its mouth for inspection (see Fig. 6.1). Then it learns natural behaviours on cue. Learning to come when called is essential for the ball balancing sequence, as is allowing the keeper and ball within close proximity and 'stationing' (staying in one place).

Changing the animal's motivation before a training session: the keepers get Bill excited by calling '*Ready Bill, let's go*' and showing him the fish bucket. Before a show, Bill sees the trainers getting ready and can hear the audience taking their seats, anticipates being rewarded and his motivation increases.

Number of training sessions per week 15
Duration of session 10 minutes
Time taken to learn 4 months

In the process of shaping the final behaviour, the trainer:

1. Habituated Bill to the ball. Animals that never approach the ball do not learn the behaviour. The ball must be seen as a positive cue. To introduce the ball the trainer began by simply placing it under one arm during feeding.
2. Fed a fish and said '*Good*' as soon as Bill first sniffed the ball. This encouraged him to focus on the ball.
3. Held the ball above Bill's head and, while continually giving fish rewards, gradually lowered the ball until it touched his nose. Once Bill associated the ball with fish, he would follow it with his head while it was held in contact with his nose and moved around in circles and from side to side. The keeper could then occasionally let go of the ball. If it was balanced off the ground, for no matter how long or through what means, Bill was enthusiastically rewarded.
4. Shaped the keeping of the ball off the ground. Bill began to flex and extend his neck to keep the ball balanced on his nose. The period of time that Bill kept the ball aloft was extended by waiting slightly longer each time to reward him.

5. Placed the ball on Bill's nose while he was in the pool. Then, by rewarding him for approaching the ball as on land, Bill was encouraged to balance the ball himself when it was dropped in the water. As the ball was associated with balancing, Bill tried to balance it and was rewarded for each successive improvement in his attempts. He was ignored if he started playing with the ball.

6. Recalled Bill whenever he was balancing the ball in the pool but rewarded him only when he came out with the ball.

7. Shaped Bill to resume his position at his feeding station with the ball in place on his nose.

Stumbling blocks: establishing the balancing as a key to being rewarded takes the greatest patience. After that the main problem is that the seal may begin playing with the ball. He may also initially tend to drop the ball before exiting the pool.

General processes in training

Clicker-training: yes.

Use of restraints: none.

Other equipment: bucket and ball.

Aversive stimuli: if Bill does something incorrectly, the keeper turns away and all requests for food, attention or play are ignored. This is the only punishment used. No physical restraint is used during training.

Auditory cues: 'Good' and the whistle are used to finish the behaviours.

Visual cues: each step in the training process and ultimately each successive behaviour in the show is dependent on a visual cue. For example, when Paul throws the ball into the water Bill knows he has to ball balance in order to either proceed to the next behaviour or receive a reward. Paul takes a step towards the pool to indicate that the seal should begin the exercise. When Bill is lined up to emerge from the pool. Paul takes a step back and Bill knows that he should come out and return to his station.

Use of reinforcers

Rewards used: the rewards used are the bridge 'Good' (or variations) and fish. Bridging is used so Bill knows immediately he has done the right thing, even if he cannot be rewarded with fish at that moment. Bill eats whiting, herring, yellowtail, mullet, mackerel, pilchard and squid, rationed into a daily food intake keeping Bill motivated but content.

Variation in the size of a reward: yes. The size of reward varies with the quality of response.

Variety of rewards used: the perceived value of the reward varies with the quality of response. If an attempt is half-hearted but correct, Bill may only get a 'Good' or one fish. The first time a seal exhibits a behaviour e.g. face-washing or a new noise, it may get a handful of fish or even squid – a seal's favourite!

Reinforcement schedule: continuous rewards are given every time the behaviour appears including during shows.

Highlights: a drop in the quality of responses is probably not due to forgetting, just a relative lack of motivation. Generally, trainers do not signal in advance that a big reward is potentially available to get a really good performance. Therefore a seal cannot know in advance what size reward he is to get. On occasions when the seal puts less effort in he must simply accept a smaller reward. Any reward gradient is therefore used *post hoc* rather than as an apparent incentive or 'bribe'.

Monitoring motivation to forage is of pivotal importance when eliciting conditioned responses from this animal. In summer, Bill eats only about three to four kilograms of food and so there is less reward available. In winter, there is a need for up to ten kilograms so sessions are more frequent. During the breeding season, seals go off their food entirely so no training takes place.

Case 20	Green-winged macaw *Ara chloroptera*

Training profile

Target behaviour:	riding and steering a tricycle
Name:	Romario
Age:	2 years
Trainer's assessment of temperament:	nervous, quiet, cautious
Trainer's name:	Alan Drayton

Background

The birds at Yorkshire's Flamingoland Parrot Show are almost all macaws. They work for a living in that they receive a large part of their daily ration only after performing the learned behaviours on cue. There are up to four shows per day during which the birds exhibit a fascinating variety of behaviours including

lying on their backs, climbing, 'laughing', talking, apparently counting to any number between one and ten, and adding together two such numbers. Although free to wander at will, each bird waits its turn while perched at the back of the stage. Some of the birds have their feathers clipped to minimise the distance they can cover if they are startled.

Habituation of display birds to crowds, the noise of the park, different handlers and the equipment is central to their training. Riding a tricycle looks comical and reasonably technical, but trainers point out that getting the bird from the perch to the tricycle to do some pedalling and then place it back on the perch without any signs of feather fluffing, fearfulness or unhappiness is the really hard part.

Training programme

Before commencing training the animal must: be habituated to the stick (mobile perch). Be target-trained. Be fully habituated to trainers and associating trainers with rewards.

Changing the animal's motivation before a training session: birds have their weight monitored daily to ensure they do not get fat (which, apart from being bad for their health, causes a plummet in their motivation to perform). Being placed on their perches at the start of each show primes the birds to expect to perform the tasks.

Number of training sessions per week   4 per day
Duration of session   10 minutes
Time taken to learn   3 weeks

In the process of shaping the final behaviour, the trainer:
1. Habituated the bird to the tricycle.

2. Rewarded the bird for climbing onto the pedals.

3. Rewarded the bird for gripping the handlebars with his beak.

4. Rewarded the bird for any accidental movement of the pedals in the right direction.

5. Shaped increasing movement in a straight line, using a target.

Stumbling blocks: it takes time for the bird to learn how to pedal correctly and establish the rhythm we all need to ride a cycle. Getting past the rocking stage takes a great deal of time and patience.

General processes in training

Clicker-training: no.

Use of restraints: none.

Other equipment: tricycle, target and stick.

Aversive stimuli: none.

Auditory cues: none.

Visual cues: early on in the training process, Alan's hand is used in advance of the tricycle to encourage forward movement. The target eventually replaces the hand and then the bird grows to rely on the sight of a distant food reward as a cue for cycling. Food rewards are removed if the bird simply gets off the vehicle and marches up to the food to help himself (omission training).

Use of reinforcers

Rewards used: contact with familiar humans, peanuts, bananas, pecans and the occasional brazil nut.

Variation in the size of a reward: yes, to balance the energy value of reinforcers, highly calorific rewards such as brazil nuts are generally broken up and delivered in small pieces. Occasionally, a whole brazil nut is given as a jackpot.

Variety of rewards used: yes. Different food rewards are employed, but human attention alone is a weak reinforcer for Romario.

Reinforcement schedule: continuous for eight months then variable reinforcement is used during the shows.

Ratio of variable reinforcement: 1:2.

Use of rewards as lures or targets: food is used around the handlebars to attract the bird's attention to that part of the equipment.

Highlights: as with the pinnipeds, macaws make poor display animals when they are under the influence of breeding hormones. Because they are especially fractious and flighty, females are never trained while in season (see Chapter 1).

Case 21	Asian elephant *Elephas maximus*

Training profile

Target behaviour:	blow water from her trunk on command
Name:	Chandrika
Age:	7.5 years
Trainer's assessment of temperament:	lazy, cautious, aware
Trainer's name:	Lynn Thomson

Background

As part of a shift in management policy at Woburn Safari Park (in Bedfordshire, UK) that placed more emphasis on the demonstration of the trainability of elephants in the park's pachyderm exhibit, Chandrika (meaning moonlight) was imported from India with her female companion shortly after being weaned. One of three young Asian elephants in the current group, she had received some early training in her country of origin and bears a few scars to prove it. The handlers at Woburn use negative reinforcement in combination with considerable patience to shape an impressive range of behaviours.

Here are some of the commands that the elephants at Woburn respond to: *steady; move up; move out; come here; here side; get over; get around; back up; easy; foot lift; foot down; feet lift; trunk lift; trunk down; stretch (lie down); head down; head up; come in line; get over in line; alright (good - stop what you are doing); bow; change; quit; tail up; ear (move the ear nearest the handler); ears (move both ears); mouth; pick up; drop (let go); give (place object in trainer's hand) hold; step up; step down; push; speak; blow; cross; shake; sit; sit up; stand up.*

In this case study, Chandrika blows water through her trunk, a very popular behaviour with the public. With comic effect Chandrika then directs a jet of water at her audience - something wild elephants would rarely do. From the trainers' perspective the aim is to see a large volume of water ejected over a considerable distance.

Whilst some might argue that Chandrika's having to hold water in her airway under a human's orders is undignified, there is at least some educational importance to this part of her daily display. She demonstrates an element of elephantine drinking behaviour that many of us overlook. Unlike other over-sized species such as giraffes and rhinos, elephants cannot drink by simply bringing their mouths to the level of the water. Instead they must bring the water to their mouths by filling their trunks and then pouring it into their mouths.

Training programme

Before commencing training the animal must: respond consistently to the following basic commands: *steady* (hold the current position); *move up* (advance slowly); *trunk down* (lower trunk); *hold* (maintain the current behaviour being performed by trunk); *drink.*

Changing the animal's motivation before a training session: by walking to the training area, the elephant is given a series of cues that set the context for training.

Number of training sessions per week 7
Duration of session 10 minutes
Time taken to learn 2 weeks

In the process of shaping the final behaviour, the trainer:

1. Held the trunk in a bucket of water in the hope that Chandrika would suck up the water, issuing the established command '*drink*'.

2. If the first step failed, poured a volume (approximately two pints) of water into the trunk itself.
3. Held Chandrika's trunk up in combination with the command '*hold*' followed by '*trunk*'. By simultaneously feeding Chandrika, the water holding part of the chain of behaviours was reinforced. Holding Chandrika's trunk up and gradually increasing the time she spent holding the water in her trunk increased her motivation to expel the water.

4. Manipulated the trunk straight out and introduced the command '*blow*'. Using an automatic response when allowed to clear her trunk, Chandrika ejected the water and then was shaped for enthusiastic blowing.

Stumbling blocks: getting the elephant accustomed to having its trunk held in the water.

General processes in training

Clicker-training: no

Use of restraints: chains are used initially to keep the elephant in place.

Other equipment: the hook. Sometimes a human stands in front of the elephant to present a target for the water. At other times a line is drawn in front of the animal for the same reason.

Aversive stimuli: yes, the second handler (who is always present for safety reasons) helps to guide the trunk. If the elephant moves its trunk away from the trainer issuing the instructions the second handler uses his hook to move it back into place.

Auditory cues: 'drink', 'hold', 'trunk', 'blow'.

Visual cues: nil (although some visual cues may become unintentionally linked with voice commands).

Use of reinforcers

Rewards used: when a novel behaviour is being established, food rewards are given. Banana is particularly valued and therefore reserved for early training. In later training this is replaced by carrots.

Variation in the size of a reward: yes, occasionally.

Variety of rewards used: yes, vocal praise and a pat on the shoulder are reinforcing since they become closely associated with food rewards.

Reinforcement schedule: continuous for two to three weeks. Once the behaviour is established rewards are given after three to four blows.

Ratio of variable reinforcement: 1:4. More frequent food rewards can train the elephants to look for food rather than concentrating on the learned behaviour.

Highlights: this training demonstrates the ability of elephants to discriminate a wide variety of human noises (especially when visual cues are not used). As elephants hear infra-sound, human voices must sound like so-much squeaking to them. Therefore their ability to distinguish between numerous similar sounding words is impressive.

Case 22   Bottlenose dolphin *Tursiops truncatus*

Training profile

Target behaviour:	tail-walking
Name:	Tyson
Age:	3.5 years
Trainer's assessment of temperament:	assertive, active, focused
Trainer's name:	Ross Deakin

Background

Just as the fictions *Moby Dick* and *Jaws* overly demonised whales and sharks, perhaps we have mythologised dolphins too far. Recent evidence of dolphin infanticide has tarnished their idealised image. Trainers of captive-bred animals in dolphinaria acknowledge that their pupils retain an aggressive streak. The fighting among the occupants of some such tanks reminds us that they can easily kill humans they perceive as strangers.

Of the 35 dolphins at Australia's Seaworld in Queensland, 12 are home-bred and some are even third generation. Many of the dolphins do not take part in shows, but are kept in quiet groups that are used for educational purposes and with which children can swim. The show team is given intensive training 56 times per week. This includes time spent socialising with the dolphins, reinforcing show behaviours and habituating the animals to routine veterinary procedures. The behaviours that are reinforced by the trainers for the shows are largely wild behaviours that have an appeal to human observers. The weight of fish dolphins earn by performing learned behaviours is closely monitored, as is the weight of the dolphins themselves. This is achieved by first training the dolphins to launch themselves onto a specially made pad in return for a small fishy reward.

Tyson, the dolphin featured in the following case study, lives in a group with three other males and one female. He is the dominant male in the group, a position occasionally contested by his closest rival, Coen. As with many cohorts of young dolphins, the males in this group are distinguished by bearing tooth marks and scratches as legacies of previous disputes and play-fights. Dominant males are generally regarded as being among the least suitable for training. Tyson is described as being as smart as his wild-caught counterparts but, being home-bred, perhaps rather more amenable to training.

By hand-feeding and socialising with the dolphins, the trainers establish patting as a secondary reinforcer but note that patting only becomes occasionally rewarding in its own right when dolphins wish to be scratched. The dolphins hear a whistle every time they are fed and this noise, of course, becomes a bridge associated with food (i.e. a secondary reinforcer; see Chapter 2). The other noise dolphins are taught is a recall command. This is a very different sounding click that brings the dolphins back to their trainers immediately. It is very useful in stopping a dolphin from doing whatever is its current task and returning to the trainer to restart an exercise. Once the recall click has been issued, the dolphin can be sure that no further rewards will appear if he persists in his current activity. Rather like saying 'No, let's start that again', this is a very useful way of arresting sub-standard behaviour. Dolphins are taught to discriminate between a good and an indifferent performance in every training session. Responding appropriately to such a recall signal is reinforced only by the start of a new opportunity to produce a good response. They may even be recalled during a show. This is considered important in the prevention of half-hearted performances during shows (so-called 'show discrimination').

In this case study, after Ross gives a visual cue, Tyson performs a 'forward walk' which is a stylised version of a surveillance behaviour that may be used in the wild to spot other pods of dolphins. The strength of the dolphin in being able to lift himself out of the water and support himself with energetic tail-thrashing is undoubtedly impressive. The highlight for the audience is undoubtedly when he locomotes in a straight line with or without an accompanying pool-mate. Ross asks that at least 80 per cent of the dolphin's body length is out of the water.

Training programme

Before commencing training the animal must: know what a target represents. When the dolphin touches a padded stick, called a boom, he is bridged (i.e. a whistle is sounded) and rewarded. As this target is lifted out of the water, the dolphin is bridged for keeping in touch with it. The backward tail walk is taught before the forward version.

Changing the animal's motivation before a training session: the preludes to a training session follow a set routine. As trainers armed with targets and toys appear in their wetsuits, buckets are placed on the training pontoon and the dolphins are alerted to the need for their attention.

Number of training sessions per week 56
Duration of session   10 minutes
Time taken to learn   8 weeks

In the process of shaping the final behaviour, the trainer:
1. Reinforced target training so that Tyson readily followed the boom around the pontoon.

2. Moved the target backwards and rewarded the backwards motion.

3. Rewarded Tyson for following the raised target forwards.
4. Rewarded only when Tyson redirected the same behaviour in the absence of the boom towards ice that was thrown into the water as a visual lure.
5. Rewarded Tyson, in the absence of ice, for performing the same behaviour where the ice had previously tended to land.
6. Shaped elevated versions of the same behaviour.

7. Introduced the command and rewarded only when Tyson tail-walked on cue.

Stumbling blocks: persuading the dolphins to stop depending on the prompt given by the boom, which has proved so bountiful in previous training, is one of the major stumbling blocks.

General processes in training

Clicker-training: yes.

Use of restraints: none.

Other equipment: bucket, ice, target stick.

Aversive stimuli: although not strictly speaking aversive, dolphins do not like being told they have lost the opportunity to earn food. If a dolphin persistently ignores cues, then he will be given 'time out'. This is known as the least reinforcing stimulus (LRS) and marks the end of a training session and the opportunity to earn rewards.

Auditory cues: whistles and clicks act to reinforce and recall, but no voice commands are used. The presenter may give the illusion of a conversation during the show, but the dolphins are concentrating on their individual trainers at the rear of the pool rather than the human with the microphone at the front. All the animals know the sequence of behaviours that are chained together in the show. As soon as they have completed one phase of the show properly they hear a whistle. They then return to their trainer for a fish and wait for the cue to launch into their next piece of action.

Visual cues: by using their arms and hands the trainers can direct the dolphins to the next phase of the show. So the cue for a forward walk becomes ever more subtle as the sequence of behaviours in a show becomes more predictable.

Use of reinforcers

Rewards used: whiting, yellowtail, herring, whole squid up to 400 grams in weight. Tyson finds a big sea mullet of around one-and-a-half kilograms virtually irresistible. Occasionally toys are also used.

Variation in the size of a reward: yes, depending on the merit of the performance. On a good day, dolphins can earn as much as three kilograms of mixed fish per show.

Variety of rewards used: yes.

Reinforcement schedule: continuous reinforcement for as long as it takes to shape the desired response, then variable.

Ratio of variable reinforcement: for every five correct performances animal gets four rewards.

Use of rewards as lures or targets: fish are thrown in the air to encourage the emergence of aerial manoeuvres such as tail flips and spins.

Highlights: the dolphinarium is the ancestral home of the secondary reinforcer. As marine mammal trainers are swift to remind us, one cannot force dolphins to perform. Being able to inform the animals (even at a distance) when they are producing behaviours that are appropriate is pivotal and the clicker is the most effective way to transmit this message.

The use of the recall click in this case study challenges the dictum 'never say no' is antiquated and unhelpful when it comes to training animals. The dolphins seem to need a signal to follow inappropriate behaviour (technically a secondary punisher) to ensure that they move on to new solutions to the problems presented in a training context.

Case 23 — Tufted or brown capuchin *Cebus apella*

Training profile

Target behaviour:	extracting food from a hollow log
Name:	Vince
Age:	7 years
Trainer's assessment of temperament:	curious, secretive, cautious
Trainer's name:	Amy Plowman

Background

The monkeys used by organ grinders of old and by modern assistance-animal trainers are largely capuchins. While all of the great apes are known to use tools, capuchins are distinguished among the true monkeys as the only species to have been observed using tools in the wild. Monkeys in the wild spend somewhere in the region of 60 per cent of their time foraging. In a bid to normalise their capuchins' ethograms (behavioural repertoires), staff at Paignton Zoo, in Devon, who have been proactive in the field of environmental enrichment for some years decided to offer food in puzzle feeders. The food used in the feeders is neither the most nor the least desirable on the monkeys' menu, but is sufficiently sweet to attract the monkeys to the feeders and entice the desired foraging activity. Young dominant individuals are most likely to learn new foraging strategies. Aged animals that expect food delivery in traditional ways may be disinterested in learning, while the most submissive members of the troupe are often denied access to the feeders by those of higher rank. The nutrition of all captive animals has to be closely monitored and so it is inappropriate to offer the monkeys the sweetest of foods without regard for the impact this can have on their health.

When the monkey in this case study was named, it was thought to be male. Seven years later a veterinarian revealed that he was in fact a 'she'. Regardless of this technicality, Vince continues to bear her original name. Vince was the first of her troupe of five to learn to use tools to forage.

Because she was observed throughout her first interactions with the device, it is possible to authenticate a remarkable anecdote. For three days, she was the only monkey who could use the stick to withdraw food from the hollow feeding device. Intriguingly, when her companions entered the feeding area, she would drop the stick and look away from the device. Given that all capuchin monkeys monitor the feeding behaviours of others very closely, it appears that her reluctance to share the information that gave her the advantage was sufficient to motivate her to perform deceptive behaviour.

Many anecdotes featuring companion animals bear comparison to this apparent deception. A common example is of dogs that bark at the front door raising a false alarm that lures their companions away from a prized resource such as a bone or toy. The possibility of deception and cognition in these cases is questioned by those who say that, rather than using insight, dog A could have simply learned by accident or trial and error that barking at the door leads to removal of dog B from the resource. In contrast, Vince is known to have behaved in this way on first exposure to the puzzle, and her response to the approach of others was to stop her activity rather than to initiate some new behaviour. It is the termination of the behaviour and the impediment this produces to observational learning that is particularly fascinating.

Training programme

Before commencing training the animal must: be familiar with bamboo sticks, used as a food source and as rudimentary toothpicks, before they were given access to the feeders.

Changing the animal's motivation before a training session: initially the food used in the feeders is additional to the monkeys' normal ration. Once the monkeys have learned to retrieve food, the mass placed in the feeder is taken out of their normal allowance. This is an attempt to make the monkeys work for a living. In fact, the nutritional value of the food is almost certainly far less important than the mental stimulation offered by the opportunity to meet a behavioural need to forage.

Number of training sessions per week   5
Duration of session   8 hours
Time taken to learn   1 hour 45 minutes

In the process of shaping the final behaviour, the trainer:
1. Filled the hollow log with sufficient sticky food so that some of it could be withdrawn by the monkeys using their fingers.

2. Suspended the feeder from an accessible point in the roof of the enclosure and left plenty of fine bamboo sticks in the enclosure.

3. Allowed the monkeys to solve the puzzle and refine their technique.

4. Introduced identical empty 'dummy' logs to make foraging less predictable and to increase the diversity of the behaviour.

Stumbling blocks: lack of access to the feeders, as a result of the presence of a hostile companion, is the main impediment to learning.

General processes in training

Clicker-training: no.
Use of restraints: none.
Other equipment: none.
Aversive stimuli: none.
Auditory cues: none.
Visual cues: none.

Use of reinforcers

Rewards used: bananas, tomatoes and bread – in fact, anything that is soft enough to be mushed through the holes of the feeders.
Variation in the size of a reward: when the feeder is full, the mass of food removed with each use of the stick depends on the skill of the user.
Variety of reward used: various soft foods are used in rotation.
Reinforcement schedule: the monkey is reinforced every time she uses the feeder until it is empty.
Ratio of variable reinforcement: once the device is no longer brimming with food reinforcement is random.
Use of rewards as lures or targets: when first presented in the log, food is used to lure the monkeys to its central core.

Highlights: the possible role of deception in this case is truly fascinating. It is data such as these that suggest some animals can project into the future. It may be that Vince had a mental concept of the disadvantages that would befall her if she carried on foraging with her new skill in the presence of others. For example, not only would she have lost the advantage, an advantage she had invested time and energy in securing, she might also have had to relinquish access to the resource. Because it lends the deceiver a potential improvement in biological fitness, it is easy to see why primates may have evolved to be capable of deception. Unfortunately, deception is difficult to study under controlled conditions, because it has to be demonstrably free from the possibility of being based on a more simple form of learning such as operant conditioning and therefore relies on data from single trials with naive animals.

Case 24 — Common octopus *Octopus vulgaris*

Training profile

Target behaviour:	removing a lid from a jar
Name:	Philippa
Age:	2 years
Trainer's assessment of temperament:	inquisitive, shy, playful
Trainer's name:	Paul Hale

Background

Over the past twenty years or so, cephalods such as squids and octopi have been receiving increasing attention from cognitive ethologists. They have a greater ability to process information than many of us had given them credit for. An octopus from the Sea Life centre in Brighton provides a useful example of this point. By removing the lid from a jar placed in her tank, she demonstrates operant conditioning. Sometimes she even looks as though she is playing with the addition to her environment (see Fig. 6.3). This sort of learning has opened our eyes to the possibility of cognition in invertebrates. For example, there is now some evidence for deception in the signalling behaviour of squid. Legislation that previously protected only vertebrates in laboratory experiments now embraces these species in many countries.

As a graphic example of problem-solving in the common octopus, several individuals in captivity have learned to remove the lids from jars or the corks from bottles. Although naive observers enjoy the spectacle probably because it is surprising to discover that a marine invertebrate can manipulate everyday terrestrial objects, some Sea Life centres are sometimes reluctant to display the behaviour as part of the exhibit. However, regardless of whether the public are aware of the strategy, many octopus keepers give their animals an opportunity to forage in this way as a form of environmental enrichment. It is felt that time spent manipulating the jar is related to improved welfare. Using the predatory strike that equips them for crab-hunting, most common octopi launch themselves at the jars without hesitation and show a similarly swift completion of the task. Although live prey attract the attention of any octopus, they are not a prerequisite for training.

Young common octopi seem most suitable for training for this behaviour. Aged naive octopi are less likely to forage in this way because they are used to finding food in simpler contexts. The lesser octopus (*Eledone cirrhosa*) and the tropical octopus are slower and perhaps too small to manipulate the average jar.

Training programme

Before commencing training the animal must: forage on dead food items (the provision of live prey is generally unacceptable in public wildlife exhibits).

Changing the animal's motivation before a training session: food is presented only in this way.

Number of training sessions per week 7
Duration of session 5 minutes
Time taken to learn 2 weeks

In the process of shaping the final behaviour, the trainer:
1. Presented food in the jar without a lid every day for five days.

3. Increased the tightness of the lid every second day until it is secure but not tight.

2. Proceeded with lid attached very lightly.

Stumbling blocks: if the lid is too tight too early on in training, the octopus will find it too difficult to manipulate and will most likely give up. Interestingly, frustration in this species is manifested by a dramatic change in colour from sandy brown to brick red.

General processes in training

Clicker-training: no.
Use of restraints: none.
Other equipment: jar and lid.
Aversive stimuli: none.
Auditory cues: none.
Visual cues: jar may to some extent replace the food item itself as a visual signal for foraging to commence.

Use of reinforcers

Rewards used: fish and crustaceans.

Variation in the size of a reward: none.
Variety of reward used: yes.
Reinforcement schedule: continuous.
Use of rewards as lures or targets: because it is visible within the jar, food lures the octopus every time.

Highlights: the simplicity of this case is exemplary. Like Thorndike's cats and Skinner's rats, octopi that solve this puzzle are demonstrating trial and error learning that requires almost no human intervention.

b. Training for film, television or display purposes

Any work with large exotic animals involves some risks. Obviously, all such risks should be kept to a minimum except when the central purpose of one's work with the animals is to demonstrate a degree of bravery. Trainers working with large carnivores for television, film and public displays risk personal injury to provide a spectacle. It is the risk as perceived by novice observers that largely drives demand for displays of this sort – the public enjoys seeing considerable physical contact with the animals. However, some trainers of big cats indicate that the animals would perform as well if not better were they not in such close proximity to humans.

The relationship between humans and animals necessarily involves some antagonism. The way in which this is managed varies between species and trainers. When crocodiles are wrestled and venomous snakes are held aloft, rumours about the use of sedatives often abound. When large carnivorous mammals are handled one usually finds they have been hand-reared. This lends the human a strong psychological advantage by being able to impose on the youngster some crucial ideas about who is the boss. The day a big cat discovers the relative mismatch between the trainer's physical strength and his own is the day he becomes an extremely dangerous creature. This means that the cat has to be constantly reminded to 'respect' the humans.

In most cases, handling the animals as youngsters is a prerequisite to later training. For example, by preferentially acquiring animals whose parents have been trained, Jim Clubb, the trainer of Mowgli the African spotted leopard (Case 26), takes a crucial first step in the selection process that means the animals are not distressed by handling and captivity. The leopard cubs are reared by their mothers, which, if from working stock, are tolerant of humans. During the socialisation period, cubs are removed from the den for two hours each day to be handled and taught the essentials of bite inhibition. Other young exotic cats such as Mohan the Bengal tiger (Case 25) are hand-reared from the age of three weeks to socialise them with humans. This capitalises on the critical socialisation period that is open only in the first few weeks of life in most felidae (see section on socialisation in Chapter 1). This is not always successful, for example, in the case of Howlett Zoo, in Kent, which attracted a council ban on humans associating with tigers after a senior keeper died because the zoo's owner erroneously believed that he had adequately socialised the tigers.

Given an appropriately reared animal, the next requirement for training large cats is time. The key is to allow the animal sufficient time to learn that certain responses are normally followed by rewards. Being solitary hunters, cats rely very little on cues from others when acquiring food. This may account for the relatively minor significance of verbal commands in the training of all felidae when compared to, say, dogs.

Case 25   Bengal tiger *Panther tigris tigris*

Training profile

Target behaviour:	rearing on command
Name:	Mohan
Age:	4.5 years
Trainer's assessment of temperament:	reliable, steady, focused
Trainer's name:	Andy Goldfarb

Background

The tigers on Tiger Island, in Australia's Dreamworld, are trained to interact with humans in controlled play bouts. This is intended to provide an intriguing spectacle, to keep the tigers occupied and avoid the emergence of stereotypic behaviours. Unfortunately, this strategy is extremely unlikely to prevent stereotypies because many vacuum periods in the cage remain despite the handlers' best efforts to keep the tigers busy - and stereotypies in carnivores are very much linked with pre-feeding periods and with size of original home range. From an early age, tigers are taught to chase and pounce upon large pieces of sturdy bark pulled by handlers. Once they realise that pressure on the chain around their necks is not negotiable, they go on investigative walks around the park as part of their daily routine with less tension on their leads than most pet dogs.

In all play sessions the tigers have to capitulate to human demands, and in this way they are expected to be safer to handle. Any possessiveness is punished by ending the game. It is interesting to note that the trainers believe all of these behaviours could be taught to domestic cats if sufficient time was spent with them, and if the delivery of rewards was well enough timed.

The tendency to play in these structured ways tends to wane in tigers over four years of age. Handlers are careful to avoid overexposing their cats to too many stimuli, in the hope that this will delay the time by which play drive decreases. Small toys are considered preferable, since they limit the tendency of tigers to generalise from an inanimate lure moved by a human to the human itself. While all hand-reared Siberian, Sumatran and Bengal tigers are suitable for training for this response, Andy, very sensibly, avoids those that tend to chomp on shoulders during the rise and those that cling on to the human with their claws.

Training programme

Before commencing training the animal must: associate access to milk with the training area and have learned that the word *easy* means that it must not use its innate self-defence behaviours even if the trainer accidentally treads on its feet.

Changing the animal's motivation before a training session: if the tiger is sleepy he is woken with a toy and given time to orientate himself and focus on the task.

Number of training sessions per week   21
Duration of session   10 minutes
Time taken to learn   8 weeks

In the process of shaping the final behaviour, the trainer:
1. Trained Mohan to approach the human carrying the milk carton.

2. Encouraged Mohan to lie down before getting the milk. Tigers do not dog-sit very readily.

3. Used the milk carton to elevate Mohan's upper body so that he was sitting up on his haunches.

4. Gradually lifted the carton higher and higher until Mohan could reach it only by supporting himself on the human's shoulders.

Stumbling blocks: the tigers may rush at the milk because they don't want to delay receipt of the reward by lying down. Excited by the milk, they are motivated to follow the carton and seem to anticipate the delivery of most of its contents before they are on the shoulders of the handler (*see* sign tracking in Chapter 2).

General processes in training

Clicker-training: no.

Use of restraints: chains without a running link (i.e. they act as collars rather than chokers) are used around the tiger's neck. Hooks rather like crow bars are carried by all other handlers present whenever Andy is interacting with any of the mature tigers.

Other equipment: milk carton.

Aversive stimuli: the tigers are taught while still suckling that a sharp clap of the handler's hands means 'stop what you are doing and focus on me'. The tigers learn that they can expect a short sharp punch on the nose if they become dangerously rough with personnel.

Auditory cues: 'get up' means rise on the human's shoulders. '*Easy*' means stop being rough.

Visual cues: hand with milk is presented at head to encourage the cat to approach the hand rises to lure the 'rise'.

Use of reinforcers

Rewards used: every time the behaviour is performed 150 ml of full cream milk are dribbled into the tiger's mouth or, less regularly, a small meat reward is given. Meat represents less of a treat since Mohan's evening meal most days includes whole chicken breasts, emu steaks, venison shanks and ox hearts.

Variation in the size of a reward: no.

Variety of rewards used: minimal.

Reinforcement schedule: continuous.

Use of rewards as lures or targets: the cartons of milk are used to lure the tiger into the positions required.

Highlights: this case confirms the usefulness of an inhibiting command. Being able to stop a behaviour in its tracks can save lives in this context. Therefore the notion of never saying '*no*' is completely alien to long-lived big cat trainers.

Case 26

African spotted leopard *Panthera pardus*

Training profile
Target behaviour: leaping from A to B on cue
Name: Mowgli
Age: 12 years
Trainer's assessment of temperament: placid, reliable, consistent
Trainer's name: Jim Clubb

Background

We have all seen big cats making predatory leaps in natural history documentaries. Their power and athleticism is impressive and deadly. When captive animals perform the same activities on cue in the film studio, they are required to leave us with the same impression without the normal casualties. Leading animal trainer, Jim Clubb, uses techniques employed by his family for over a hundred years to manoeuvre a potentially lethal leopard. All his animals are captive-bred, either by him or by people known to him.

Leopards that have been reared by their mothers alone (especially if they had minimal contact with humans before 18 months of age) are unlikely to be suitable for training. Of the other medium-sized cats, jaguars present a serious challenge to animal trainers because they can be slow learners and yet retain their strength and volatility throughout life, while pumas are also difficult to train because they are relatively nervous. Similarly, because they can easily recognise their own strength, Jim feels that Javanese black leopards are very dangerous to train.

Generally, the essence of the training procedure used here is errorless learning. So, each advance in the training process is made so simple that the animal cannot perform it incorrectly. Each animal is trained with a tailor-made approach that allows for individual differences. Although Jim aims to keep constant the environment in which he trains, he avoids adherence to routine training times because his goal is to make trained behaviours appear spontaneous. He feels that too structured a timetable is counterproductive in that it can make the responses hackneyed and mundane. The training aims to ensure that the animal displays the behaviour sought 90 per cent of the time, and performs its leaps from one podium to the next with fluency, power and athleticism and without too many vocal prompts.

Training programme

Before commencing training the animal must: be responsive (not passive or inclined to hide in corners) to stimuli. For obvious reasons, extremely aggressive animals are avoided.

Changing the animal's motivation before a training session: the cat will receive 50 per cent of his food in the training arena; the remainder will be fed on his return to his home pen. The main preparation prior to training is a brief behavioural assessment intended to detect any shift in mood that will make the leopard aggressive or reluctant to learn. By asking the animal's carers about his food and water intake, the trainer can ensure that he is well and fit to work for food.

Number of training sessions per week   10
Duration of session   10 minutes
Time taken to learn   6 months

N.B. Sessions start at two to three minutes and extend to a maximum of 15 minutes.

In the process of shaping the final behaviour, the trainer:

1. Placed Mowgli in a round training arena – this represents the very best training environment for all animals because no corners means nowhere to adopt as a temporary den.

2. Habituated Mowgli to the training arena. It was clear when this had been achieved because Mowgli stopped investigating the pen and its contents and then became able to concentrate on the stimuli with which he was presented.

3. Taught the word '*finish*' as a prelude to the arena doors opening to allow Mowgli to return to his home pen and eat his daily ration.

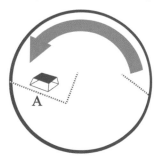

4. Trained Mowgli to know the place at which he should stay (in this case a two-metre long rostrum placed alongside the wall of the train-

ing arena, with an L-shaped radial guiding arm that prevents him wandering too far in several directions) in expectation of food rewards. This was achieved by throwing food to Mowgli only when he was on the rostrum. Mowgli began to regard this as his marked home patch.

A second piece of fencing prevented him from running at the trainer. For three to four days, while using the command place, the trainer reinforced Mowgli for finding the rostrum. As training proceeded the meat was offered from the end of a bamboo cane.

5. Taught Mowgli that when not being looked at he was expected to stay at his feeding station (point A).

If the trainer looked at Mowgli and said his name, the cat had his cue to move. It was important to take the decision as to whether the movement Mowgli executed in his future performances would be in a clockwise or anti-clockwise direction. This decision was largely driven by the nature of the cat's first film job.

6. Began to use the bamboo in different ways so that Mowgli learned that drumming on a surface with the cane invited him to approach that point. If reluctant, the cat could be prompted in movement by being gently tapped by the cane, but it remained important to avoid fear of the canes. Tapping the sticks against one another was taught as a visual and auditory cue meaning 'move away'. This told Mowgli to move away from the canes when they bear no meat to the next position to find a reward. Mowgli became sensitised to the sound of the canes being tapped together.

7. Very gradually reduced the amount of interior fencing and the size of the rostrum.

8. Placed a second rostrum (point B) three feet away from A, tapped the sticks and rewarded when Mowgli reached B.

9. Repeated in reverse. The command *stay* was then introduced and reinforced by giving Mowgli meat only when he stayed at his new feeding station.

10. Moved A away from the perimeter fence to avoid Mowgli becoming completely reliant on this as a stimulus on which all other training depended.

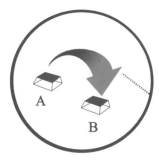

11. Moved B slightly closer to the centre of the arena and alternated between B being a rostrum and a flat plate on the ground. This was necessary to teach Mowgli to approach the trainer on the command *here*. It was also important to be able to govern the pace at which Mowgli made his approach. To invite Mowgli to walk towards the plate, the trainer withdrew. To stop Mowgli's advance, the trainer walked forward.

12. Moved B much closer to the centre of the arena and, over the ensuing six months, extended the distance between A and B very gradually. If leaps in the region of 20 feet were required, launching blocks were also introduced over the same gradual time frame.

Stumbling blocks: the main outcome that can work against efficient training is any consequence of training that causes the leopard to lose confidence. With this in mind, all surfaces should be non-slip and all raised areas should be strong enough to support the cat safely. Once training advances the main stumbling block is the anticipation of cues and food. Too high a food drive can lead to overexcitement that can manifest as possessiveness and resultant aggression. It is countered by giving modest food rewards rather than jackpots.

General processes in training

Clicker-training: no.
Use of restraints: the walls of the training arena.
Other equipment: canes and rostra.
Aversive stimuli: the cat must learn to avoid the canes when presented without meat on them or being tapped together.
Auditory cues: up, place, stay, alright, finish.
Visual cues: the consistent use of canes and rostra help the leopard know what is expected of him.

Use of reinforcers

Rewards used: small pieces of fresh meat.
Variation in the size of a reward: no.
Variety of rewards used: no.
Reinforcement schedule: continuous.
Use of rewards as lures or targets: meat is thrown onto the rostrum to attract the cat to this point as a reliable feeding station.

Highlights: with food being used in front of the animal and tapping sticks behind, this is a classic example of carrots and sticks being used in combination.

c. Training for comic effect

When animals are used for entertainment, they are often given human tasks to perform. This appeals to the side of human nature that enjoys anthropomorphism. Even though it obscures the true biology of non-human animals, this approach allows us to develop a feeling of empathy with them, however ill-informed or patronising that may be. Just as it is comical to see children dressed up as adults, so we find amusement in seeing animals behaving in a serious manner that seems almost fuelled by human values. The creation of this illusion offers some interesting insights into animal training. For instance, visitors to model farms are entertained to see sheep of different breeds being released onto a stage and stopping beside a plinth bearing the name of their individual breed. As we will discover, giving a sheep such as Bob (Case 27) reliable and uncontested access to a meal in one spot on a stage is the best means of training this behaviour.

As humans, we imagine that few of our aesthetic values are shared by non-humans. We smile at the thought of an animal appreciating art, and this contributes to the entertainment value of training an animal to paint. Although the extent to which elephant paintings can be called works of art is debatable, the charm of a painting that has not come from the hand of a human should not be underestimated. Works in acrylic on canvas by the elephants at Woburn sell for more than many of those by art school graduates. Painting requires brush holding, and this is why elephants steal the march on other species. Using its trunk, or rather one nostril, an elephant such as Woburn's Raja (Case 28) can manipulate a brush with considerable dexterity in the same way as it would use a switch or twig to deter flies. Whether he gets the same gratification moving his trunk about while having a brush up one of his nostrils is another matter.

The manipulation of inanimate objects is also seen in many avian species that build nests. Magpies and bower birds take this a step further when they decorate their nest sites. The natural use of such objects may account for the salience of manipulable items as tokens for food. Red, the Australian magpie (Case 29) at Taronga Zoo, in Sydney, has learned to carry discarded paper to a designated site to make his daily meal appear. As with Jasper the Galah (Case 30), another Taronga resident, initial training encourages the bird to hold objects and trade them for rewards from the trainer. This is the principle behind a common remedial approach to teaching the retrieve exercise to dogs that for whatever reason have failed to understand what fun a game of fetch can be. Teaching '*hold*' must always be reinforced before '*leave*' or '*drop*' is established. Continually telling puppies to leave household objects alone can make them very reluctant to fetch on demand.

It is good to see captive animals using their athleticism as their wild relatives do. This accounts for the popularity of falconry displays and free-flight shows. Red and Jasper are not caged when they perform their learned responses. They could fly off into the wide blue yonder of Sydney harbour if they were so inclined, and indeed occasionally that's exactly what happens. The birds wear radio-tracking devices, but such departures are very rare and this makes their conditioning particularly intriguing.

Regardless of the species being exhibited, there are some common features of basic training for free-flight shows. All birds must first be pet-pack trained i.e. trained to associate a pet travel cage with food. Finding and entering a pet-pack is the means by which free flying birds are caught after their performance. It is a prerequisite to training that requires tremendous patience. After habituation to being fed near the cage, the distance between the food and the cage door is very gradually decreased until the birds appear comfortable in the cage. It is important not to shut the door until the bird has repeatedly been fed inside the cage and enters it without resistance. Once that stage is reached, the door can be shut and the cage can be gently moved. It is important to remove any negative associations with the cage, and therefore the trainer should avoid slamming the cage door once the bird is inside. Timing is also critical, since shutting the door too early can establish long-lasting reluctance to enter the cage. Once these steps are mastered, the bird can be carried in the cage, but it is important to recognise that moving the cage makes it an unpleasant place to be. So this must be done with what could almost be described as reverence and for only short periods until the bird habituates to the movement implicit in transit.

Fig. 6.4 Traing a bantam to trigger the release of a banner as it approaches its pet pack.

The macaws in this chapter are tea-stand trained under similar principles. For ease of handling, they must be taught that their perches (the tea-stands) are where most of their rewards are delivered, and must also know that they can expect rewards if they climb onto the stick when presented with it. As with all performing birds, the macaws must be habituated to equipment, crowds and personnel. Attempts are also made to habituate them to change. A change as simple as slightly raising the socket board, used as part of the birds' show, can throw their performance completely.

One conditioned response in the current section is of particular interest because it requires cued inhibition of learned responses. By serial repetitions of a simple behaviour we can create an on-switch. Subsequent reinforcement of the termination of behaviour creates an off-switch. By deploying such an off-switch a trainer can arrest a repeated response. For example, a macaw such as Jake (Case 32) who uses repeated iterations of a behaviour as if he is counting, can be reinforced for stopping the counting. Passive but inquisitive birds are the easiest to train. Aggressive birds are unsuitable, as are those who lose interest in operant devices after only five or six actuations. With the right bird, all that the trainer must do to create an illusion of mathematical skill in his bird is make the stop cue as subtle, and therefore as difficult for human observers to detect, as possible. It is wise to consider that certain animals can actually do the real thing e.g. really count, and sort articles according to their shapes and colours. The cases here simulate what can be real parrot abilities, for example, as demonstrated by Irene Pepperberg's parrot, Alex.

A similar off-switch technique has been used with tremendous success in resolving barking dog problems. The normal human knee-jerk reaction to a barking dog is to tell the dog to shut up. By necessity one usually issues this request loudly because that is the only way to be heard. This is more often ineffective, not least because many dogs respond to human vocalisation by barking, perhaps as a result of social facilitation (i.e., it is almost as if they perceive the human as barking too). Compare this to the subtle off-switch used by Jake's trainer and one can see that by first training a dog to bark one can train it to stop on cue without raising one's voice.

Case 27   Sheep *Ovis aries* (Devon Longwool)

Training profile

Target behaviour:	finding a specific site on a podium
Name:	Bob
Age:	2 years
Trainer's assessment of temperament:	cheeky, timid, easy-going
Trainer's name:	Stuart Barnes

Background

Sheep on farms are usually left pretty much to their own devices. This does not mean that they are not learning all the time. They certainly seem to pick up the most salient details about their home range, and their memory is impressive. Knowing where to find food, and the ability to recognise flock-mates as individuals using their facial features, are core skills for a sheep. Some breeds, of which the Herdwick is an example, show a hefting instinct, a lifelong memory trace it uses to reliably return to the area of its birth. Whole flocks of sheep learn that the sound of a particular make of vehicle is associated with the delivery of food. While grazing beside a busy road, they rapidly learn to discriminate between that sound and those of other vehicles and come running towards the former while completely ignoring the latter. They also learn to spot certain sheepdogs and seem to understand that some deserve more respect than others.

The shepherds at the Big Sheep rural exhibition centre in Devon have harnessed their rams' ability to memorise food stores for their sheep display. Bob Marley, a Devon Longwool, takes his place on a pyramidal podium very happily every day in the knowledge that it gives him access to his favourite concentrated ration. When the display rams are released from their holding pen, they march down the track to the exhibition hall, and one by one come to call when they hear their names, so that they can be arranged in order in the race behind the stage. As each is released from the race they assume a position in front of their breed's name plate on the podium. To the audience this gives an impression of self-awareness. For the trainers, it is important that the rams do not stray to feed bowls on other parts of the podium and that they do not struggle once they have been chained up. Free-range mature rams are unsuitable because they tend to fight this sort of handling.

Training programme

Before commencing training the animal must: have an appetite.

Changing the animal's motivation before a training session: nothing. In fact, because the Big Sheep offers bags of sheep nuts for its patrons to feed to the sheep, many of the rams are full of food immediately before being allowed to travel to the exhibition hall. Strangely this does not appear to have any deleterious effect on their performance.

Number of training sessions per week   14
Duration of session   20 minutes
Time taken to learn   6 days

In the process of shaping the final behaviour, the trainer:
1. Habituated Bob to 'nuts', a form of concentrated food (a novel delight for many of the rams that have been fed only on grass and hay before).

2. Habituated Bob to wearing a collar.
3. Shaped a suitable response to collar pressure i.e. taught Bob to be led.
4. Taught Bob alongside his peers to expect to get fed in the shed.
5. Put all rams into the race in a consistent order.

6. Allowed Bob to learn that ramming the sides of the backstage pens does not get rewarded by effecting an escape route.

7. Physically manoeuvred Bob to his appointed part of the podium where he immediately gained access to the nuts.

8. Habituated Bob to being chained up while waiting (for up to five minutes) by his feed bowl for more nuts. If Bob found his way to another ram's feeding station he was physically displaced and tied to his own. Therefore all rams learned to discriminate which place to choose.

Stumbling blocks: at every stage in the process, the rams seem to be looking for escape routes. So before being used all equipment has to be made ram-proof.

General processes in training

Clicker-training: no.

Use of restraints: chains are used to keep the rams in place while the presenter continues to explain some of the more interesting features of sheep breeds, shearing and the history of the wool industry.

Other equipment: none.

Aversive stimuli: nil.

Auditory cues: although each animal is called by name to take its place in the backstage race, the rams seem to perform the correct response even when different names are called.

Visual cues: nil.

Use of reinforcers

Rewards used: sheep nuts.

Variation in the size of a reward: no.

Variety of rewards used: no.

Reinforcement schedule: continuous.

Use of rewards as lures or targets: the bowl of nuts is used as a target.

Highlights: this is a form of place training (see Chapter 2). Once they work out that this response brings access to a brimming bowl of nuts that does not have to be contested with other sheep, the rams race to the podium. In animals that feed in groups, the value of such a foraging opportunity seems considerably greater than the nutritional value of the food alone.

Case 28   Asian elephant *Elephas maximus*

Training profile

Target behaviour:	painting within the margins of an A3 canvas
Name:	Raja
Age:	7.5 years
Trainer's assessment of temperament:	happy, co-operative, inquisitive
Trainer's name:	James Lingard

Background

Using a series of trained responses linked to one another, the elephants at Woburn apply one colour after another to create futuristic pieces. Each elephant has its own individual painting style. Interestingly, the keepers at Woburn note that their animals paint better with the brush held by their left nostrils than their right. Bold characters are the preferred candidates for this sort of training, since nervous animals seem to find the behaviour too complex. When they are performing at their best, elephants pick up the brush with confidence, make smooth progress to the canvas and proceed to use smooth brush strokes that stay within the confines of the canvas. Vendors of elephant art note that these pictures can be viewed from every angle as you rotate them through 360 degrees.

Training programme

Before commencing training the animal must: be habituated to having its trunk held by humans. Further to this the animal must know to move away from the hook and be responsive to the following commands: *steady* (hold the current behaviour); *alright* (stop the current behaviour); *pick up* (the nearest object); *hold* (that object); *drop* (that object); *bucket* (drop that object - in the bucket).

Changing the animal's motivation before a training session: a drill of behaviours is routinely applied every morning when the elephants are fresh. This helps to get them focused and therefore painting is most often attempted in the morning after drill.

Number of training sessions per week   7
Duration of session   5 minutes
Time taken to learn   8 weeks

In the process of shaping the final behaviour, the trainer:
1. Manually moved Raja's trunk to the paintbrush and inserted the brush into his left nostril.

2. Issued the command '*pick up brush*' as he moved the trunk over the brush then said '*hold*'.
3. Moved Raja's trunk on the canvas in combination with the command '*paint*'.

4. Gave the command '*alright*' once there was a series of strokes in that colour on the canvas.

5. Said '*bucket*' to encourage Raja to move his trunk to the bucket.

6. Repeated steps 1-5 with the next brush i.e. a different colour. Raja is encouraged to select brushes himself but generally the selection process is guided by the trainer.

7. Gave a food reward.

Stumbling blocks: the elephants tend to hold the brush sloppily and often seem to hover it at a distance from the canvas, either because they cannot locate its surface or because to do so is uncomfortable.

General processes in training

Clicker-training: no.

Use of restraints: chains are used initially to keep the elephant in place.

Other equipment: hook, brush, easel, canvas, paint and bucket.

Aversive stimuli: the hook is used in painting training, but sparingly since it tends to make the elephants nervous. Better results are obtained if the elephants are working for positive reinforcers.

Auditory cues: pick up brush, hold, paint, alright and *bucket.*

Visual cues: the keeper's hand can be used as a guide when elephants are painting since they move their trunks away from the trainer's hand more smoothly than they do from the hook.

Use of reinforcers

Rewards used: chocolate muffins, bananas, apples.

Variation in the size of a reward: yes.

Variety of rewards used: yes, it is important to reward enthusiastic painting with a jackpot such as a whole banana given in two-inch pieces.

Reinforcement schedule: initially rewards are given every time after a complete brushstroke, then the elephant is weaned onto a reward after every complete use of a single colour, and then finally on to every complete four-colour cycle. Delaying the arrival of food in this way helps to stop the elephant anticipating the end of its paint-work. Too many food rewards are distracting.

Highlights: because they seem to lose concentration and seem almost too excited, anticipation of the end of work and the arrival of food can make animals difficult to train.

Case 29   Australian magpie *Gymnorhina tibicen*

Training profile

Target behaviour:	placing litter in a bin
Name:	Red
Age:	3 years
Trainer's assessment of temperament:	reliable, hard-working, resourceful
Trainer's name:	Matthew Kettle

Background

Like other members of the crow family, magpies are resourceful birds that rapidly learn to exploit their environment for all the food it can provide without expenditure of too much effort or exposure to too much danger. As scavengers, they have to be able to adapt to changes in the way edible material is presented. Naturally reared older birds are poor candidates for training and especially those with bad experiences around humans or those with flight injuries. Any bird that has learned to acquire food in more natural ways will not adapt easily to training procedures. Similarly, wild birds would at times be more motivated to breed than feed and, provided the right extraneous stimuli were present, this could cause an early departure stage left. Although hand-reared birds also have the urge to breed, this may be redirected to humans. Habituation and imprinting are pivotal to these animals' learning and therefore only foundlings/orphan birds are used in this collection.

Red appears on the stage at the front of the show's auditorium at Taronga Zoo. He strolls up to a piece of freshly discarded paper, picks it up, marches busily to the litter bin in the corner and deposits the rubbish where it belongs. Then he exits stage right. It is amusing to see a workmanlike magpie arrive on stage when the presenter, who has just wiped his hands on and discarded a paper towel, is nonchalantly discussing the dangers litter represent to wildlife. The humour continues when the bird raises his wings as he runs to the bin appearing just a little exasperated with the continued hypocrisy of the presenter.

The bird should be responsive to stimuli regardless of the weather. Notwithstanding the state of his plumage, he should fly onto the stage with confidence and perform the chained behaviours with a fluency that helps to convince novice observers that he is doing the right thing with litter despite the presenter's misbehaviour.

Training programme

Before commencing training the animal must: hop onto the handler's hand for food and know that the word '*good*' is a secondary reinforcer worth working for. The birds are also habituated to the pet pack and learn to look for this as a landing pad on which they can expect a large reward whenever they have finished a training session.

Changing the animal's motivation before a training session: all birds in free flight shows have their body weight closely monitored. They usually get most of their food allowance as a result of trained behaviours and rarely get free food. At the beginning of training every piece of food has to be justified. If they perform with less enthusiasm than usual, their body weight is likely to have increased. Daily weighing helps trainers discriminate between ill-health and a lack of motivation due to satiation as a cause of substandard performances.

Number of training sessions per week   14
Duration of session   10 minutes
Time taken to learn   2 weeks

In the process of shaping the final behaviour, the trainer:

1. Used a key initially instead of a piece of paper. The advantage of this object was that it made a characteristic noise when Red dropped it into a target receptacle (a dish). The sound was used as a bridge to herald the arrival of a reward.
2. Placed the dish in the rubbish bin and rewarded Red for placing the key in the new site.
3. Replaced the key with paper and shaped the final behaviour.

4. Habituated Red (over the next six weeks) to flying in open air and under windy conditions and in the presence of a faux audience before being used in front of the public.

Stumbling blocks: the big hurdle is building up the association of an inanimate object (be it key or paper) with food. A close second is the challenge of training the bird that dropping the item anywhere other than the bin is not good enough.

General processes in training

Clicker-training: no.

Use of restraints: a cage is used as a landing pad. As the bird eats his reward the cage door is closed and the bird is taken back to his home cage. Red wears a tracking device on one leg to facilitate his recovery should he fly away from the auditorium.

Other equipment: bin, key and paper.

Aversive stimuli: nil.

Auditory cues: nil.

Visual cues: dropping litter is the bird's cue to fly on to the stage and perform.

Use of reinforcers

Rewards used: portions of the bird's regular daily diet are delivered as rewards during training. Red's diet includes kangaroo meat, mealworms, crickets and (dead) newborn mice.

Variation in the size of a reward: yes. For a single reward, Red can receive anywhere between ten and twenty per cent of his daily intake, which varies between five and ten grams depending on the time of year, his moulting or his performance. Once fully trained he can receive 100 per cent of his daily intake at the end of a spotless performance.

Variety of rewards used: yes.

Reinforcement schedule: in the first ten days or so, all correct performances are continuously reinforced with very small portions of food. As rewards become more intermittent, their size increases. The jackpots (biggest rewards – 100 per cent of daily intake) arrive after particularly fluid performances. After approximately two weeks of training 'good' is established as a secondary reinforcer and primary reinforcement becomes variable.

Ratio of variable reinforcement: 1:5.

Use of rewards as lures or targets: food is used to lure the bird into his cage.

Highlights: using the sound of the key being dropped as a bridge is an excellent example of a secondary reinforcer that might occur during learning in the wild or at least in the absence of humans (see Chapter 2). The case is also impressive when we consider how hard it can be to train animals to release an object which they have come to associate with food (see discussion of misbehaviour in Chapter 2).

Case 30 | Galah *Cacatua roseicapilla*

Training profile

Target behaviour:	stealing coins
Name:	Jasper
Age:	3 years
Trainer's assessment of temperament:	fun-loving, cheeky and friendly
Trainer's name:	Cathy Saunders

Background

Jasper is a galah, an Australian parrot, that performs in the Free Flight Bird Show, at Sydney's Taronga Zoo. She was brought to the wildlife rehabilitation staff at Taronga Zoo as a fledgling after she fell into the back of a truck at a set of traffic lights. At this time, the Free Flight Bird Show was little more than a germ of an idea, and Taronga Zoo was looking for galahs that could be hand-raised and later trained for use in the show. Galahs are particularly suited to training as they have a playful disposition.

At Taronga Zoo's free-flight show, trained behaviours are demonstrated under very testing conditions in front of a large, seated crowd in an open-air amphitheatre with Sydney's magnificent harbour as a backdrop. The liberty this venue offers means that training has to be meticulous if the loss of exhibition birds is to be avoided. (Of equal concern, given the outdoor setting, is the threat of mobbing by wild birds such as members of the local crow population.)

During the three years of her involvement in the show, Jasper has only ever performed the coin trick. Although she has performed consistently, things have not always run smoothly. In one show, there was a bird of prey circling around the amphitheatre. On sighting the bird, Jasper flew to a tree and refused to move until she saw her pet-pack (a proprietary cat cage). This is an example of why pet-pack training is such an important element in the training of free-flying birds.

Galahs are renowned for their ability to bond with a human. This trait can be capitalised upon and used as reinforcements because galahs may perform tasks for contact. Galahs that have bonded to humans learn this series of responses most readily. Those that are aggressive, nervous, poor fliers and naturally reared older birds are poor candidates for training.

When training Jasper for this show, the initial shaping was done by one person, and gradually more and more handlers were introduced in order to dilute the attachment she had to her primary keeper. Despite implementing this strategy there was a time at the zoo when the Free Flight Bird Show was short-staffed and had to employ several temporary keepers. Some simple peculiarities in their handling technique prompted Jasper to become reluctant to fly to people with hats or sunglasses. Jasper needed to be retired temporarily from the show and retrained.

When performing the coin trick, which Jasper shares with another galah (JoJo), she collects a dollar coin from an audience member and returns it to her trainer's pocket. Some time later she returns the coin to its original owner. This trick is used to add humour and lighten the mood. It also helps to demonstrate the aptitude of psittacine species to problem-solving exercises and it allows people to have actual contact with a bird at the zoo. When performing optimally, Jasper waits to be cued and doesn't anticipate the next move. She places the coin in the pocket and on the hand precisely, and carries the coin without dropping it. Perfect execution also requires Jasper to fly to any point and to anyone in the audience.

Training programme

Before commencing training the animal must: be consistently flying hand to hand on cue. The training process begins in the bird's cage and uses food as a lure to get the bird to step onto the hand from the perch. The hand must be held like a perch, upwards of the wrist to maximise control of the bird and to prevent the bird travelling up the arm. After this is well established, the distance between the perch and the hand is gradually increased, but at this stage the reward is hidden behind the hand. Reinforcement is given initially for hopping to the hand and eventually for flying to it. A visual sendaway cue is introduced by reinforcing only when the bird flies when cued. Once this has become consistent, hand-to-hand flying is taught. This is achieved by using another person's hand as the perch, and gradually increasing the distance between the people.

Changing the animal's motivation before a training session: keeping galahs at a target weight of 300 grams controls their motivation. A change of only five grams can result in anxiety or unco-operative behaviour. This ideal weight is maintained by weighing the galahs and their food every day.

Number of training sessions per week 21
Duration of session 10 minutes
Time taken to learn 4 months

In the process of shaping the final behaviour, the trainer:
1. Presented the coin to the bird and gave reinforcement initially for mere interest in the coin, then for touching it. As shaping progressed, rewards were given for picking up the coin and, finally, only if the coin was held.

2. Trained the bird to take the coin from someone's hand. Because the bird had been taught to fly from hand to hand, and was focused on the coin, this was readily achieved. When the bird picked up the coin, the '*sendaway*' cue was used to send the bird, across a small distance, to another person. Initially, any approximation to the desired behaviour was reinforced. As training proceeded, reinforcement was given for closer approximations until finally only for the exact behaviour. Once this was achieved, the distance between the people was extended, the arm holding the coin was swapped and volunteer audiences were used to habituate the bird to crowds, hats, sunglasses, beards and children.

3. Trained the bird to place the coin in a pocket. It was imperative that the bird was given the best possible chance at completing this task correctly, allowing reinforcement and repetition of the behaviour. Cardboard was placed in the pocket, making it stick out, and the bird was held, holding the coin directly in front of the pocket. Reinforcement was initially given when the bird dropped the coin even if it lay on the breast. Eventually only the correct behaviour was reinforced and if the coin was dropped in the wrong place, the bird was asked to repeat the behaviour.

4. Trained the bird to return the coin to the palm of a hand. The bird was sent, holding the coin, to a person with an outstretched hand. Reinforcement was given for dropping the coin anywhere initially, but eventually only for placing it on the hand.

5. Linked the components of the chain together and reinforced the bird for executing the entire behaviour within an aviary before attempting free flight.

6. Habituated the bird to the amphitheatre and crowds.

Stumbling blocks: dropping the coin is a common problem especially if the distance between hands is increased too rapidly.

General processes in training

Clicker-training: yes, bridging allows immediate reinforcement when the actual reward might be delayed. Saying 'good' and giving a reward at exactly the same time allows verbal praise to become a secondary reinforcer. The delay between the primary reinforcer and secondary reinforcer can then be extended.

Use of restraints: nil.

Other equipment: the equipment needed for training includes an aviary, pet-pack and a cage of in-between size, which allows the bird to be separated during meals for maintenance of target weight.

Aversive stimuli: nil.

Auditory cues: nil.

Visual cues: a circling hand is used as a sendaway command and the coin represents a visual cue to fly to the second person.

Use of reinforcers

Rewards used: the secondary reinforcer is the word '*good*' and the most usual primary reinforcer is sunflower seeds, which are removed from the daily ration. Although, being hand-reared, Jasper relishes human company, peanuts are her personal favourite and therefore these are used in her pet-pack (small carrying cage) as her ultimate goal. Jasper performs two shows a day and her reinforcements for the show come out of her exact food ration. After the show, she is given the remainder of her meal only if she has performed consistently.

Variation in the size of a reward: no.

Variety of rewards used: no.

Reinforcement schedule: continuous then variable.

Ratio of variable reinforcement: once the initial training is in place, an approximate ratio of 1:2 is used and the number of required responses and the latency before reinforcement arrives is randomised.

Use of rewards as lures or targets: food is used as a lure during pet-pack training and the initial stages of hand-to-hand training.

Highlights: weight control is central to this training protocol. By plotting the bird's weight on a graph, trainers can determine whether satiation is to blame if performances deteriorate. It is worth considering how food rewards can be managed more elegantly in dog training. Perhaps it is the distensible nature of the canine stomach and the tendency to over-eat that makes dogs so readily trainable with food rewards. Having said that, when lives may depend on conditioned responses by keen canidae (such as in Case 41), trainers monitor weight and food intake very closely.

Case 31

Catalina macaw *Ara ararauna x Ara macao*

Training profile

Target behaviour:	matching shapes to holes and colours
Name:	Matilda
Age:	18 years
Trainer's assessment of temperament:	inquisitive, assertive, intelligent
Trainer's name:	Darren Beasley

Background

Birds share good colour vision with humans, and many can see additional colours using their sensitivity to UV light that we cannot even imagine. By using their visual abilities they can perform impressively in tasks that require movement of manipulable shapes. Using equipment that looks as though it has been acquired from an aptitude test for humans, the birds assign blocks to their respective destinations with speed, accuracy and charming nonchalance. The bird selects blocks that fit into a socket board with spaces of the same colour as the block. This has the appearance of a colour discrimination task but is made easier by the use of different shapes. Each bird has to be assessed on his or her own merits because there appear to be certain birds that pick up the behaviour quicker than others. This may reflect differences in colour vision or past history. It should be noted that although this task is somewhat simplified, there is evidence that parrots can conceptualise colours. For example,

Irene Pepperberg's Alex demonstrates this when cued verbally to select an article based on its colour.

Training programme

Before commencing training the animal must: have learned that the stage provides a context for a bountiful feeding regime.

Changing the animal's motivation before a training session: the macaws at Longleat are not weighed. Instead, their reward quota is determined by reviewing their behaviour on a given day and reducing food intake if their performance declines in a way suggesting reduction in the reward value of food.

Number of training sessions per week 21
Duration of session 5 minutes
Time taken to learn 5 days

In the process of shaping the final behaviour, the trainer:
1. Encouraged the bird to pick up any of the shapes and traded them for rewards.

2. Working entirely with a single colour, placed the shape away from the bird and established a retrieval exercise.

3. Introduced the socket board. The trainer positioned his hand as close as possible to the relevant hole in the socket board and successively rewarded the bird for placing the shape near, on, and then in, the socket.

4. Added a second colour and repeated steps 2 and 3.

5. Added a third colour and repeated steps 2 and 3.

6. Added a fourth colour and repeated steps 2 and 3.

7. Juggled the shapes around to refine the bird's recognition of the relevance of shapes and colours.

Stumbling blocks: over-enthusiasm – once the behaviour is established and the deal is struck such that rewards come for the final shaped behaviour, it is common for a bird to rush the task. This is most obvious when the bird spends more time ramming the wrong shape into the wrong hole than carefully selecting the correct destination for the shape in its beak. Shoddiness creeps in very easily if the bird is rewarded for it during a show, so the good trainer has repartee up his sleeve to excuse time spent waiting for the performance to improve. For example, Darren will keep the audience interested by apparently engaging in conversation with the bird with remarks such as '*Come on, you can do better than that*'.

General processes in training

Clicker-training: no.

Use of restraints: no.

Other equipment: shapes and socket board.

Aversive stimuli: if the bird hears '*You can do better than that*' it knows that no reward is forthcoming. The next warning command is '*Hey come on*' which alerts the bird to the real possibility of being ignored or returned to the tea-stand.

Auditory cues: minimal. Despite the illusion of there being an ongoing chat between the human and his birds, the presenter's monologue during the show is of little importance to the birds.

Visual cues: the only visual cue the birds need to prompt the behaviour is the arrival of the equipment on the stage.

Use of reinforcers

Rewards used: peanuts, brazil nuts, pulses and sunflowers.
Variation in the size of a reward: yes.
Variety of rewards used: yes.
Reinforcement schedule: continuous.
Use of rewards as lures or targets: sometimes peanuts are used in key positions to get the birds to focus on the task.

Highlights: by occasionally peeling the peanuts, the trainer can deliver rewards more rapidly for especially impressive performances. This is not so much a reward gradient as a time-to-reward gradient by adopting a gratifyingly short interval between response and reinforcement (see Chapter 2).

Case 32

Blue and Gold macaw *Ara ararauna*

Training profile

Target behaviour:	'counting'
Name:	Jake
Age:	12 years
Trainer's assessment of temperament:	inquisitive, assertive, intelligent
Trainer's name:	Robert Savin

Background

Like Clever Hans, the counting horse described in Chapter 4 who was given spoken and written puzzles to solve and pawed at the ground until the correct number was reached, birds can be taught to perform a discrete task repetitively and to stop when given very subtle signals.

Jake at Longleat Safari Park, in Wiltshire, is asked to count up to a number between one and ten that has been nominated by a member of the audience. He pulls a lever that rings a bell for the desired number of rings. He repeats this with a second number and when asked, correctly adds the two together.

The illusion is impressive. Naive observers can scarcely believe that a bird can add numbers together quicker than an average seven-year-old child. Jake's trainer looks for confident use of the device and above all a precise and abrupt halt to the ringing without any hint of slowing down, which tends to give the game away.

Training programme

Before commencing training the animal must: be trained to adopt the tea-stand as a feeding station and the stick as a target and, by observing other birds, must have learned to expect food in the context of the show. Fundamentally, the bird must have learned to associate both handlers and novel toys with food rewards.

Changing the animal's motivation before a training session: the macaws at Longleat are not weighed. Their motivation to work for attention and food is heightened by their being taken from their home cages and placed on their tea-stands on the parrot show stage. It may be that the presence of other birds being fed in this context becomes a strong cue for an individual bird that it will also get fed.

Number of training sessions per week 21
Duration of session 5 minutes
Time taken to learn 3 days

In the process of shaping the final behaviour, the trainer:
1. Rewarded the bird for holding the trigger element of the custom-built counting equipment.

2. Withdrew the reward for holding the trigger. This leads to a frustration effect and consequently the bird holds more firmly.

3. Rewarded the bird only for holding the trigger firmly enough to ring the bell.

4. Kept rewarding the bird for ringing the bell but introduced a reward gradient so that while the biggest rewards (the jackpots) are given for the greatest number of bell rings, rewards are still likely for any number of effective actuations of the trigger. Using this procedure the discriminative stimulus ('on-switch') for strong bell ringing is the presentation of the device.

5. Arbitrarily added an obvious signal, such as a raised palm, that marks the end of reward availability ('off-switch'). The trainer never rewarded bell-ringing after this signal has been issued.

6. Refined his body language (a raised palm can very gradually be replaced by a quivered finger) as much as each bird could tolerate. Birds must learn to discriminate increasingly smaller cues that act as off-switches of the counting behaviour.

Stumbling blocks: because many birds seem to get secondarily reinforced by audience responses, they can begin to stop counting because this leads to a burst of audience laughter. Birds have to be taught to watch the trainer rather than listen to observers.

General processes in training

Clicker-training: no.

Use of restraints: nil.

Other equipment: the bell ringing device.

Aversive stimuli: depending on his previous progress with the task, a bird may be sidelined for unwelcome behaviour. If the bird is experienced and yet fails to count up to the appointed number, he is given one further chance to improve his performance before being replaced on his tea-stand. If he keeps counting regardless of the cue, then he is immediately sent back to base.

Auditory cues: the number that has been nominated by the member of the audience is called out to the bird, but this is more to do with showmanship than being of any relevance to subsequent use of the device.

Visual cues: after the audience has chosen a number, the arrival of the device on stage is the discriminative stimulus for the bird to start ringing when it is allowed while the ever more subtle hand (or for that matter foot) signal arrests activation of the trigger.

Use of reinforcers

Rewards used: peanuts, brazil nuts, pulses and sunflowers.

Variation in the size of a reward: yes. However, Jake is a bird who seems to find being rewarded as rewarding as the reward itself. So, eight pieces of an average sized peanut are more rewarding than an average peanut. This marks him out as a bird that is meeting a behavioural need to forage rather than simply meeting its calorie intake target.

Variety of rewards used: yes – without frightening the bird the trainer aims to maintain an element of surprise in the delivery of rewards.

Reinforcement schedule: continuous.

Highlights: with some experienced and motivated birds, signals that halt counting can be so subtle that the trainer loses an accurate understanding of how he is communicating this off-switch. This is not only because birds have better vision than humans. They also have faster flicker fusion times and can process visual cues quicker than a human bystander. When the name of the game is sleight of hand, these attributes make the macaw a preferred species for this behaviour. But for the fact that Clever Hans' trainer did not intend to give a signal in the first place, the similarities with his famous case are of particular interest to students of learning theory (see Chapters 2 and 4).

Fig. 6.5 Maggot getting a nose job.

d. Training for veterinary procedures and to maximise the safety of personnel

Compared with domestic species, wild animals are highly intolerant of changes in their environment. While a trip to the veterinary clinic can cause some distress to a domestic pet, the introduction of veterinary paraphernalia into the enclosure of an experienced zoo animal can cause abject panic. The strength of wild animals combined with their resolve to escape from danger is a major source of self harm and a considerable hazard for personnel. Therefore for humane and practical reasons dart-guns are used rather than physical restraint.

By habituating exotic animals in zoological collections to personnel and equipment involved in routine handling procedures, staff can reduce the need for repeated sedation or analgesia. This seems beneficial for animal welfare, since each episode of psychotropic drug use necessarily involves the subjects' 'coming round' as they wake up. Recovery from such agents is sometimes accompanied by physical trauma and some evidence of distress while transient removal from a social group can have unwelcome consequences such as hierarchical disputes during and after periods of separation.

The African fauna in this section, all of which are potentially very dangerous, illustrate three successful conditioning programmes that have reduced the need for physical or chemical restraint. While Maggot, a White rhino (Case 33), has been trained to stand still for horn trimming (see Fig. 6.5) and to comply with her trainer's cues to lift her hind feet for pedicure purposes, Nyota, a young female giraffe (Case 34), has been habituated to enter a crush cage and undergo gynaecological examinations as part of a conservation effort.

By way of final example M'kali, a juvenile elephant (Case 35), has been trained to hold the tail of another elephant. Her training involves the use of some aversive stimuli. Elephant keepers have been killed in zoos throughout the world and therefore, if one is going to handle elephants, the argument for using aversive stimuli (in a process of negative reinforcement) is reasonably convincing. For example, an elephant that has been solely trained with a clicker may be difficult to halt once it has started a behaviour. If the behaviour sought to be brought to an end is 'crushing a human against the nearest wall', then an instant response is vital.

The relationship between control of elephants and the maximal use of the space available to them is neatly illustrated when male elephants are in musth. Their uncontrollability means that for safety reasons, and despite the apparent frustration they have to undergo, they have to be penned for the length of their cycle.

Case 33

White rhino *Ceratotherium simum*

Training profile
Target behaviour: lift hindleg on command
Name: Maggot
Age: 33 years
Trainer's assessment of temperament: gentle, trustworthy, patient
Trainer's name: Nick Whiting

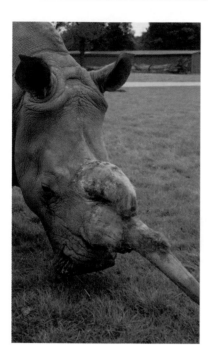

Background

Maggot is probably the most charismatic of the four White rhinos at Woburn Safari Park, in Bedfordshire. She is slightly unusual in the extent to which she seeks out the company of other rhinos, and shows a preference for being able to lie alongside her long-time companion, Mary. As she approaches her dotage, Maggot has to receive regular attention to her feet. It would be unfortunate if this required chemical sedation, and so her keeper elected to train her to have her feet handled for this husbandry exercise. The rhino should hold each foot up for enough time for podiatry to be performed. With incredible patience, the keeper has won the rhino's confidence. Indeed, such is his affinity with these potentially very dangerous animals, that he can even prune their horns without the use of a sedative.

Although rhinos may look very steady, the prevailing message from anyone who has worked with them is that their flight response is extremely easily triggered. With notoriously poor eyesight, rhinos rely on their sense of smell and hearing. The problem of flightiness is compounded by the fact that, in addition to their poor eyesight, rhinos have a blindspot around their hindquarters. This makes them especially jumpy when they detect stimuli from behind. Horse owners with fearful animals could learn a lot from this keeper. Softly softly catchy monkey.

The public is often surprised to find that an animal of such size can demonstrate a willingness to co-operate and can respond correctly to subtle tactile signals.

(Note: despite the fact that all the rhinos in this group have been exhibited for more than twenty years, taking the photos that appear in this book with safety required 15 minutes of habituation to the scent of the cameraman and the sound of a motor drive on the camera.)

Training programme

Before commencing training the animal must: have developed predictable responses while around the keeper. The essence of safe rhino handling is being able to determine when the animal is not in the mood for human company.

Changing the animal's motivation before a training session: the key is not to alert the animals to anything different happening in its world. Therefore the emphasis is on making these procedures a normal part of the animal's day rather than anything that might cause excitement or arousal.

Number of training sessions per week   3
Duration of session   15 minutes
Time taken to learn   4 weeks

In the process of shaping the final behaviour, the trainer:

1. Ensured Maggot was in the right sort of mood for this sort of handling. If she appeared too reactive to extraneous stimuli, he left her alone.
2. Put some food on the ground to keep Maggot occupied.
3. Reaccustomed Maggot to his voice.
4. Reaccustomed Maggot to being touched by hand all over her body.

5. Moved his hand to a trigger spot on her inner thigh (the thigh is less sensitive lower down than this spot but the stimulus remains effective all the way down the limb). The presence of the keeper's hand causes a reflex outward movement that in habituated animals causes no alarm. The response is reinforced by removal of the hand pressure.

6. Applied gentle pressure to the fleshy cushion above the big middle toe (the third metatarsal).

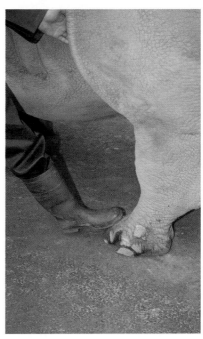

7. Provided nominal support under the lifted leg and began habituating Maggot to the sound and feel of the pedicure rasp.

8. Generalised the learning to the other hind leg.

Stumbling blocks: changing moods can lead to danger. It is important to minimise extraneous stimuli, e.g. mobile phones have to be switched off, but little can be done about smells wafting across the rhino's nose and disturbing it.

General processes in training

Clicker-training: no.

Use of restraints: none.

Other equipment: none.

Aversive stimuli: none.

Auditory cues: none.

Visual cues: none. The only cues are tactile. Placing hand in signal areas alerts the rhino to the request.

Use of reinforcers

Rewards used: food (horse mix) on the ground rewards the rhino for staying put. Because it associates food on the ground with being handled, the handling itself will become reinforcing. As a special treat Maggot sometimes receives the bark of oak and chestnut trees.

Variation in the size of a reward: no.

Variety of reward used: no.

Reinforcement schedule: continuous.

Use of rewards as lures or targets: food is used to bring the rhino to the correct spot before handling starts.

Highlights: the biological constraints on learning in rhinos are mainly to do with their nervousness. Arousal in rhinos rises readily over a threshold beyond which they show a flight response. Distress in these animals is a similarly predictable consequence when members of this species attempt to escape from confined spaces. Further to this, rhinos have not evolved to live in large social groups and defer to conspecific leaders. For all of these reasons, one can see why rhinos have never served humankind as elephants have.

Case 34	Giraffe *Giraffa camelopardalis*

Training profile

Target behaviour:	standing in a crush cage
Name:	Nyota
Age:	7 years
Trainer's assessment of temperament:	jaunty, juvenile, mischievous
Trainer's name:	Frank McFaddyn

Background

Nyota is the youngest of four giraffes at Taronga Zoo. She was born in captivity at Taronga to dam, Hope, and sire, Charity. At seven years of age, Nyota is ready to be mated; however, her father is the only male giraffe at Taronga. Plans for her relocation to Dubbo Western Plains Zoo for breeding purposes were abandoned because it was thought the move would be too disruptive for her. Instead, she remains at Taronga for what will be Australia's first attempt at giraffe artificial insemination (AI). The behaviour modification programme was designed by her keepers to entice her slowly into the crush (the sturdy temporary holding chamber that accommodates the animal safely and comfortably but denies her the opportunity to move backwards or forwards or to turn around) using daily food rations as rewards and to acclimatise her to physical restraint and handling for AI. Although inquisitive and placid, giraffe are considered dangerous under most zoo safety policies, so Nyota's learning to relax in the crush is pivotal to the AI process. Nyota must enter the crush and remain settled in this confined area, while being handled around her hind quarters.

Pre-weaned giraffe calves are too delicate to isolate from the herd and therefore would never be handled in this way. Compliance generally increases with age. Indeed most training difficulties involve juveniles that are wary of humans, and more anxious or nervous than adults.

Nyota's training began two years before this interview. Although occasionally stubborn and aggressive, she is usually playful and mischievous. Nudging, head-butting, biting her keepers' elbows and stealing their microphones are among her favourite attention-seeking strategies. The eagerness with which Nyota has learned to enter the crush and remain placid, while physically restrained, has pleased the keepers.

Habituation of the giraffe is paramount to the successful use of a crush. It requires repeated exposure to the crush environment and pressure around Nyota's hind quarters. Sessions are initially short to minimise stress. Kicking and head tossing call for soothing vocalisation from the keepers. Nyota may feel vulnerable when physically immobilised, so keepers must ensure the crush does not become associated with danger and discomfort. Nyota must be confident that release will eventually be granted. She is showing steadily increased compliance with the trainer's requests when being called into the crush; a confident and rapid entry, without hesitation or diversion of her attention to environmental distractions such as zebra, which share her paddock.

Over time Nyota has developed an eagerness to reach the crush and occasional dribbling upon hearing the top house door open, without being called. As an unusual example of classical conditioning, it seems she has come to associate a previously neutral sound with the food she receives in the crush. The sound of the door is a conditioned stimulus and her heightened activity and dribbling a conditioned response.

Training programme

Before commencing training the animal must: be comfortable when separate from the rest of the herd and familiar with the top house and raceway into which the crush is built. To reach this level, Nyota had to spend frequent periods alone while Hope was in the top house and raceway. Nyota also had to habituate to the personnel present during this handling process.

Changing the animal's motivation before a training session: she must have spent two to three hours wandering around the display yard and built up an appetite since the morning feed before she is motivated to work. In order to retain its position in the giraffe's daily routine, training must commence strictly at 10:30 am.

Number of training sessions per week   4–5
Duration of session   Initially about one hour, however time spent enclosed in the crush never exceeds 10–15 minutes
Time taken to learn   4 weeks

In the process of shaping the final behaviour, the trainer:
1. Called Nyota and Hope into their house from the display paddock. The keepers entered the paddock and used encouraging voice tones to manoeuvre them. Once inside, Hope was called out leaving Nyota alone in the house.

2. Called Nyota into the crush. A food trough was initially hung as a lure at the entrance of the crush, so she could see and reach it while still standing in the house.
3. Moved the food further inside the crush, once she was comfortable feeding at this spot, so that she had to walk inside to reach it. As she did so, a keeper stood next to her on a platform and said '*Good girl, Nyota*' throughout the exercise. When she was comfortable with this increased level of confinement, the trough was moved further in again, until eventually the food was hanging beyond the crush so that she had to be completely within it to feed.

4. Left Nyota to feed in the crush until she was completely calm. Then the crush gate was closed behind her. Nyota was watched for signs of distress such as kicking and head tossing. When they occurred, a keeper used carrots and a gentle encouraging voice to calm and distract her. Because it was clear that stress reduced learning, Nyota was released if she began to struggle. As Nyota became more tolerant of the crush, its sides were drawn together to hold her more securely. Initially, this was done for only 30 seconds, but the period of confinement was gradually increased.

5. Applied hand pressure to Nyota's rump, anus and vulva. Touching was firm and gentle; tickling was avoided in case it caused kicking which can easily spiral into full-blown flight response.

Usual stumbling block in training: every so often Nyota fails to enter the house: generally this occurs if Hope will not enter first. Nyota is deterred further if other giraffes linger around the doorway. Either way, the reluctance of other animals to move nearer to the house seems to increase the youngster's fear response. Failure to enter the crush itself is the next stumbling block. Nyota will freeze or back away if she hears loud noises or senses any movements around the crush. Giraffes are very sensitive to movements in their surroundings and a windy day will cause Nyota to become anxious, so her co-operation is substantially diminished. She will gallop and circle about the house. If she does not settle, the day's training is abandoned.

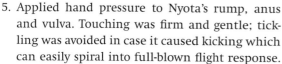

General processes in training

Clicker-training: no.

Use of restraints: the crush is used to keep Nyota still while her hind-quarters are touched.

Other equipment: none.

Aversive stimuli: an indoor gate sometimes used to encourage Nyota into the crush may be considered as a manoeuvring goad. The gate does not contact Nyota; however, by moving it toward her, she has less space behind her and prompted to move forward into the crush. Five months after her initial training, Nyota occasionally started entering the crush backwards. To reverse this behaviour, she was touched with a stick on her hind limb and given the command '*Stop*'; however, the success of this only lasted for a short period. Rather than use aversive stimuli, Nyota was allowed to enter backward as her behaviour was considered a protective mechanism in the same vein as 'facing the predator'.

Auditory cues: '*come on*' and '*stop*'. Calling and positive voice tones also encourage her to enter, though these certainly seem less effective than the food.

Visual cues: none.

Use of reinforcers

Rewards used: favourite foods: cattle cubes and carrots are most important for rewarding entry and behaviour. Familiar voices are also thought to reward her calmness and are used pre-emptively to alleviate stress.

Variation in the size of a reward: no, Nyota always receives the same quantity of food (one scoop of cattle cubes and carrots) each time the exercise is correctly carried out.

Variety of reward used: no, food is unconditionally rewarded for an entry and made available throughout her time in the crush. She is always released upon completion of the exercise.

Reinforcement schedule: continuous. Nyota is always rewarded, provided she completes her entry into the crush. If she halts prior to the crush, she will not be able to reach the food, hence there is no reward. Once handling has commenced carrots are administered before Nyota becomes stressed, to reinforce that staying calm is the correct response.

Use of rewards as lures or targets: food is hung to lure her into the crush at each session. Seeing Hope (after being separated) beyond the crush encourages Nyota to enter it. Therefore, in a sense, Hope is also used as a lure.

Highlights: the need to minimise injury as a result of flight responses is probably the reason why this response takes so long to counter-condition. Despite there being occasions when she was released because she was thrashing around, Nyota has gradually learned that nervous responses will not be followed by instant release. Over time her tendency to struggle has waned, so signs of distress are now rarely seen although time spent in the crush has increased significantly.

Case 35   African elephant *Loxodonta africana*

Training profile

Target behaviour:	holding the tail of the elephant in front
Name:	M'kali
Age:	8.5 years
Trainer's assessment of temperament:	loving, unassuming, independent
Trainer's name:	Andy Hayton

Background

African elephants are considered intractable, but that is something of a myth. As their keepers explain, comparing the two species of elephants is rather like comparing a thoroughbred racehorse to a Shetland pit pony. The African is flighty and reactive, while the Asian is steady and happily resigned to a working life. Despite this reputation, African elephants were put to considerable use as hauliers during the height of the Belgian Congo, and King Leopold set up a transiently successful elephant training school. As the young animals at Wiltshire's Longleat Safari Park illustrate, African elephants can be more biddable than many pet dogs.

The tailing-up is useful since it allows two keepers to control all the elephants in the herd. This means that they can be easily and safely moved as a group from their overnight stables to the safari park itself, and has welfare advantages because it generally increases the extent to which the animals can be exercised. The aim of the training is to get all members of the herd performing the same behaviour, on cue. Uniformed behaviours give the appearance of regimental order. The members of the herd are trained to hold a tail neatly just above the hair-line without any snaking up towards the buttocks of its owner. When we visited these animals they were seen without human company hundreds of yards away walking along in a tailed-up line. The public enjoy watching elephants performing this behaviour, perhaps because it reminds them of a scene from Disney's *Jungle Book*.

In early training, the elephant must be habituated to having its trunk handled. Two trainers were required to establish a pleasant association with trunk handling. Many horse owners could learn from this approach to the introduction of potentially aversive handling technique, for example, foot handling. While the trunk rope must be regarded by the elephant as a non-negotiable lead, it is important never to fight with an elephant wearing a trunk rope. Interestingly, keepers describe a placid response to this nose noose that seems remarkably similar to that seen in horses wearing a twitch, a traditional means of restraining horses that comprises a noose that is tightened over the top lip and known to activate endorphins.

Training programme

Before commencing training the animal must: be habituated to humans and the restraining chains which help to keep them in one place during early training. They must also have learned the commands '*no*' and '*ho*' (hold the current position). They must also have learned that '*good*' is reinforcing.

Changing the animal's motivation before a training session: it is usual to run through the established learned responses before training sessions

Number of training sessions per week 21
Duration of session 10 minutes
Time taken to learn 2 weeks

In the process of shaping the final behaviour, the trainer:
1. Applied a trunk rope with one handler on either side of M'kali and one of her hind legs chained. M'kali was fed simultaneously to counter-condition her response to this potentially alarming equipment.

ulate the trunk by hand to show M'kali the desired technique.

2. Issued the command '*give it to me*' as the rope was used to guide M'kali's trunk to the hand.

5. Trained M'kali to hold the linear-shaped object for longer periods using the '*ho*' command to maintain the desired behaviour.

3. Massaged M'kali's trunk aiming to persuade her to relax and give the trunk happily while waiting for the release command, '*OK*', which was combined with the release of the trunk.

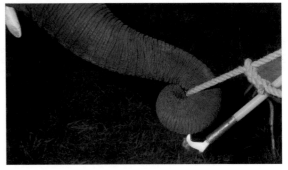

6. Moved from rigid objects to a rope that could be hung close by a real tail.

7. Shaped good tail-holding, as described above, in combination with the novel command '*tails*'.

8. Moved to real tails to link two elephants.

4. Trained M'kali to pick up a stick or rope by wrapping her trunk around it and issuing the '*pick it up*' command. The trainer had to manip-

9. Formed a chain of elephants and got them all working as consistently as one another.

Stumbling block: inconsistency on the part of keepers.

General processes in training

Clicker-training: no.

Use of restraints: chains are used initially to keep the elephant in place.

Other equipment: hook.

Aversive stimuli: yes, the elephants are encouraged to move away from the hook to which they must be sensitised. The hook is used on the skin, especially of the shoulders, to repel the elephants if they fail to respond to voice commands. Hook use by a good trainer is very subtle, rather like spur use by a sensitive dressage rider.

Auditory cues: 'give it to me' and 'tails'.

Visual cues: the main visual signal the elephants respond to is the hook. Because they keep a very close (some would say fearful) eye on where it is, it can be used to guide movements of both their trunk and their limbs.

Use of reinforcers

Rewards used: carrots and bananas.

Variation in the size of a reward: yes.

Variety of reward used: yes, by being vocally praised and scratched the elephants receive auditory and tactile reinforcement.

Reinforcement schedule: continuous until the response is established. Then few rewards are given because the behaviour is seen as an essential rather than a special skill. It may be that by tailing-up the elephants facilitate their own environmental enrichment and therefore the behaviour may become self-reinforcing.

Highlights: safety is particularly important when working with elephants. Trainers never attempt to work with their animals unless they are carrying a hook, and many elephants are not released from their chains in overnight stables until their handlers carrying hooks have reminded them of their conditioned responses to a number of verbal cues (see avoidance learning, Chapter 3).

Case 36
Black Canadian timber wolf *Canis lupus occidentalis*

Training profile
Target behaviour:	lying down when asked
Name:	Madadh (pronounced Maddie)
Age:	8 months
Trainer's assessment of temperament:	energetic, cautious, enthusiastic
Trainer's name:	Tony Haighway

Background

Founded in 1993, Wolf Watch UK is a project designed to promote wolf conservation. With facilities to house rescued wolves and take surpluses from zoological collections, Wolf Watch UK provides facilities for non-invasive research and supports creative conservation initiatives. Madadh came from Port Lympe Wildlife Park with her brother Kgosi as eight-day-old cubs. They are socialised to humans and are an excellent example of the adaptive nature of canidae if exposed to appropriate stimuli during the sensitive period for socialisation. Completely wild wolves (i.e. those that have not been socialised with humans during their sensitive period) are complete non-starters for this sort of training.

Clicker-training is being used to improve the communication between these representatives of wolfdom and humans. What Madadh is capable of being taught is limited more by the trainer than by her own ability to learn. Having said that, one can see why wolf training is not a popular pastime. Despite being well socialised, Madadh opportunistically snatches and grabs at the trainer's hands because they taste of the reward, and she may have learned that the trainer can be forced to relinquish food when accosted in this way. Com-pared to a juvenile domestic dog of the same size, Madadh shows little inhibition of biting. It is the first response she makes to access food and defend herself. Whereas in the past we may have seen this as an illustration of the archetypal greed of a wolf, we are now beginning to appreciate that it is simply one of the attributes that has allowed them to survive to the present day.

The differences between dog handling and wolf handling are striking. During our visit to the Wolf Watch UK Centre, in Shropshire, the animals for individual training were removed from their group individually. They were easily distracted by the intriguing possibilities of food being available elsewhere, i.e. other than from the trainer. They were keen to help themselves from the trainer's cache of food and responded far more rapidly to a howl than the sound of their names. Perhaps as a result of a disinclination to respond in what may be perceived as a submissive manner, males seem rather less keen than females to lie in front of a human.

Training programme

Before commencing training the animal must: be socialised with humans and be habituated to the training area. Clicker-training is instituted by exposing the wolf to five clicks in association with the arrival of free food (i.e. without having to perform any response). Before training sternal recumbency (i.e. lying down on the brisket), the wolf must be taught to sit. The word *'no'* must be understood as a signal to terminate any unwelcome behaviour.

Changing the animal's motivation before a training session: withholding the evening meal.

Number of training sessions per week 1 session every 2 weeks
Duration of session 10 minutes
Time taken to learn 3 sessions

In the process of shaping the final behaviour, the trainer:

1. Asked the wolf to sit and then withdrew the clicks (and any primary reinforcers) for sitting to present the wolf with a problem.

2. Waited for the wolf to lie on her chest and clicked for any approximations of the desired behaviour, e.g. looking at the ground or moving the forelegs forward. If the wolf failed to remain in one spot the trainer lured her to the ground with a small food reward.

3. Clicked when the desired behaviour emerged, and rewarded by throwing a morsel of food above the head. This terminated the behaviour and allowed the wolf to approach the problem afresh. By throwing the food the trainer extinguished the snatching response the wolf was tending to self-shape (to grab food out of the trainer's hand).

Stumbling blocks: distractions in the training area can lure the wolf away from the trainer, since being wild animals the promise of free food elsewhere and the excitement of a scenting and foraging mission is highly attractive.

General processes in training

Clicker-training: yes.

Use of restraints: none. While a collar and lead are optional in this process, they certainly help to keep the youngster focused on the quest for clicks rather than the distractions offered by other stimuli in the training area.

Other equipment: nil.

Aversive stimuli: none.

Auditory cues: 'down' is introduced once the final behaviour is offered regularly.

Visual cues: trainer's finger pointing to the ground.

Use of reinforcers

Rewards used: cheese, liver, raw chicken and even, on hot days, water.

Variation in the size of a reward: yes.

Variety of reward used: yes. A single training session can herald the arrival of a variety of food rewards.

Reinforcement schedule: Every time for the first four to five responses. After that a click is given alone for every improved response.

Ratio of variable reinforcement: food is given for every four clicks.

Use of rewards as lures or targets: occasionally, during initial stages, food may be used to lure the wolf's attention to the ground.

Highlights: being unable to concentrate on the task in hand seems to have provided a serious obstacle to learning in this case. During a single training session, Madadh successfully worked out where the food supply was being stashed and helped herself. Most domestic dogs would probably not have done this during training because they defer to humans for food.

Chapter 7

True working animals

Of all the species humans have recruited to help them at work, dogs are the most ubiquitous. Dogs are social problem solvers with a quality often referred to as 'a will to please'. Without consciously making the choice, humans have historically selected dogs with this trait. But how can a dog know how the alpha member of its pack is feeling? It is probably sufficient to note that as social animals, dogs are sensitive to social reinforcement (e.g. attention) and to socially aversive events, such as being ignored or isolated. They work well as members of a team not least because they watch those around for indications of a desired effect. The role of initiator in dog–human dyads is fascinating since it is usual to find the human dominating in successful working pairs. However, at the same time there has to be sufficient flexibility for the dog to demonstrate initiative, as in the case of working sheepdogs or indeed leadership in the case of guide dogs.

The dog's many impressive and exploitable qualities include a very superior sense of smell. The cases in this chapter include dogs that use their noses to detect explosives, truffles, termites and even the scent of broken grass for competitive tracking trials. Also, the domestic dog's characteristic drive to play can be redirected towards humans – both alive-and-kicking and dead – for police and search and rescue work. Then again there are the guide dogs that inspire us with their eagerness to behave in a manner that protects their owners from unseen harm. In Case 47 we question the role of altruism and consider more likely motivations for their work. Training guide dogs involves rewards for not doing certain things as well as for doing others. For example, the dog must be trained to cross a road only when there is no evident vehicle moving in his direction, regardless of prevailing instructions from the owner. If there is a friendly looking puppy on the other side of the road making enticing playful overtures in the direction of the guide dog, prior training has to have vanquished the innate motivation to play.

By focusing on particular traits employed by wild hunting canidae, humans have selected dogs that can be trained to demonstrate elements of a hunt as trackers, sniffers and attackers on our behalf. Along with horses, reindeer (Case 37) and oxen (Case 38), dogs of the

Fig. 7.1 Dog sled team raring to go.

appropriate breeds can be given the most basic of tasks i.e. haulage (Case 39). Here it seems to be the thrill of the chase that motivates members of a team to exert themselves. Spurring each other on as if hoping to be first to locate and apprehend their quarry, they will continue to run even with painfully abraded paws.

The stamina and speed of the so-called working breeds of dog predicated their suitability for use in warfare. It is interesting to note the effect of breed upon behaviour. Among the messenger dogs, lurchers, whippets and collies were highly regarded, while hounds were considered too independent, and poodles and terriers too frivolous.

Dogs of the right physique and temperament were especially useful in World War I when communication units relied on them to carry vital messages back from the front. While carrier pigeons were regularly shot out of the sky by the enemy and flew poorly in wet and foggy conditions, dogs were often favoured because they could slip through towns and villages unnoticed. Over a period of three to four weeks, from initially being released only three hundred yards away from their handlers and called back for morsels of food, the dogs were taught to return to the base camp from a distance of five miles (a form of place-training, see Chapter 2). They were then transported to the front and released with messages in panniers or attached to their collars. Their desire to return to the 'pack' is what later drove them to traverse hostile terrain. The major impediment to this process was the tendency of soldiers at the front to feed and make much of the dogs, so distracting the dogs from their handlers and rations at base camp.

Food is a tremendous motivator for all species and that is why the tastiest morsels are central to the training of one of our other traditional hunting companions, the falcons (see Case 40). A trained bird chooses to fly to, not from, its handler. A well-trained bird makes an immediate response to the presentation of the fist because it associates it initially with choice food items, then with tougher morsels and finally with the opportunity to launch a further hunting mission. While most falconers train their birds to fly to a fist to travel

Fig. 7.2 Hooded falcon.

the short distance from a kill, longer distance recalls are usually to a lure. In many fully trained birds, the drive to prey prevails over the need to eat. One of the characteristics of falconry is the use of a hood to 'switch the bird off'. A similar approach was used to pacify working cheetahs. It contains the animal's prey drive and helps to make hunting the default response when the hood is removed.

Police dogs used for explosive detection (see Case 41) are a good example of animals that have been trained to link work directly with food. The element of classical conditioning in this training programme is that the dog associates the explosive with food and this evokes salivation. This physiological response is replaced by a behavioural one when the dogs learn to sit to receive part of their daily food ration if the correct scents are concurrently present. Ultimately, these dogs do not get fed unless they have detected explosives and responded appropriately. At the end of the day, the dogs are given one large bone-shaped biscuit each to signal the end of the mission/exercise/hunt. The incorporation of this off-switch helps them relax after work.

Similarly, in her early training, Teela the competitive tracker dog (Case 42) learned that tracing the smell of broken vegetation was associated with her favourite delicacy, cheese. The same olfactory cues were later linked to Teela's toys that had been hidden. Using the innate skills that helped her wild ancestors track and harry prey, this dog eventually locates conditioned stimuli that provide her with fun not food.

Fig. 7.3 Foxhounds work as a pack not for food reinforcers but because they enjoy chasing prey.

It seems to be the excitement of hunting that keeps dogs keen when we give them jobs that employ analogues of predatory behaviour. Dogs looking for toys that have been associated with certain olfactory or visual stimuli seem to relish locating and securing the items that represent their prey. Toys are favoured as a reinforcer by the trainers of some working dogs who believe that feeding routines may interfere with work. Because police attack dogs can be required to work at any time of day, one can see how a food-driven dog would be of little use directly after it has received its evening meal. Therefore, as with the dogs tracking termites and truffles (Cases 43 and 44), it is considered preferable to motivate dogs for search-and-rescue work (Case 45) and man-work (Case 46) with resources (such as toys) that allow them to express their drive to hunt, kill and possess.

Dogs have an acute sense of smell and hearing and are fast at covering the ground, which makes them suitable for wilderness searches. Search and rescue dogs are trained to track airborne scent (rather than ground tracking) that can be up to one kilometre away, wind permitting. By contrast, police siege dogs respond to visual stimuli. The sight of a human running away holds the promise of rare fun indeed. It is fascinating to note that the same drive (to play) can be used to save and to attack humans. By manipulating their expectation we can modify animals' behaviour without necessarily inculcating traditional obedience.

Although guide dogs are trained in traditional obedience exercises which arguably elevate the human to an alpha status, this relationship has to change when the dog guides the human. When wearing the harness, the dog (such as Robyn, Case 47) must have the confidence to know when commands from the human are unhelpful and ignore them.

A similar sense of independence is required in the upper echelons of competitive sheepdog trials. For success in farm work and more especially in trials, sheepdogs first need to respond predictably, rapidly and consistently to approximately 60 commands. These are used to place the dogs in situations that present problems which they must solve using their own creative strategies.

By first teaching the dog verbal commands and then largely replacing these with whistled commands, Bruce (Case 48) ensures that he can communicate with Craig from a distance of more than 800 metres. Whistled commands replace verbal commands by becoming associated temporally. Commands are composed from a palette of seven basic cues: go clockwise, go anticlockwise, stop, go, come away from the sheep, look for more sheep and stand still.

By modulating his voice, the shepherd can develop more subtle signals such as 'proceed steadily'. Intonation in the voice of a shepherd can also be used to encourage a dog to speed up. Just as horses seem universally to respond to 'giddy-up' noises, so too dogs seem to respond innately to certain quickly emitted vocalisations. It is surprising that we do not make more use of our voice in handling horses. Indeed, despite its ancient origins in the raucous hurly burly of mounted combat, competitive dressage requires riders to remain silent and impart their signals to the horses using tactile stimuli alone.

Of all the working animals, the horse has been most highly prized for its speed. Its drive to run is admired and, in the best cases, sympathetically bridled. The fear response that naive horses show in the presence of humans means that we can easily train horses to move away from us in round-pens. Conversely, using the advance-retreat training system, we can shape them to approach the handler and stay close by assuming less predatory postures when they respond appropriately. This negatively reinforces the desired responses of so-called bonding or joining-up. A similar system of pressure-release training is used to train horses to move away from a leg or a whip. The sooner the horse responds to the pressure, the sooner it will be relieved of it. This is why the best riders are those who can apply instructions to their horses with the greatest subtlety. Having a 'good seat', in other words, being able to sit on a horse at all paces with a minimum of movement in the saddle, allows such a rider to change tactile contact with the horse only to issue instructions. Compare this to the novice rider who uses the reins to stay aboard, apparently oblivious to the pain this causes in the horse's mouth. By swinging his weight around in the saddle and gripping with his legs, the rider is sending a great deal of confusing information to the horse. The ability to habituate to such painful stimuli is what makes some poor wretches in riding schools regular cannon fodder for the complete beginner. The same rider on a Grand Prix dressage horse would send the animal off in all directions at a variety of speeds before falling off.

When riders lack the patience or education to treat their horses humanely, force is often used to tame the beast. Metal bits from the days of Roman charioteers were rimmed with spikes intended to cut into the cheeks. Dropped nosebands, designed to keep the mouth shut and reduce evasion of the bit were so tight that the nostrils of the horses were cut open to allow them to breathe. The perceived need to control horses rather than educate them has prompted the invention of more devices for restraint and control of horses than for the rest of the domestic species put together. Yet the safest horse to ride is a calm, relaxed horse. Modern training methods like those of the so-called horse whisperers use few devices, little or no coercion and an acute understanding of horse behaviour. The codes of body language used by the hunters and the hunted can be applied to the domestic horse with tremendous tact and subtlety. While traditionalists still use some force, albeit with increasing subtlety, the modern approach appreciates that the horse is innately so fearful of predation, he can be rewarded by a human simply looking in the opposite direction.

Of all the ways to modify innate equine responses, habituation is the most firmly established. This is illustrated by the case study on Star the police horse (Case 49). Mounted police perform a wide variety of duties, ranging from park and street patrols to parades, escorts, demonstrations and crowd control at special events. In all such functions, horses work in pairs, and are required to remain calm and steady regardless of often highly unusual surrounding circumstances. The conditions under which horses are expected to work are frequently stressful, in terms of loud noise and aggressive human behaviour. Their role in crowd management involves controlling the movement of pedestrians, dispersing riots or conducting arrests. Mounted police are highly efficient at working with crowds, with one horse regarded as being as effective as ten police officers on foot. This is partially due to their elevation, mobility, size and power, and is helped by the fact that the majority of city dwellers regard horses with an element of fear.

When confronted by tremendously aversive stimuli Star has been trained to remain still. Meanwhile the most subtle of stimuli make Peruano (the last animal in this chapter) rear up on his hind legs and paddle the air with dramatic effect. Peruano is a stunt horse and must be able to demonstrate stylised responses on cue. Despite the rarity of rearing in the equine behavioural repertoire, ignorant humans expect horses to rear up whenever they are frightened or even angry. As an animal working in film and television, Peruano can produce this behaviour even without his trainer in shot.

Case 37

Reindeer *Rangifer tarandus*

Training profile

Target behaviour:	pulling sled left and right on cue
Name:	Rando
Age:	7 years
Trainer's assessment of temperament:	territorial, greedy, willing
Trainer's name:	Steve Swinnerton

Background

While male rein-deer in rut are noto-riously incalcitrant and often downright dangerous, they are at most other times less skittish than females and there-fore more useful in public. In their natu-ral state, when they lose their antlers at the end of the rut, the males lose their precious place

in the pecking order allowing the females and pre-vious year's calves to get the best of what meagre lichenous pickings are available. This takes a great toll on the males' ultimate fitness and is the main reason for their rarely surviving longer than four years in the wild, compared with approximately 12 years in captivity.

With their responsiveness and pulling power derived from an innate ability to haul them-selves through snow, reindeer adapt from the free-ranging state to draught work with remarkably little fuss. When purchased from a wildlife park, Rando was unused to human contact but now he is completely habituated to large crowds at close quarters (especially during the run up to Christ-mas when his presence is in great demand at carol concerts, shopping arcades and fairy grot-tos). From a public liability perspective it is very important therefore that he should be quiet at all times and should listen to the handler's ver-bal instructions. Despite the seasonal nature of Rando's work meaning that he is laid off for six months at a time, his return to work is always uneventful.

Training programme

Before commencing training the animal must: have had few negative experiences with humans.

Changing the animal's motivation before a training session: nothing.

Number of training sessions per week 7
Duration of session 60 minutes
Time taken to learn 5 weeks

In the process of shaping the final behaviour, the trainer:

1. Halter broke the reindeer by tying him to a solid post in a very sturdy head collar with a strong rope. All of the flips and rolls of the ensuing struggle were difficult to ameliorate with food because, when a naive prey animal is trapped, its drive to flee prevails. After three or four hour-long training sessions, these animals have learned to stand quietly when tied up. They have by then also learned that uncomfortable pressure from the head collar is likely to con-tinue until they move in an appropriate direc-tion. This lesson was a prerequisite to learning to be led.

2. Led him around for the next week of training and introduced him to the commands *whoa* (stop), *walk on* (advance), *gee* (turn right) and *come around* (turn left) immediately before he

was forced to do any of those behaviours. The central task here was to associate the words with the behaviours while increasing the reindeer's confidence around humans. Simply trying to pull a reindeer that has put his brakes on is futile and therefore a second person was required

to push the animal forward when the *walk on* command was issued. Alternatively, a rope placed just above the hocks was an excellent means of propelling the animal forward.

3. Habituated the reindeer to wearing the harness while tied up. For a prey animal, being bombarded with tactile stimuli all over the body can be alarming, but being secured to a fixed point reduces the extent to which a response of arousal can turn into one of flight. It did not take the reindeer more than three sessions to learn that he was being neither pursued nor gobbled.

4. Began leading him around with the harness on. The sensation of moving with the harness on is rather different from when standing still, but this step in the habituation process took only another three days.

5. Tied ropes to the harness and an old car tyre to the ropes. Being heavy and offering plenty of friction, the tyre did not slide too easily and the reindeer learned to engage both his shoulder and hindquarter muscles to advance the load. When cornering, care had to be taken since the camber of the road surface was otherwise sufficient to tilt the tyre upright.

6. Spent the next two weeks consolidating the animal's responses before risking damage to the valuable sled.

7. Introduced the sled and worked the reindeer with it for at least a week before venturing out in public.

Stumbling blocks: Though more agreeable than oxen, reindeer can be very assertive – some would say stubborn. During early training, when they plant their feet into the ground, any amount of shouting *walk on* will prove useless. The use of force from behind is required to help the animal learn that when in harness, it does not make the rules.

General processes in training

Clicker-training: no.
Use of restraints: head collar.
Other equipment: harness and sled.
Aversive stimuli: we do not know how aversive it is for a prey animal to be placed in a compromising position such as a harness attached to a sled, with all locomotion controlled by a potential predator. However, judging from the speed with which habituation takes place it seems likely that these threats can be tolerated.
Auditory cues: gee, come around, whoa, walk on.
Visual cues: nil.

Use of reinforcers

Rewards used: nil. A big bucketful of commercial reindeer mix (similar to horse food) is given at the end of every training session regardless of the level of performance and cannot be viewed as reward. Pressure on the head collar is relieved when the animal turns in the correct direction. This is negative reinforcement.
Variation in the size of a reward: none.
Variety of reward used: none.
Reinforcement schedule: negative reinforcement.

Highlights: when using traditional training to teach animals to lead, the animals must become sensitised to pressure from elements of the head collar and must react to these cues with increasing responsiveness. By instrumental conditioning, the animal learns that to get relief from pressure (i.e. to achieve negative reinforcement), it must move in the appropriate direction.

Case 38

Training profile
Target behaviour: walking in a yoke
Name: Bill and Ben
Age: 3 years
Trainer's assessment of temperament: dominant, playful, bossy
Trainer's name: Kathy Pegg

Background

Far from being used daily for haulage duties as some inner city delivery horses still are, the oxen seen pulling carts in period dramas are used only periodically. The demands of working for hours on end on sets awash with expensive equipment and human actors are very different from those of the oxen originally driven as plough and cart pullers. Indeed the passivity of their responses to novel stimuli has to be better guaranteed than that of any of their agricultural forebears. The animals should be responsive to all verbal commands and, above all, dependably quiet. The main process in bullock training is habituation. They must also learn how to move as a pair, especially when turning corners. This bullock team can go for six months without training and yet become instantly biddable when their halters are in place.

In these days of hornless (or polled) breeds, Longhorns are particularly popular because they give an extra sense of authenticity to the piece. With their bowed horns, animals of this breed are easier to work side by side than those with straight horns. The traction comes from the withers via a yoke that is held in place by two loops of willow. A central ring on the yoke is attached to a pole that ensures a low slung connection to any load. The low set of the pole helps to keep the yoke in place.

Training programme

Before commencing training the animal must: nothing.

Changing the animal's motivation before a training session: nothing.

Number of training sessions per week   14
Duration of session   60 minutes
Time taken to learn   6 weeks

In the process of shaping the final behaviour, the trainer:

1. Spent one week halter breaking the animals by tying them up to a fixed point. They attempted to evade this aversive imposition, sometimes even hurling themselves onto the floor.

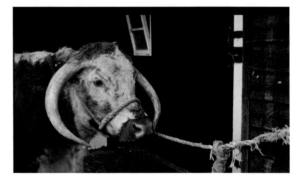

2. Led the animals around alone for the next week and began teaching the commands *walk on, gee, come around* (all of which were negatively reinforced with the use of a stick) and *whoa.*

3. Always tied up the oxen alongside each other to get them working as a team, with Bill on Ben's left. In the same way that some trotters are trained, the pair were secured to the rear end of a tractor that was gently advanced when the *walk on* command was given.

4. Yoked the team together for the next week's training sessions and again towed them around as a pair behind a tractor.

5. Introduced the central pole over the following seven days. While still bound to the tractor, the oxen habituated to the sound of the pole being dragged between them.

6. Attached a vehicle to the pole and habituated the oxen to the sensation of having their withers loaded.

7. Finally led the stock around without the tractor.

Stumbling blocks: oxen usually fight the halter and generally object to coercion until they learn that resistance is futile.

General processes in training

Clicker-training: no.

Use of restraints: halter.

Other equipment: the ropes that link the two animals before the introduction of the yoke and the central pole.

Aversive stimuli: a stick.

Auditory cues: gee, come around, whoa, walk on.

Visual cues: nil.

Use of reinforcers

Rewards used: nil. Concentrated food is given at the end of every training session regardless of the level of performance and cannot be viewed as reward. Pressure on the halter is relieved and tapping with the stick stops when the animals turn in the correct direction. This is negative reinforcement.

Variation in the size of a reward: none.

Variety of reward used: none.

Reinforcement schedule: negative reinforcement.

Highlights: there is no negotiation in this form of training. It is quicker than teaching to lead by hand because the animals have so few opportunities to ignore or learn incorrect responses to the four commands. The oxen must learn through negative reinforcement that they have to respond in a certain manner whenever they hear a command.

Case 39

Dog *Canis familiaris* (Siberian Husky)

Training profile

Target behaviour:	turning on command
Name:	Kodiak
Age:	2 years
Trainer's assessment of temperament:	enthusiastic, nutcase, anxious
Trainer's name:	Sue Hull

Background

Any dog can be trained to pull its owner to the park but it takes a lot of work to train one for sled competition (unless one is dealing with purpose bred sled dogs such as the Eskimo Dogs, Samoyeds and Malamutes). As with many working dogs, good practices in sled dog breeding have negated the need for rewards in this pursuit. Whilst other breeds that are physically similar to huskies may appear equipped for the job, they usually lack the enthusiasm to stay out in front and keep running. Any dog that has not been bred for draught purposes will struggle with this sort of training because it lacks the motivation to keep running. Sled dogs seem to find running self-reinforcing. They are trained first and foremost to get out in front of the handler (or musher). They are trained not to look at the handler. When you are haring along aboard a dog-drawn vehicle with an average speed of 20 mph, the last thing you want them to do is focus on you. Dogs that attempt to glance round in the direction from which they have come are the stuff of serious pile-ups.

Just as pet dogs love to go for a walk with all the thrills of investigating, meeting friends new and old, and staking claims to territory, so too do sled dogs love to run. This enthusiasm has to be nurtured, never bridled. That is why sled dogs should never be restrained by their collars once they are in harness. Racing dogs are not trained in the traditional obedience-dog sense. Rather like a racing greyhound, if you ask a sled dog to *sit*, the best response you can hope for is a clueless glance as the order is interpreted as nothing more than a distraction.

Since there are no reins, the team must be turned left or right, as part of a team, in response to voice commands. This is, strictly speaking, something that only lead dogs have to master. However, swapping the members of a team is facilitated by having all dogs trained in this way. Lead dogs are not necessarily the alpha in the dominance hierarchy within a social group of working dogs, but they are certainly the fastest and most willing. They are the mushers' direct line of communication to the team, which can have up to 20 members. Members of a large team can learn by cultural transmission, but dogs that have been individually tutored by humans are thought to be more reliable.

With pups, the turns can be taught by throwing toys around a corner off a corridor. However, this is not a practice that Sue, the trainer in this case, adheres to throughout the dogs' lives because, contrary to the goal of getting the dogs to keeping running on, it teaches them to stop and search for an article immediately round most corners.

The voice is the main stimulant of extra effort. Once it has become associated with an exciting portion of a training run, a key command can be used to generate excitement during races. The sight of another team is one of the most exciting stimuli for sled dogs. It is almost as if two teams in close proximity begin to compete for an unseen goal.

By responding correctly the dogs get more reward – tearing round the countryside at speed. After turning, the dogs are faced with a wealth of more exciting stimuli on a new track and the chance of something more stimulating than that they have just left behind. Dogs soon learn to prefer turns to straights. Because the team needs to race round corners and change direction at speeds of up to 30 mph, it is important that the dogs respond confidently and without hesitation. Generally the dogs make better turns at higher speeds.

Note: Kodiak is described as anxious because he is the least dominant member of the team.

Training programme

Before commencing training the animals must: have learned they will not get punished for pulling and so, effectively that they should stay out in front of the handler.

Changing the animal's motivation before a training session: putting the harness on gets the dogs very excited and increases their motivation to run in or out of a team.

Number of training sessions per week 2
Duration of session   15 minutes
Time taken to learn   3 months

Note: Since dogs work as part of a team with a mixture of experience, it is often difficult to determine how much each team member is contributing in a turning response. So, the extent to which an individual dog's training is often obscured until a change of lead dog exposes the reliance other team members have had on him or her.

In the process of shaping the final behaviour, the trainer:

1. Planned the route she would take for training runs. Long straight forestry tracks less than ideal as they include few turns. The turns available in a training area lend considerable advantage to serious competitors and are pivotal in the learning process.

2. Took the dog out alone on a harness and lead.
3. Clipped the lead to a waist belt and jogged behind the dog as it headed out in front. Pulling the handler simulates the pulling of a vehicle. Increasing fitness in the dog over time can mean that the human is less able to keep up with the team and there can be a resultant loss of control.

4. Let the dog investigate deflections in the track.

5. Gave the verbal command ('gee' or 'haw') the moment the dog changed direction.
6. Praised the dog and hoped that another animal (such as a rabbit) would appear around the corner to reward the dog. Eventually the command evolved to mean 'look for a turn to the left or right'.

Stumbling blocks:
1. Shortage of terrain with plenty of turns.

2. Lead dogs in a team can begin to behave as the alpha (and take charge of the pack activities rather than waiting for cues from the musher) or the team as a whole learns to ignore signals. There are few ways of penalising the team when it becomes autonomous.
3. The dogs can become familiar with the training track and so take those turns beautifully without learning to respond to the voice.

General processes in training

Clicker-training: no.
Use of restraints: collars attached to neck-lines are used to stop the dogs pulling out sidewards, the padded nylon harnesses are attached to the vehicle to provide traction.
Other equipment: toys.
Aversive stimuli: some mushers use noisemakers to send the dogs forward, but these are banned in the UK.
Auditory cues: not applicable, continuous. 'haw' – turn left, 'straight on' – straight on, 'whoa' – slow down, 'hike' – speed up.
Visual cues: nil. The dogs cannot see the musher nor are they encouraged to look round, so hand signals are redundant.

Use of reinforcers

Rewards used: three types of reinforcers are used:

A. Self-rewarding thrill of the chase.
B. Naturally occurring stimuli that emerge unexpectedly once dogs have turned a corner. The biggest reward for these dogs is close contact with prey species.
C. Engineered rewards such as toys thrown around corners to encourage turning in a given direction.

Variation in the size of a reward: yes, especially B rewards such as deer or rabbits.

Variety of reward used: yes, A and B rewards vary with the terrain, weather conditions and the proximity of prey species.
Reinforcement schedule: the availability of rewards varies with the rewards themselves:

A – terrain dependent
B – dependent on chance
C – dependent on time available to spend on training of juveniles.
Ratio of variable reinforcement:
A – limited by physiological fatigue
B – dependent on chance
C – not applicable, continuous.

Use of rewards as lures or targets: toys are used when the puppies are being trained to obey the turning commands.

Highlights: habituation to the harness and hitching up to the vehicle becomes a reliable prelude to a pack outing and certainly gets the dogs in the mood for work by classical conditioning. Similarly, the *post hoc* introduction of commands after the dogs have started to turn or are committed to a turn is perhaps an example of what we have dubbed *reinforcement-to-command transfer* (see Introduction to Case Studies).

Case 40

Falcon *Falco peregrinus x F. novaeseelandiae* (Peregrine x New Zealand Falcon)

Training profile

Target behaviour:	fly to the fist
Name:	Dynamite
Age:	12 months
Trainer's assessment of temperament:	sociable, juvenile, excitable
Trainer's name:	Nick Fox

Background

Just as sheepdog trainers must be able to predict the behaviour of both sheep and dogs, so do falconers have to know how both their birds and the birds' quarry will react to stimuli. It is the falconer's job to launch his bird only at quarry that can be caught with a degree of effort and skill. If the quarry escape too often, the falcon will lose interest, its rewards will be too infrequent and the hunting response will be extinguished. If the quarry is too easily caught, not only does this eliminate the sporting component of the activity, but also the bird will learn to expect easy kills.

Shaping the flight to the fist is achieved by gradual increments that depend on the wildness of the bird. A particularly cautious bird might take two days' worth of training sessions to fly to the fist, while another can be flying to not just the fist but a lure in 20 minutes. More important to a falconer than the distance over which the bird is learning is the latency with which it leaves the perch. This can be shaped once the bird is habituated to the glove, the trainer and the training area, and therefore is able to focus exclusively on the signal. The fist comes to represent quarry that allows itself to be caught. An immediate response to the presentation of the signal (the garnished fist i.e. the glove holding meat) is desirable because, if the bird decides when it is going to respond, then the falconer has a less co-operative hunting companion and, to an extent, has lost control.

The aim is to make the airborne element of the behaviour an analogue of the innate response the bird might make to the appearance of a rabbit. The bird should land on the fist with speed and confidence. It is important to present the signal for no more than five seconds. If the bird does not respond, the signal is removed and the window of opportunity closed. There is a falconer's expression that many a pet dog owner could learn from: 'never call in vain', meaning that one should never teach the bird not to come. This can be achieved by ensuring that the bird is always correctly prepared for exposure to the signal and that it learns to respond quickly and almost as a reflex.

Wild birds are rather troublesome candidates for training because they can simply fly away as soon as they leave the post for the first time and their stress response to human contact impedes learning. The chief impediment to learning in wild-caught birds especially is stress. This can only be remedied by habituation. The traditional approach adopted by ancient falconers was to flood, say, a sparrowhawk by placing it in a stocking with its head popping out, placing it on the mantelpiece and inviting their friends round for a party or 'waking' (keeping the bird awake for 48 hours). It is, of course, more humane to rear the birds of choice and expose them to stimuli more gradually. Captive-bred parent-reared hawks can be habituated to humans, dogs and all of the paraphernalia of a busy training centre by simply keeping them near all of the activity.

Training programme

Before commencing training the animal must: be able to stop on command once it has launched into flight; be habituated to the glove and the training area and must associate the fist with feeding and perching.

Changing the animal's motivation before a training session: the preparation of the bird before training in this way includes monitoring its weight and its appetite. Fat falcons should not be flown. The bird's stress responses must be monitored since these can have a deleterious effect on learning.

Number of training sessions per week 5
Duration of session 20 minutes
Time taken to learn 5 days

In the process of shaping the final behaviour, the trainer:
1. Took the bird to the training area with a line tied to its legs. Selected a glove (the same colour and indeed the same trainer must be used for most of the subsequent training steps). Carried the bird to the training area on the fist and fed it a bechin (small piece of meat) from the fist.

2. Placed the bird on a fence post at about the same height as the fist (birds prefer to fly horizontally or slightly upwards) as soon as it had finished feeding.
3. Presented the fist, holding a larger piece of meat, at a distance of six inches or so from the post. The meat was held so that it could not simply be reached for and grabbed. Proper feeding work on the meat involved the bird using its feet and therefore

the bird had to travel onto the fist to forage effectively. By grasping the morsel in the fist the trainer could hide it after the bird had engaged in some feeding activity. This kept the bird interested and prevented satiation with food. The disappearance of the food into the fist increased the bird's interest in the fist.

4. Increased the distance flown.

5. Enhanced the visual signal by tapping the meat with the free hand. By this stage, the fist should represent, to the bird, a prey item that allows itself to be caught.

6. Introduced the whistle or call to complement the visual signal and facilitate recalling the bird from a wooded area.
7. Introduced a variable ratio.
8. Removed the reward completely so that the fist represented a bridge for the start of the next hunting opportunity.
9. Generalised the bird's response to the gloves, their colour, the trainers and the training areas.

Stumbling blocks: novice birds can become fearful of taking the leap off the post if they have yet to accomplish an effective braking system. Nick speaks of the panic he can detect in the faces of some birds when they cannot find the brakes and he feels this is likely to account (at least in part) for reticence to take off or reluctance to fly fast. Frustration manifests itself with intention tremors and multiple attempts to take off.

General processes in training

Clicker-training: no.

Use of restraints: jesses (thongs tied to the birds' legs), creance (the line) and the walls (if training takes place indoors).

Other equipment: glove and post.

Aversive stimuli: none.

Auditory cues: whistle or a call.

Visual cues: the fist (garnished or otherwise).

Use of reinforcers

Rewards used: food, company (but less than in a social falcon species such as Harris hawks) and the fist as a perch from which to launch further hunting forays. Ultimately the biggest reward for a working bird such as Dynamite should be catching her own food in the form of a rabbit.

Variation in the size of a reward: yes, a reward gradient is used and the tougher offerings make the bird commit to engaging on the fist with its feet.

Variety of reward used: yes.

Reinforcement schedule: continuous reinforcement is used until the flying response is prompt and confident.

Ratio of variable reinforcement: from continuous down to zero when the fist becomes a prerequisite to further hunting.

Use of rewards as lures or targets: food in the fist is the key to early training.

Highlights: To build up the desired associations, birds are first fed easily consumed, tempting morsels of food from the fist. As time goes by, the food offered from the fist becomes tougher, involving more sinew than muscle, to encourage the bird to use its talons and beak in innate foraging activity and increase the time associated with getting rewards from the fist.

Case 41   Dog *Canis familiaris* (Labrador retriever)

Training profile

Target behaviour:	detecting explosives
Name:	Yeller and Oleo
Age:	2.5 years
Trainer's assessment of temperament:	Yeller: hard working, old-fashioned, reliable
	Oleo: affectionate, defensive, tough
Trainer's name:	Janet Pengelly (Yeller)
	Lara Raymond (Oleo)

Background

Prior to the Sydney Olympics, NSW police 'sniffer dog' trainers participated in an American programme to teach them food reward-based training methods. American Labradors were provided for these trainers, which were subsequently brought back to Australia. The two dogs described in this case study, Yeller and Oleo, were sourced from the United States as part of this programme. In the USA, the police 'sniffer dogs' are all guide dogs that have been deemed unsuitable because, for example, they were too frantic or energetic.

In Australia, the Police Service (Dog Unit) has an agreement with the Customs Service, which breed their own Labrador retrievers. Labradors are currently the favoured breed of dog for explosive detection. They are chosen because of their notorious food drive. Despite extraneous noise that other dogs may find very distracting, most Labradors remain very interested in food even just after their evening meal. Skittish, overly excitable

dogs and those unfocused on food are undesirable because they are easily distracted. Similarly, the police avoid taking on dogs that just want to sniff, play or fight with other dogs. Particularly unattractive dogs are also considered undesirable (due to a possibly negative public reaction). The most important step in the selection process identifies animals that are most highly driven by food. The Customs Service is particularly interested in breeding dogs with high retrieval and energy levels, hence a high food drive. Once it makes its selection from these litters, the Police Service then can make its selection. The Dog Units also obtain 'unfit' Labradors from the Guide Dog Association. If the dogs (whether donated or selected) are young, or if there is no training programme about to begin (they occur only every six months), the dogs are placed in a puppy-walking programme. This involves members of the public who 'foster' the dogs for a period of time, and expose the dogs to a family

Fig. 7.3 Photograph of the tins used in the training of police dogs for drug and explosive detection.

environment, shopping centres, other dogs, people and places etc. To ensure that the dogs are indeed well socialised, and exposed to a wide variety of experiences, the dogs are rotated between puppy walkers – generally every three months.

Depending on their age and the availability of training programmes, the dogs may stay in the puppy-walk programme for as little as a month, or for as long as a year. Further habituation to everyday stimuli occurs in the initial six week period of training.

To be useful as explosive detectors the dogs must identify a thumbnail-sized sample with the odour of a substance used in explosives, which is placed inside two tins, each with perforated lids, which are then placed into a larger, open tin (see Fig. 7.6). Well-educated dogs salivate clearly when they find explosives.

Explosive in a small sniffer can (about the size of shoe polish tin) with holes in the lid is pre-sented to the dog. When the dog makes an audible inhalation, immediate verbal praise is given and a food reward is offered on top of or adjacent to the tin. The tin is moved over the trainer's body to generalise the response. The passive response of sitting as an operant response in the presence of the stimulus is then trained by pushing down on the dog's rump while the dog is feeding after a correct sniff. Then the trainer starts holding the tin away from the body, placing it on walls and in boxes and always quickly rewarding the passive (sit) response. During this phase the trainer has to keep changing hands and placing the tin at different heights and positions to avoid the learning becoming context specific, i.e. to ensure that the dog is sniffing the tin not just the location. The next step is to place the tin on the ground and reward the dog for the correct response. Over the ensuing months, the trainer must move the tin to an enormous variety of locations.

Basic training takes four months. This comprises six weeks of habituation and shaping (i.e. associating the explosives with food), then ten weeks' follow-up teaching the dog increasing levels of discrimination. Regular assessments are performed every six weeks. Ongoing assessment and the introduction of new scents, should any new explosive become available, occur every six months.

When the dog has recognised the scent and distinguished it from any similar, innocuous accompanying odours (preferably using audible, deep sniffs), it must communicate its recognition to its handler with a very rapid change in behaviour – a sit. The sniffs must be emphatic because training sessions are measured in terms of the number of sniffs early in training: an average of approximately 1,200 a week (approximately 130–50 per day). To maintain a trained dog, generally about 200 sniffs a week are sufficient. At least one training session is required per day to feed the dog, and the amount of food per reward depends on how many targets are used. The dogs must learn to discriminate between explosives and distracters, but discrimination between explosives is not necessary.

'The wheel' is a rotatable device (so dogs do not just learn position or location) with four arms, each of which bears a can. Usually there is one hot can (a can containing traces of explosive) while the remainder are cold (empty). However, if only exposed to this template, dogs will often learn to do three sniffs and then just stop at the fourth. To keep dogs attentive and to overcome this element of anticipation, there are sometimes negative wheels (with no hots) and double hot wheels with two hot cans. Different wheels have different distracters and explosives in them.

Training programme

Before commencing training the animal must: simply be socialised and habituated to a wide variety of environments and have at least an average food drive.

Changing the animal's motivation before a training session: the dogs are brought out of their pens and allowed to have a run around. When they see the training room (where the wheels are) they learn what to expect and get excited. Seeing the wheel and hearing the command '*seek*' is the trigger to start work. Dogs are fed only as a reward to prevent any laziness or lack of keenness to work. This also avoids the dog learning that even if it does not work, it will still be fed. So if a dog has not worked all day, it must be worked, for example on the wheels, to get its ration of food. Once a dog's optimal ration of food has been calculated (on the basis of its shoulder height), it is adhered to stringently, and each handler rewards the dog from this daily ration. The ration keeps the dogs lean, keen and in very good working condition.

Number of training sessions per week   Up to 84
Duration of session   15 minutes
Time taken to learn   16 weeks

In the process of shaping the final behaviour, the trainer:
1. Put the sniffer can on the bottom of an upturned 'quart' tin (about the size of a 200 g coffee tin) into which the dog had to put its nose to perform a correct sniff. Empty tins were added to train the dog to discriminate between hot and cold cans.
2. Used distracters once the dog was effectively identifying all hot tins. The trainers keep a cupboard full of all the foods that act as inviting distracters including peanut butter, confectionery and chocolate. They also use household

products such as cassette tapes, rubber bands and adhesives since these have similar scents to the phenylurethane found in explosives.

3. Put the lidded quart tin inside a 'gallon tin' (like a very large coffee tin). It is this set up that is used on 'the wheel'.

4. Introduced the dog to the training wall which was primed with sniffer cans, hot and cold. The

purpose of holding the tin in the initial stages of training becomes apparent because despite the absence of the tin in the trainer's hand, the dog learns to follow the hand. At 'the wall', five or six small sniffer tins are placed behind slits in the wood of the screen. For assessment by external personnel, a tiny piece of tape on the wall indicates the presence of hot cans (those containing explosive).

5. Taught the dogs to sit and resist being led away from a hot can to receive their reward. Training continues with changing the working environment of the dog, e.g. putting the sniffer cans in boxes, bags, in bushes, long grass etc.; and also, in busier environments with more people, other dogs, more noise etc.

Stumbling blocks:

Handler error: not being clear with the hand signals, or the rewards (e.g. not rewarding quickly enough), or inadvertently cueing the dogs with the Clever Hans effect, for example, by a change in voice or body language. For this reason, eye contact is avoided, and the lead is kept as slack as possible. Interestingly, the trainers note the effect of handler demeanour on the dogs and their work. Happy handlers seem to get more accurate responses from their dogs.

External distractions: are important especially early in the training programme, e.g. noise, people, other animals. Habituation to such distracters under controlled conditions is an important facet of training.

Contamination of cans: is a problem that underlines the sensitivity of the dog's olfaction. For example, handling a hot one before a cold one can transfer hot scent to it. The problem here is that the dog sits in response to the contamination on the cold can and gets confused by not being rewarded.

Contamination of the equipment: can occur if, for example, another dog has done the course previously. Pieces of food may have landed unnoticed in the gallon tin, or there may be traces of saliva on the equipment, causing the dog to identify that instead of the explosive.

General processes in training

Clicker-training: no.

Use of restraints: the dogs wear only cloth choker collars – not chains. Dogs are checked extremely rarely, only when voice aids are insufficient and to give a stimulus that brings back the dog's attention.

Other equipment: training wheel, wall, tins, distracters and lead.

Aversive stimuli: none.

Auditory cues: seek.

Visual cues: the dog tends to follow its handler's hand.

Use of reinforcers

Rewards used: food and praise. When they hit the jackpot by responding with accuracy and conviction, the dogs receive a good handful of food and especially high praise.

Variation in the size of a reward: usually the response is standard. Only if the response is exceptional or there is a limited time available for training would the reward be noticeably bigger.

Variety of reward used: no.

Reinforcement schedule: continuous.

Highlights: this training protocol exemplifies the combined use of classical and instrumental conditioning followed by discrimination training. Classical associations are built between the smell of explosives (conditioned stimulus) and food (unconditioned stimulus) producing salivation (unconditioned response) while the passive sitting response and the strangely emphatic inhalations are developed as a result of instrumental conditioning (see Chapter 2).

Case 42   Dog *Canis familiaris* (Working sheepdog)

Training profile

Target behaviour:	tracking a scent
Name:	Teela
Age:	6 years
Trainer's assessment of temperament:	gentle, keen, determined
Trainer's name:	Moira Rogerson

Background

For centuries, tracking dogs have been trained to find people by scent. Most working breeds can learn to do this, especially those that have not been selected to hunt with their vision (e.g. greyhounds are particularly unsuited to train for this exercise). The images that many of us conjure up when these animals are mentioned are largely derived from films and so include either baying Baskervillian bloodhounds or rabid Dobermanns or canine heroes such as Lassie who intuitively know which human is being sought without so much as a whiff of his or her casually discarded undergarment. While many myths seem to have evolved around the learning processes in these dogs, the training process used for tracking dog competitions is elegant in its simplicity.

Teela, the subject of the current case study, holds an 'Excellent' title in working dog trials as a companion dog, a utility dog, a working dog and a patrol dog, but her forte is as a tracking dog. She tracks with confidence, commitment and precision especially when the track changes direction and sometimes gives the impression of travelling on tramlines. In competitions she must find three dropped items while tracking a human scent that is at least three hours old and includes up to 25 changes in direction. Novices are sometimes baffled because they cannot understand how a dog can track a human without prior exposure to that person's scent. The secret is that the dogs are primarily tracking the trail of broken vegetation.

Training can be broken down into two components: training to follow a trail, and training to find objects on the trail and sit beside them.

Training programme

Before commencing training the animal must: have at least an average food drive.

Changing the animal's motivation before a training session: the dog is shown the food, toys and harness. In pups, an association is built with the tracking harness and line (see photographs) by introducing these items of equipment at 3.5 months of age. For older dogs commencing their training in this skill, the harness can be introduced from the beginning.

Number of training sessions per week 7 for two weeks then two per week–ongoing
Duration of session 10 minutes
Time taken to learn 6 months

In the process of training to follow a trail, the trainer:
1. Planted a starting pole in the ground that acts as a consistent cue for the dog to begin tracking.
2. Placed tiny pieces of food a foot or so apart making sure that an assistant shuffled from one spot to the next to link the food items. This technique, known as *scrubbing*, breaks the vegetation under foot and releases volatile plant aromas, which become associated with the promise of rewards ahead.

3. Laid freshly scrubbed tracks in novel arenas but always using the pole as a constant feature.
4. Very gradually placed the items of food further apart while simultaneously increasing their value to maintain motivation.
5. Introduced simple right angle changes of direction in the track.

6. Increased the length of the track.

7. Used tracks of increasing age.
8. Used tracks with increasing numbers of turns.
9. Used tracks laid prior to rain.
10. Used tracks with more and more distracters.

In the process of training to find objects on the trail and sit beside them, the trainer:

11. Used food targets only in early training. The shaping of the correct response to dropped items on the track develops from there.
12. Placed the food on top of small containers such as film cases.
13. Placed the food underneath these characteristic containers.
14. Placed the food inside these characteristic containers.

15. Taught the dog to sit before receiving rewards. This teaches the dog that the containers are prized targets. *Fetch* games are played with them once the dog has sat.
16. Replaced the containers with novel items and used these for *fetch* games as long as the dog is happy to have them in her mouth.
17. Habituated dog to retrieve metal objects.

Stumbling blocks: most commonly the dogs fail to stop at the dropped items because they want instead to continue tracking. In later training the main stumbling block is that dogs learn to predict the placement of reinforcers and this can lead to them making mistakes so the key is to place articles at unpredictable distances apart.

General processes in training

Clicker-training: no.

Use of restraints: nil. The dog is encouraged to move out in front of the handler and become self-reliant and confident in his/her choice of direction.

Other equipment: harness, line and pole.

Aversive stimuli: none.

Auditory cues: nil.

Visual cues: the pole is a visual cue to start tracking.

Use of reinforcers

Rewards used: the track itself rapidly becomes a secondary reinforcer because it leads to the primary reinforcers (food and toys).

Variation in the size of a reward: yes, a reward gradient is used so that better reinforcers (jackpots) are placed towards the end of the track to maintain levels of motivation in subsequent work.

Variety of reward used: yes, unusual toys are used to keep dogs excited. As soon as the dog responds optimally to novel articles, it pays to replace the article with a favourite toy and institute play with that as a reliable reinforcer.

Reinforcement schedule: the track is continuously reinforcing. Food and toys begin as being very predictable and then becomes less so, i.e. more variable.

Use of rewards as lures or targets: yes. The essence of this training is that the track brings its own rewards.

Highlights: by being shown the food or toys, dogs being trained to track are given a concept of what it is they are tracking. Previously sighting a target helps the dogs during training, but this contingency is not available during competition. Training is designed to make the tracking behaviour context specific (see Chapter 2). In tracking competitions, the trainer must hope that all the contextual cues (including the harness, the start pole and the passivity of the trainer who follows but does not interfere as she might usually do on a regular walk) will encourage the dog to assume that valuable resources are available for collection.

Case 43 — Dog *Canis familiaris* (English Cocker Spaniel)

Training profile

Target behaviour:	termite detection signalled by scrabbling
Name:	Charlie
Age:	3.5 years
Trainer's assessment of temperament:	vibrant, enthusiastic, affectionate
Trainer's name:	Cathy McCauliffe

Background

Cocker Spaniels are favoured for termite detection work because their size allows them to fit under the floorboards and inside the ceilings of houses. Because they weigh only approximately 15 kg, they can walk on the plasterboard of ceilings without breaking them. Because they are erratic workers, Beagles or Jack Russells are least suitable for training for this behaviour. Their general wilfulness and inability to focus on human driven tasks when off the lead seem to cause them to miss sections of a wall where termites are located.

Termite detection by dogs is unusual, but actually more reliable than detection by humans who rely on tapping the walls and floors of dwellings in order to discern the different sounds that accompany termite damage. Cathy looks for a strong focused positive response, such as scratching, ripping, barking at the area/object, where the termites are located. It is important that termite detection dogs are able to discriminate between the scent of damp timber and termite-ridden timber. When timber gets damp it grows fungi, which release pheromones, and consequently attract termites. If the dogs actively respond to damp tim-ber, they may not always be successful locating the termites. The smell of damp wood is therefore taught through scent discrimination training. Because the dogs are rewarded only when they smell termites, the damp timber becomes just part of the overall background odour. Thus, the smell of timber by itself causes an 'interest' but not a strong 'indication'.

With daily training, it takes less than three weeks to teach the active response and to build up the desire for retrieval. The PVC pipe filled with termites becomes the recognised toy. Games of throw and retrieval are played so that the dogs become excited when they see the pipe. Search patterns are then taught over the next ten weeks using different training strategies that allow the dog to find the odour by itself without the aid of the trainer. The dog therefore learns work by looking for its own reward. The dog is rewarded with play when the termites are located by scent. The whole desire for work therefore becomes the opportunity to play with the toy.

Training programme

Before commencing training the animal must: be trained to search for objects following the command *seek*.

Changing the animal's motivation before a training session: prior to the scent discrimination exercises involving the termite containers, the dogs are given a few minutes to play with the toy and retrieve it. When the toy is placed in the designated container, the dogs are encouraged to play with the toy.

Number of training sessions per week 14 reducing to 7

Duration of session 5 minutes or more depending on the dog

Time taken to learn 2 weeks

Note: initial three weeks of training two sessions per day. This drops to once daily until completion of the 12-week training schedule. The length of each session depends on the dog. Training should stop when the dog has reached the peak of its 'training plateau'. An effective five-minute training session is more productive than a 20-minute training session that may cause the dog to lose interest.

In the process of shaping the final behaviour, the trainer:

1. Trained the dog to associate the scent of termites with a toy by placing a small number of them inside a hollow PVC pipe with porous ends.

2. Hid the toy in a close, clean site and then encouraged Charlie to *seek*. Verbal praise encouraged the dog to scrabble and whine at a positive site to deliver a clear indication of the presence of termites. Whining helps handlers locate dogs when they make a find while working out of sight, e.g. under floorboards.

3. Added other distractive odours such as food and damp timber.
4. Asked a third party to hide the toy while the trainer pretended to hide the toy in several other areas to break down any dependence that may have developed on cues from the trainer.
5. Trained the dog in an old and rather distressed scout camp so that he could familiarise himself with the peculiarities of houses (he is a kennelled dog).

Stumbling blocks: the trainer may believe that the dog knows a given exercise and jump ahead, thereby confusing the dog. On the other hand, the dog may get bored and lose interest if the exercise is repeated too many times. Each exercise must have strong foundations on which the dog can build.

General processes in training

Clicker-training: no.

Use of restraints: flat collars – with no choking capacity.

Other equipment: harness – helps the dog to discern between general interaction with the owners and work.

Aversive stimuli: the word 'no' used to redirect the dog when it is conducting an obviously unhelpful search such as through a concrete portion of a building.

Auditory cues: seek.

Visual cues: the dog follows the hand in the initial stages of training but then becomes self-directed.

Use of reinforcers

Rewards used: apart from the PVC tube toy with termites in it, praise and play are the only rewards used. Praise is always used and the toy is always the same. Food is used for puppies and adult dogs, but this is phased out. Retrieval and tug-of-war with the toy is the main reward driving the dogs. Once they start working, the Cocker Spaniels usually favour the toys over and above food.

Variation in the size of a reward: the amount or type of play may vary depending on each dog's response. Praise is given at the completion of each task. However, the frequency of the 'play' reward is gradually reduced to encourage the dog to work harder in the hope that its next 'hit' will merit some play interaction with the handler.

Variety of reward used: Play and praise are both used for adult dogs.

Reinforcement schedule: The frequency of the 'play' reward is reduced after three days of training to once every time there are three successful hits. Praise, on the other hand, is used continuously.

Use of rewards as lures or targets: in the initial stages of training rewards are used as targets and lures all the time, so that the dog has a reason to follow the command. The investigation sites in this trained behaviour are the walls. When the dog locates the termite odour it gives an active response (scrabbling, pawing and whining) to that area.

Highlights: rewards are always given for the correct response, but targets are scattered and randomised in training otherwise the dog may stop if it fails to hit after a certain period of time. Because in working contexts, the time taken to find termites is unpredictable, the timing of rewards in training is varied, so the dog will keep working until a reward is given. So the dog is on a variable interval reinforcement schedule (see Chapter 2).

Case 44
Dog *Canis familiaris* (Border Collie)

Training profile

Target behaviour:	detecting truffles
Name:	Bobby
Age:	9 years
Trainer's assessment of temperament:	enthusiastic, playful, keen
Trainer's name:	Steve Austin

Background

Recently truffles, those rare and treasured lumps of fungoid material, have been developed as a farmed product in the island state of Tasmania. Under special conditions that involve the planting of oak and hazelnut trees a set distance apart, Australian truffles are being cultivated with some success. Finding the truffles depends on dogs like Bobby. Bobby sniffs around a designated site when encouraged to by his handler, Steve Austin, one of Australia's foremost animal trainers.

Bobby, who is also an accomplished narcotic detector, can spend a day in the paddocks, working with his fellow truffle dogs. With good predictions and a great deal of enthusiasm from their trainer, they can unearth tens of thousands of dollars worth of delicacy. Beyond the treasure troving aspect of this behaviour, novice observers are also impressed by the dog's ability to detect the faintest scent of truffle.

The main task is to discriminate between truffle odours and the full gamut of distracters. Given all the distracters dogs may encounter (such as the scent of interesting wild animals and their droppings), accurately hitting the correct sites with truffles set 12 inches below the surface is no mean feat. Non-target desensitisation is an important part of the overall training process. Non-targets include bandicoot, wallaby, deer and quail droppings that are placed around the training ground. Dogs are trained not to respond to non-targets by extinction training, i.e. no reward is given for a response to a non-target. No reprimand is used, because this may make the dogs reluctant to respond generally.

Sniffing to find secreted articles is one of the best activities for dogs that work in this field. Dogs with a good play drive are preferred, but not those that have become obsessed with one sort of game. Steve suggests that all dogs are encouraged to play a number of different games. Only one in ten dogs has the drive to focus on a task such as this with sufficient attention to be useful as a working dog. Focused dogs that are not easily distracted are particularly favoured as are those that show striking behavioural changes when they encounter the scent of truffle. A radical departure from a normal left-to-right quartering activity (used by dogs as they scan the olfactory terrain) helps the handler know when the dog should be helped in his digging activity. Having said that, the help that dogs need from their handlers in the preliminary searching process should be minimal. Not surprisingly, handlers favour dogs that are consistent and neither make false responses nor miss 'hot' targets.

Training programme

Before commencing training the animal must: sit, stay and, above all, play.

Changing the animal's motivation before a training session: playing retrieve games in the company of other keen dogs is the very best way to get Bobby motivated for the truffle-flavoured toy hunt.

Number of training sessions per week   7 to 10
Duration of session   Up to 15 minutes
Time taken to learn   4 months

In the process of shaping the final behaviour, the trainer:

1. Focused dog on a retrieve game.

2. Distracted the dog.
3. Hid the retrieved article in the ground litter.

4. Encouraged dog to sniff at the litter to find the toy.

5. Encouraged dog to dig at the litter to find the toy.
6. Repeated steps 3 to 5 with the toy being successively deeper.

7. Repeated steps 3 to 5 without using the toy - instead, a drop of truffle oil on cotton wool was buried in the litter, motivating the dog as before. When he dug up the tell-tale white fibres, the trainer hurled the toy into the site of his digging activity. This was swiftly followed by praise and play retrieve games. In this way the smell of truffles becomes linked to that favourite toy and the hunt represents a thrilling game that keeps the dog very interested indeed.

Stumbling blocks: the move from the training shed with all its controlled conditions to the field scenario represents the biggest challenge, since the chances of the dogs encountering distracters are increased in many unpredictable ways.

General processes in training

Clicker-training: no.

Use of restraints: none.

Other equipment: toy

Aversive stimuli: none.

Auditory cues: truffle = sniff for truffles not narcotics; *find* = focus and dig.

Visual cues: hands drum on handler's chest – accompanies verbal truffle command. Right hand sent forward as if scattering seed – accompanies verbal *find* command.

Use of reinforcers

Rewards used: plastic retrieve toys specially designed with a hollow core to accommodate tiny volumes of odiferous liquids. Because he has a huge play drive, Bobby is particularly keen on chases and tugs-of-war.

Variation in the size of a reward: yes, a reward gradient is deployed. Depending on the speed of finding the toy, the length of the resultant games vary.

Variety of reward used: as well as play, food is used occasionally. Interestingly the reverse is the case for dogs when searching for narcotics (food replaces toys).

Reinforcement schedule: continuous. In the field, there is much more variability because truffles occur so far apart in nature. Meticulous records are brought up to date after every training session so that Steve can know for sure that Bobby's learning is improving or at the very least not extinguishing.

Use of rewards as lures or targets: during training the toy is thrown into the earth to confirm and reinforce the dog's interest in 'hot' sites (i.e. those hiding oil-laced cotton wool targets or real truffles).

Highlights: apart from classical conditioning (the association of truffle odour with toys), this case highlights the ability of dogs to locate different resources according to different auditory cues.

Case 45
Dog *Canis familiaris* (German Shepherd cross)

Training profile

Target behaviour:	search and rescue
Name:	Lizzy
Age:	8 years
Trainer's assessment of temperament:	bold, devoted, fearless
Trainer's name:	Mick McCauliffe

Background

The Australian K-9 Search and Rescue Association was founded in 1998. The inspiration came after the Papua New Guinea tidal wave, when search and rescue (SAR) dogs were flown in from America and Canada. Unfortunately, Australia was not in a position to offer such a service. Since that time the association has sought assistance from members of a specialised profession, including Mick McCauliffe.

The Australian K-9 Search and Rescue Association is a volunteer association and registered charity that aims to provide a valuable community service. The organisation consists of volunteers who train their pets as SAR dogs for the purpose of finding people lost in the wilderness or buried under rubble following building collapse (earthquake, explosions etc.).

While many pet dogs do whatever they please even when their owners stand over them and threaten the use of physical force, the SAR dogs demonstrate impressive distance control and a willingness to move in different directions according to hand signals. Dogs selected for basic training must have a good play drive. Dogs over two years of age are generally avoided because they are thought to have learned too many other behaviours. Brachiocephalic ('short-skulled') breeds, such as bulldogs, that have limited ability to breathe naturally and others having simply too much bulk to carry themselves across rough ter-

rain all day are not considered for basic training. Only 20 per cent of dogs have the necessary physical qualities and sufficient play drive to be selected for training.

The behaviour showcased is a combined control and detachment exercise. The aim of the exercise is for the animal to move away from the handler in a specified direction (forward, back, left or right) in response to specific commands.

The first part of the combined exercise involves the dogs learning that they can be rewarded if they leave their owners on cue. This is the *detachment* component of the exercise. Many dogs are so attached to their owners that they find it difficult to leave their side.

In addition, dogs learn to respond to single commands, such as *stop, left, right*, hence the control aspect of the exercise. The aim is to maintain *control* of the dog even when the dog is working at a distance from the handler.

Subsequent training can then be broken down into two components: the *bucket* run and the *show me* run. The *bucket* run is a control and detachment exercise developed by the Swiss Alpine Rescue Group. The bucket acts as a visual target that provides the dog with a focus away from the handler. The *show me* run is an extension of the bucket run. Once the dog returns from the bucket to the handler it must then return to the bucket with the handler, where it receives a second reward. The aim of the *show me* run is for the dog first to find the target (i.e. the missing person) and then return to the handler and take the handler back to the target, hence showing the handler where the missing person is.

Generally food is used to establish the movement away from the handler. Since toys are most valuable when the owner is close enough to be able to play with them, they come into their own when the dog is required to return to the handler.

Punishment (such as using a harsh tone, choker chain or striking) results in a compliant but often unenthusiastic dog. Since SAR dogs are expected to expend large amounts of energy in difficult conditions for extended periods of time, punishment is avoided in their training. Instead emphasis is placed on rewarding correct behaviour.

Apart from the obedience commands discussed in this study, a fully trained SAR dog must respond to *get on* (meaning go forward) and *across* (meaning look at the handler and wait for the indication to go left or right). These verbal commands are accompanied by hand signals.

To work effectively in unfamiliar terrain, SAR dogs must quickly become habituated to a wide variety of distractions, including other people, noise, running prey species and working environments in general. Discrimination is used in advanced training of SAR dogs to teach them to track only human scent; not the scent of other animals. Since the scent of humans changes rapidly after death, dogs are taught to discriminate human scent on this basis. Specialist chemical manufacturers produce synthetic analogues of the volatile molecules associated with decomposing human flesh that can be used in discrimination training.

Training programme

Before commencing training the animal must: obey the following basic obedience exercises (even in the face of tempting distractions): *sit, drop, stay, fetch, heel* and *come*. The dog must also demonstrate some interest in scenting work. This can be readily confirmed by hiding one of the dog's toys and waiting to see whether the dog sets about searching for it with his nose to the ground.

Changing the animal's motivation before a training session: harnesses always help to build an association with a particular sort of work. Since the dogs are trained to expect a toy reward when they bring the handler to the target, an initial play session is a helpful means of focusing the dog.

Number of training sessions per week 10
Duration of session 5–20 minutes
Time taken to learn 3 months

In the process of shaping the bucket run, the trainer:
1. Placed a reward on the bucket.

2. Sent the dog to the bucket and allowed it to eat the reward. This teaches the dog to move away from the handler and towards the bucket.
3. Told it to *stay* briefly, then recalled it. This teaches the dog to stay at the bucket until given the command to return to the handler.

In the process of shaping the show me run, the trainer:

4. Said *show me* and then returned to the bucket with the dog. Giving the dog a second reward for this return trip is necessary, especially during the early stages of training.

5. Replaced the bucket with a human decoy and gave the *find* command. The human target hides a pair of toys behind her back. On finding the human the dog gets to play with the first toy. The dog returns to the trainer for a good game with the first toy. On returning to the decoy with the trainer the dog gets to play with the second toy.

6. Asked the human target to hide. This gradually becomes more complex as the dog's task develops into a search for the human.

7. Introduced the bringsels. Bringsels are cylindrical tabs attached to the collar. They replace the toys. When the dog finds the decoy, it swings the bringsel, picks it up in its teeth and retrieves it back to the owner. This indicates to the handler that the dog has made a find, and the dog then takes the handler back to the find. This behaviour is referred to as a 'bringsel alert'.

Stumbling blocks: teaching the dog to leave the handler on command is probably the most difficult and seems to be related to the competing drive to stay close to the trainer because he is the source of reinforcement. This is overcome by moving the bucket target away from the handler in small increments.

The next problem arises when dogs start to move away too far from the handler too soon. This can easily result in loss of control and is best avoided by teaching the dog the *stop* command while close to the handler. For the dog's own safety, it is not allowed to work out of sight of the handler. Since experienced trainers supervise the owners handling their own dogs in this exercise, one of the most awkward stumbling blocks remains the vacillating motivation of owner-handlers.

General processes in training

Clicker-training: no.
Use of restraints: none.
Other equipment: toys, harnesses and bringsels.
Aversive stimuli: none.
Auditory cues: find and *show me.*
Visual cues: a hand signal sends the dog forward towards the target.

Use of reinforcers

Rewards used: toys used in ways that meet the dog's individual preference. For Lizzy, games of *fetch* with the ball rank well above food and praise.
Variation in the size of a reward: yes. Rewards increase with the complexity of the task being tackled and the quality of the performance.
Variety of reward used: yes.
Reinforcement schedule: continual reinforcement continues until the dog performs the exercise perfectly every time it is asked to. From then on intermittent reinforcement is used.
Ratio of variable reinforcement: once the dog has learned the behaviour it is not necessary to reward it every time. Instead the dog is rewarded with primary reinforcers intermittently for correct behaviour. There is no set variable reinforcement ratio, the delivery of primary reinforcers depends on the task, stage of training and ability of the individual dog. It may be 1:3, 1:5 or 1:7.
Use of rewards as lures or targets: rewards are used to attract the dog to the bucket.

Highlights: this case reminds us of a key distinction between food and toys when they are used as primary reinforcers in dog training. Toys are most reinforcing when the handler is available to play with them. While a dog may be trained to find anything associated with food, it is less likely to need the human present to enjoy making a find. Therefore, when detective work must be performed by a dog at a distance from its handler, the use of toys is ideal if the dog can be taught that he must bring the owner to the secondary reinforcer (the hidden human) before being reinforced with a game.

Case 46

Dog Canis familiaris (German Shepherd)

Training profile

Target behaviour:	apprehension of human
Name:	Ruger
Age:	5 years
Trainer's assessment of temperament:	cheeky, playful, keen
Trainer's name:	Steve Collier

Background

Bold, playful, athletic dogs are welcome recruits to the dog squad. Submissive, gun-shy dogs are not selected for police work. Dogs with no innate play drive or more commonly those that have had it knocked out of them, i.e. they have learned not to exhibit play behaviours in the presence of humans, are especially difficult to motivate. There are also overaggressive dogs that are dangerous even to their own handlers. To protect the public, these dogs are not selected for attack work.

Dogs used by the police for apprehension of suspects and siege work are presented to the novice observer as being singularly vicious and sometimes even useful in detecting criminal activity perhaps through some sense of justice. According to police dog handlers, the public like to believe that they feel they have a 'dangerous beast' as an ally.

When the police consider the hierarchy of force available to them for the control of dangerous suspects, dogs rank just below guns. It may surprise some readers to learn that Ruger is described by his handler as a cheeky, affectionate dog who really loves his work. Unlike a bullet, Ruger can be called back. As we will see, to him the motivation to work is probably eclipsed by the concept of play. Training takes place every day until the dogs are fully operational. Once possessiveness has been nurtured, dogs must be habituated to flailing arms and legs so that they do not learn to release when the 'suspect' struggles or defends himself. Then weekly sessions with the training sleeve are administered. In these lessons it is the quality of the exposure of the stimulus rather than the number of times it appears that is crucial.

In training for man work, police officers are used as decoy suspects. If dogs fail to respond to the all-important leave command or if they bite the wrong part of the volunteer, they are physically punished (with a choke-chain across the rump). This is considered necessary not only to enhance public confidence but also to ensure good volunteering rates by police officers.

Ruger demonstrates his 'man-work' by seizing criminal suspects if they fail to stop when requested to by the officer handling him. Officers assessing dogs at the end of training look for good control, a firm bite and focused attention to the job in hand.

Training programme

Before commencing training the animal must: know the words *sit, down, come, fetch* and *drop* (the word *leave* is somewhat sacred in that it is reserved for use when dogs are using their teeth on humans).

Changing the animal's motivation before a training session: nothing.

Number of training sessions per week 5
Duration of session 5–15 minutes
Time taken to learn 12 months

In the process of shaping the final behaviour, the trainer:

1. Introduced the puppy tug. By being hurled around and pulled in unpredictable directions on a rope, a roll of hessian increases play drive and excites the dogs into being highly possessive of this special toy.

2. Used the same toy in a so-called 'aggression line' in the presence of dogs. As they lunge and bark, dogs compete with two or three others for access to the toy. They are all given access to the toy, but the sight of another dog with this treasured possession seems to increase the dogs' motivation to hold on with tremendous resolve once they have bitten.

3. Showed the dog the same toy in the arms of a handler as he ran away from the dog.

4. Introduced a protective sleeve covered in the same hessian. This replaces the puppy tug and training focuses on controlling the bites delivered to the sleeve as the dog's new best toy.

5. Issued a verbal attack command (this is a monosyllabic word that, in the interests of safety, cannot be published) whenever the dog is released to seize the sleeve.

6. Hid the sleeve under normal clothes to complete the transition from toy to ostensibly normal human.

Stumbling blocks: early on in training some dogs do not take possession of the toy in their mouths but instead chase it and then stand over it. Perhaps as a legacy from previous unpleasant experiences, other dogs will bite but then release when the handlers play tug-of-war with it. Towards the end of the 20-week training programme, there are always the really keen dogs that take a while to be persuaded that they should ever wait for permission to bite the sleeve. Dogs that have been trained to have considerable motivation to seize human flesh, long to be allowed to bite and retain possession for a long time. Not surprisingly, the same animals are sometimes also reluctant to let go on command.

General processes in training

Clicker-training: no.

Use of restraints: choke chains are used to restrain dogs prior to a bite.

Other equipment: toy.

Aversive stimuli: physical punishment if the dog fails to release the human when told.

Auditory cues: while many dogs pick up on the regulation 'Stop, Police' and 'Stop, or I will release the dog' overture that represents a prelude to a possible bite, the dogs are trained to wait for the single verbal command to attack.

Visual cues: no visual guides are used. Instead the handlers praise the dogs when they gaze in the right direction.

Use of reinforcers

Rewards used: play.

Variation in the size of a reward: yes. The value of the game depends largely on the agitator's ability to give the dog a good tug-of-war game.

Variety of reward used: no.

Reinforcement schedule: continuous. This behaviour seems to be largely self-rewarding in that the bite is the reward for responding to the control commands. Just the sight of a training sleeve is enough to send some dogs into paroxysms of irrepressible play drive. Dogs that become uncontrollable at this point are not given a bite.

Ratio of variable reinforcement: not applicable.

Use of rewards as lures or targets: the toy is used to lure the dog to the volunteer. This teaches all dogs to expect to find the equivalent of a toy in every fleeing human.

Highlights: the use of conspecifics to increase the motivation to possess the roll of hessian is a particularly interesting highlight of this case. The young dogs focus each other's attention on the puppy tug and teach naive animals that the tug is highly prized. This example demonstrates that social facilitation and social learning can occur simultaneously (see Chapter 2).

Case 47   Dog *Canis familiaris* (Labrador retriever cross)

Training profile
Target behaviour:	guiding around obstacles
Name:	Robyn
Age:	1.5 years
Trainer's assessment of temperament:	sensitive, willing, happy
Trainer's name:	Julie Clarke

Background

It takes a special sort of dog to be a guide dog. For this job the most trainable dogs have a balanced temperament and moderate play and food drives that can be modified by sensitive training. Dogs with a strong motivation to interact with conspecifics can be difficult to train because they can be easily distracted by other dogs while working. That is why the attrition rate in guide dog training is high and why considerable efforts have been made to identify bloodline and crosses that are physically fit and have the behavioural attributes for the job. There are several reasons for deselection from guide dog training. These include aggression and an inability to ignore other dogs. Those dogs with extremely high or low body sensitivity require time and effort to moderate their responsiveness. This is particularly important in guide dog training. Bumptious young dogs with low sensitivity are easily spotted because they readily knock things over. An under-sensitive dog can be improved by tickling him and encouraging him to enjoy detecting contact. Dogs with extremely high sensitivity, on the other hand, find tactile stimuli generally aversive and must be habituated to being touched by slowly increasing the tension on the collar and very slowly introducing rough and tumble games.

Guide dogs have to learn one thing above all others: to lead their users in a straight line and to regain their course after having manoeuvred past an obstacle. This allows visually impaired people to have confidence that they are still travelling in the desired direction. Dogs are trained to avoid obstacles by a fixed distance that allows suf-

ficient clearance by both the handler and the dog. This is known as 'right shoulder work'. This allows a completely blind person to walk at a normal pace through congested streets with confidence. Training aims to produce a dog that executes the required manoeuvres with safety and confidence.

The dogs are not programmed to head for a given destination (such as the post office or the greengrocer's). Instead the people they are guiding must memorise the straight lines and turns that are involved in navigating there. Sometimes chaining helps to reinforce the dogs. Robyn, for instance, has a strange affiliation for Boots the Chemist and her ultimate arrival there reinforces her decision-making on the way through town. Obviously, the challenge then becomes encouraging her to find other destinations unless the owner with whom she is eventually matched can be persuaded to work at Boots the Chemist. Most dogs very quickly become motivated to locate new destinations in their owners' home areas. Crossing roads also has to be done in straight lines to minimise confusion and also time spent among traffic, which is the guide dog users' ultimate bête noire (apart, that is, from well-meaning folk who stop the dog to feed, coo and bill at it). Motor vehicles have to be avoided and the dog is taught to do that even if it is being actively encouraged to leave the kerb. A process of repetition achieves this. Trained stooge drivers are used on suburban roads with numerous corners behind which to hide.

Training programme

Before commencing training the animal must: know *stand, steady, sit* and *wait.* Before these commands are taught all young dogs are puppy-walked to build confidence in crowds and learn the commands *down,* and *on your bed,* and a reliable recall response to their name or a whistle. Interestingly, guide dogs are conditioned from an early age to associate the word *busy* with defaecation and urination as soon as they leave their kennels for training. This facilitates each training session by removing distractions and in later working contexts allows visually impaired users to be confident that their dogs are not going to relieve themselves while on the job.

Changing the animal's motivation before a training session: lots of cuddles before a training session help to relax Robyn and renew the bond with the handler and prime her for work with that person.

Number of training sessions per week 12
Duration of session 25 minutes
Time taken to learn 8 weeks

In the process of shaping the final behaviour, the trainer:

1. Approached a practice obstacle in the path of the dog while saying '*watch*'. Taught the dog to break away from the human by stepping slightly in advance of the dog.

2. Issued the command *over* as soon as the dog looked to the right and got out of the handler's way. When the dog was at right angles to her original path, the trainer stopped her and rewarded her with physical praise and sometimes a toy or some food.

3. Introduced a backwards step, once the dog is readily making a generous turn. This ensures that the dog gets no closer to the line of the obstacle. Once past the obstacle the handler took a step back towards the line of the obstacle while saying *in*. This brought the dog back to the centre of the pavement and the straight line it was pursuing.

4. Repeated until the dog was breaking away and returning to its centre line with confidence.

5. Reinforced correct turns. If the dog was not making turns, the trainer simply stopped it and waited for any movement, only praising the movements in the correct direction. Some dogs look up at their handlers at this point and invite eye contact. This is not encouraged since the dog may develop an overdependence on the handler that potentially reduces the dog's ability to focus on its environment.

6. Approached obstacles that were less well defined, such as lampposts, pedestrians, overhanging branches and potholes in the ground.

7. Allowed trial and error learning to take over from errorless learning as the dog had to take

more decisions and people were moved into the dog's path.

8. Repeated steps 1 and 4 in town with the harness off.
9. Repeated steps 1 and 4 in town with the harness on.
10. Tested the effectiveness of training by challenging the dog to make errors with poor following of its guidance or actively interfering in its decision making.
11. Wore a blindfold and repeated the exercises with an observer on hand to assess the dog and to avert any disasters.
12. Wore a blindfold and repeated the exercises while behaving unhelpfully or naively, in front of an assessor.

Stumbling blocks: some dogs over-compensate for obstacles and can begin to rush past them with an unhelpful crabbing action.

General processes in training

Clicker-training: no.

Use of restraints: a flat collar is preferred by this trainer but sometimes a half-check chain or check chain is used.

Other equipment: harness with rigid handle.

Aversive stimuli: by gently tapping the obstacles, trainers alert the dogs to the presence of barriers that must be avoided. No negative associations with the barriers are established. Gentle correction is applied via the check chain.

Auditory cues: 'watch', 'over' and 'in'.

Visual cues: at the discretion of the trainer, hand signals are used to alert the dog to the next element of each day's challenge.

Use of reinforcers

Rewards used: approval from the handler, praise and games.

Variation in the size of a reward: yes.

Variety of reward used: not with this dog.

Reinforcement schedule: continuous reinforcement throughout basic training. When assigned to their guide dog owners, the dogs are supposed to get continual training. This is why owners are encouraged to keep up a monologue with their dogs while working.

Ratio of variable reinforcement: once trained behaviours become chained together on a regular trip, praise can be delivered at variable points (1–4) in the chain.

Use of rewards as lures or targets: no.

Highlights: this case demonstrates the impressive level of complexity of information that can be established using backward chaining (see learning theory). Furthermore, the way in which guide dogs arrive at designated spots is testimony to the ability of canidae to form mental maps.

Case 48   Dog *Canis familiaris* (Border Collie)

Training profile

Target behaviour:	sendaway (gathering sheep unseen)
Name:	Craig
Age:	6 years
Trainer's assessment of temperament:	keen, reliable, creative
Trainer's name:	Bruce Englefield

Background

Craig waits very keenly for the release command and then gallops away from Bruce to find sheep that may be out of sight, e.g. behind a hedgerow or hill. In trialing terms this is known as 'gathering sheep unseen'.

Two days before this interview, this team won the West of England Sheepdog Trials. As both a leading trainer and a companion animal behaviour counsellor, Bruce considers obedience and trust essential if the dog is to take commands graciously before it has seen the sheep. The zeal with which dogs such as Craig leave their masters' sides is particularly striking until one appreciates that the sendaway is an analogue of the start of a hunting trip. With their innate need to chase, working sheepdogs seem to find complying with this command as easy as most pet collies find chasing a ball. This particular task is a gathering exercise that involves moving the sheep as a group towards the human. It is part of an innate hunting strategy. Of the dogs with the motivation to move stock into a group, the more useful and hard to find are actually those that are excellent at 'driving', i.e. moving stock away from the human.

Given that the dog learns that responding to the *sendaway* command will help him find sheep, it is important to establish what is expected of the dog once he has found the flock. The dog must therefore be trained how to gather sheep. This skill involves the dog learning how to judge the flight distance for a particular cohort of sheep (the flight distance is the radius of a circle around an animal or group of animals within which an approach by a potential predator will prompt fleeing). Shepherds speak of dogs' showing eye when working sheep. This means they can adopt an impressive stare that seems to make sheep take them very seriously. Bruce believes that more important than the dog's eyes themselves is the dog's use of a stalking profile. This contention is supported by the fact that a number of outstanding collies have worked sheep even after disease has blinded them.

The dog must become habituated to distractions that occur in working contexts. Paradoxically, since he must be stopped from working every single sheep he ever sees, he must also be habituated to sheep in general. Simultaneously, the dog must be sensitised to certain signals that bring trouble if they are ignored. Bruce teaches his pups, in a passageway, that *keep out* means 'get away from whatever you are close to'. Bruce is something of a pioneer in his field because he uses auditory secondary reinforcers, i.e. clicker training, with his pups to establish the initial seven commands.

Words like *leave, no* and *get out* are unwelcome from the dog's perspective because they mark the end of a working session and usually the end of a very engaging chase. These commands have to be instilled with some rigour since they can save sheep from being bitten in the wrong place (contrary to popular belief, dogs are trained to bite on command . . . but only at the head end of the sheep).

There is always an element of the unexpected or unpredictable that seems to maintain dogs' keenness to work. Because it is a command used to bring a dog away from a group of sheep (but trust that there will more to work with any moment), *that'll do* should never mean the absolute termination of that day's access to sheep.

Training programme

Before commencing training the animal must: know whistled commands for *stop, clockwise, anticlockwise, cast in* (approach sheep), *cast out* (move away from sheep), *look back* (leave the sheep you are currently eyeing – I am going to send you somewhere else – but I guarantee you will see sheep again) and *no.*

Changing the animal's motivation before a training session: very occasionally sheepdog trainers tie up their dogs in view of other dogs working. This is believed to increase motivation to get involved. Bruce feels this is counterproductive because it may precipitate so much frustration that the dogs are difficult to control when finally allowed to work. The motivation to work sheep is innate in sheepdogs. Bruce maintains that they do not have a will to please so much as a will to work as part of a team.

Number of training sessions per week 3 per day, 6 days per week
Duration of session 10 minutes
Time taken to learn 1 week

In the process of shaping the final behaviour, the trainer:
1. Issued verbal commands at the moment that the dog performed an innate response to moving sheep.
2. Taught the dog to stop and hold sheep. This is achieved by giving the dog many opportunities to keep a small flock steady using his 'eye' while the handler pivots the group around him.

3. Taught the '*look back*' as described above. This is an important recall command that should be used carefully. It is especially important that the dog is never put back into his kennel after this command until he has seen and worked with a second group of sheep.
4. Taught '*cast in*' and '*cast out*' by issuing the commands at the very same time that the dog is moving towards or away from the sheep, respectively. Once all of the above commands are in place the dog should know that his job is to keep the sheep coming towards the shepherd and he should have the skills to achieve that.

5. Exposed the dog to small groups of sheep further and further away and allowed him to apply his innate gathering skills.

Stumbling blocks: Bruce believes in the merit of setting situations up so that the dog has every chance of learning the commands the first time they are issued. However, mistakes can emerge when the trained behaviours become context-specific. For example, the dog may learn to look for sheep every time he turns left through the gate in the far right corner of the top paddock. If rewards (of continued opportunities to herd sheep) are always coincident with the left turn command, ritualisation can be sufficient to teach the dog that it should always turn left in that corner.

Unfortunately, some trainers do not allow the dogs to develop their innate herding skills. If trainers interfere and use instructions for each and every turn, turns that the dog would be about to make anyway, then the dog may quickly become frustrated and begin to lose its creativity. In this sense, timing is one of the most important skills in sheepdog training.

General processes in training

Clicker-training: not in this exercise.

Use of restraints: none.

Other equipment: whistle and crook to guide sheep in penning exercises.

Aversive stimuli: Bruce's dogs seem to know that if they fail to follow instructions they will be told *no* on two occasions. If they continue to transgress they are grounded. Whether dogs can keep a tally of their sins (count), project into the future and even judge when to stop misbehaving remain moot points, but like a firm-but-fair parent Bruce tries to be as consistent as possible in his use of such threats. Because his dogs' performances are usually so much better after a period in the 'cooler', Bruce firmly believes that this gives them the opportunity for learning through reflection.

Auditory cues: whistled commands are used in sequence to create an impressive language that can be used to guide large flocks through tight gaps and into races.

Visual cues: while fairly crude arm movements are used to support whistles and move dogs at a distance, the crook is used with great subtlety to help move sheep in a penning exercise.

Use of reinforcers

Rewards used: access to sheep, the occasional 'good boy' and mouthful of sheep droppings. Food is never used in sheepdog training. Given that they are indulging themselves when working, the alacrity with which good dogs find sheep is a reflection of the self-rewarding nature of this hunting analogue. Individual attention in combination with a relaxed (some would say even understated) 'good boy' from Bruce, seems to be especially reinforcing.

Variation in the size of a reward: the size of flock can vary. While a single sheep can represent too little fun, flocks can also be too big to manage.

Variety of reward used: none.

Reinforcement schedule: continuous.

Use of rewards as lures or targets: sheep are 'planted' in contrived situations to reward dogs for turning in a given direction on command.

Highlights: herding dogs have been working with humans for tens of thousands of years. It is therefore perhaps not surprising that we have been able to select for the motivation to herd. Craig is a finely bred animal who works sheep as if it is his raison d'être. Because of his genetic make-up, Craig finds access to sheep the most potent primary reinforcer when out of his kennel. This appears to be a particularly powerful example of reinforcement-to-command transfer (see Introduction to the case studies) so that eventually the command controls the response. One of the other learning highlights of this case is the impressive way in which the dog learns to associate two events that are separated in time (i.e. the sendaway and finding the sheep).

Case 49

Horse *Equus caballus* (Thoroughbred)

Training profile

Target behaviour:	moving pedestrians for crowd control
Name:	Star
Age:	6 years
Trainer's assessment of temperament:	wary, willing, kind
Trainer's name:	Andrew Mackay

Background

Few horses are genuinely suited to the role of police mount, and the selection process is understandably demanding. Mares and stallions are avoided, as they are considered rather less predictable and seem easily distracted when working with other horses. Flighty or nervous horses are deemed particularly unsuitable for crowd control. Criteria applied to mounts entering the NSW police horse training programme demand bay geldings of over 15.3 hands, either part or pure thoroughbred. Preferred animals are between three and five years of age.

There is no specific source for these animals, although many come from the racing industry. Despite the thoroughbred's reactivity to stimuli, racehorses are regarded as being particularly suitable, as they are already accustomed to crowds and traffic, through frequent exposure. Ex-track thoroughbreds are cheaply available and this is reflected by the considerable attrition in the selection and training of police remounts. Of the horses that commence training, ten per cent go on to perform all desired behaviours adequately and only five per cent extremely well.

Proficiency in crowd control tends to increase over time, and occasionally a horse will show particular initiative and pre-empt the rider, but this is rare. One such horse has been with the NSW force for 25 years, and is said to seek out and target the agitators in a group without prompting from the rider. This same horse has been retired three times, and on each occasion has pined and refused to eat until brought back into active service.

Newly acquired horses spend six weeks with a general trainer who carries out initial evaluation and selection based on temperament and responsiveness, in addition to providing basic training. The trust and partnership between a mount and his rider that develops over time increases their capacity to cope with new situations. The horse must learn to stand firm under physical pressure from a noisy, pushy crowd and to push pedestrians when directed by the rider. People are surprised that the horse is unperturbed by a crowd, especially in aggressive circumstances when it may come under direct attack.

The trainers and riders of police horses aim to teach the horse to be obedient and responsive in almost any situation. This requires the horse to be relaxed and unflappable, and to remain stationary unless instructed otherwise. When given signals, the horse should follow them precisely, irrespective of jostling people, noises, lights and other distractions. Initially horses are trained to respond to basic signals. Each horse is paired with a single rider for both training and work over a number of years, which encourages a mutual trust to develop. The benefits of this appear in later schooling, where the horse is asked to perform unfamiliar tasks, facilitated through rider reassurance. The basic training programme generally lasts for six weeks, before specific behaviours are trained.

During crowd control training, the aim is for the horse to continue responding to these signals, despite external distractions. The process is one of a stepwise habituation.

Each new factor such as a banner or a loud noise is introduced to the horse when it is stationary, and has no current instructions. Once it has become accustomed to the changed conditions, and seems unperturbed, the horse is asked to respond to normal signals (e.g., it may simply be signalled to walk and then halt) under the new circumstances. The horse thus becomes habituated to the new stimuli. Further potential distracters are introduced in the same manner, until the horse is able to work in a wide variety of situations.

Training programme

Before commencing training the animal must: have been given a basic education, to respond to leg, seat and rein signals. On command, it will then move sideways, forwards or backwards. It is essential that police horses tolerate standing for extended periods. Horses are handled daily during grooming and saddling. They come to accept contact on all areas, even sensitive regions such as the groin or head.

Changing the animal's motivation before a training session: nothing.

Number of training sessions per week 7
Duration of session 45 minutes
Time taken to learn 1 week

In the process of shaping the final behaviour, the trainer:
1. Initially made the horse to stand with a pedestrian in front of him touching his neck and chest.

2. Made the horse stand still while the pedestrian applied pressure to the horse. In this situation, horses have a tendency to move away from persistent pressure. The horse was shaped to pay attention only to commands from the rider.
3. Trained the horse with leg and rein signals to advance towards the applied pressure, i.e. towards the pedestrian.
4. Simulated contact from multiple directions within a crowd by organising several people to surround the horse. The horse was again trained to respond to the rider's signals, and walk forward as directed.

5. Gradually added other distractions to the horse's repertoire. This included pedestrians holding or waving strange objects, or broadcasting loud noises. If the horse behaved fearfully, the training reverted to the last step with which the horse was comfortable, before attempting the problematic step again. Verbal and physical reassurance from the rider was particularly important during this stage.

Stumbling blocks: having many people in close proximity can disturb some horses, horses can become distracted and try to turn and see people behind them.

General processes in training

Clicker-training: no.

Use of restraints: double bridle (see glossary).

Other equipment: none.

Aversive stimuli: mock distracters. Aversive stimuli are an essential part of training, but their use is solely as part of the habituation process.

Auditory cues: constant reassurance and the command *steady*.

Visual cues: none.

Use of reinforcers

Rewards used: none.

Variation in the size of a reward: relief from leg pressure.

Variety of reward used: none.

Reinforcement schedule: negative reinforcement.

Highlights: discrimination plays a central role in this training protocol because the horse must learn to discern between pressure on the flank that comes from the rider and that coming from other humans.

Case 50 — Horse *Equus caballus* (Andalusian)

Training profile

Target behaviour:	rearing on command (without a bridle)
Name:	Peruano
Age:	15 years
Trainer's assessment of temperament:	outgoing, flamboyant, eccentric
Trainer's name:	Gerard Naprous

Background

While most riders prefer their horses not to rear, some actively train their animals to lift their forelegs off the ground as high as possible. These are the stunt trainers who need their horses to rear on command for film and television work. Powerful and threatening, the rear is a species-specific defence reaction (see Chapter 1) elicited by a threat in front of the animal that, when produced on cue, speaks of tremendous control on the part of the handler. Gerard maintains that if the horse regards the trainer as a leader with whom he is comfortable and consistently treated, then for him the biggest reward is a positive reaction and respect from the trainer.

Gerard's horses are general purpose animals; they can pull Roman chariots, stage coaches and carriages and act as the mounts of Cossacks, jousting knights and cowboys.

Being the traditional Spanish parade and bull-fighting horses, Andalusians have a helpfully high-stepping gait that lends itself well to being fashioned for display purposes. Being responsive and sensitive, they are favoured by expert riders who find them especially trainable.

The airs above the ground are advanced manoeuvres that have their origin in defence behaviours that fighting horses might occasionally use. Rearing without a rider or a bridle is impressive behaviour because it defies popular understanding of how best to control horses. In training this behaviour, Gerard looks for active forelegs, balance in the body (i.e. not collapsing to one side or the other) and power in the hindquarters.

Training programme

Before commencing training the animal must: know virtually all the haute-école ('high school') movements that one sees dressage horses and display horses perform. The horse must be keen to move forward whenever ridden or led. Only then can this forward impulsion be harnessed and channelled with ever-increasing subtlety to arrive at the sort of dramatic behaviours required for film work. Because a high-school trained horse is both multipurpose and extra safe, it is particularly well suited to work on set where expensive cameras and lighting rigs abound and it may be ridden by many VIP novices.

Changing the animal's motivation before a training session: the horse is simply warmed up physically.

Number of training sessions per week 6
Duration of session 10 minutes
Time taken to learn 3 weeks

In the process of shaping the final behaviour, the trainer:
1. Set the horse up, when riding him, with plenty of forward impulsion (from increasingly subtle leg pressure) but blocked any actual movement

forward (with increasingly subtle rein checking) so that he was almost jogging on the spot. Because the horse was well balanced this would not cause him to spin in one direction or the other. The trainer anticipated and responded to any attempts by the horse to escape from the block in front of him (effected by the bit) and the block behind him (effected by both of the rider's legs). The aim was to keep the hands and legs so well balanced that the cue to rear could be given by raising the hands very slightly while issuing the *up* command. The behaviour was reinforced simply by relaxing. The trainer asked for no more than 20 centimetres of elevation during the first training session and ensured that the head remained tucked in throughout the behaviour.

3. Commanded the same degree of collection (of energy) with the stallion in-hand, i.e. with the trainer on the ground. Using the same verbal signals, a rise was asked for and a schooling whip used to encourage the first step in the elevation.

2. Gradually increased the persistence of the hand signal so that the elevation is maintained for longer periods. As the horse climbed to greater heights he needed to use his flailing forelimbs to balance. This was encouraged because it gives the impression of flamboyance and expression. For instance, as part of a staged jousting drama where the white knight is in grave danger of being run through by the black knight, the white stallion races to his rescue and trounces the 'baddie' with this behaviour.

4. Finally, the same signals were used with the horse at liberty (without any tack). The whip, used to guide the legs up, can be replaced by any linear object such as a sword in the jousting sequence. Ultimately, the raising of an arm at a considerable distance from the horse can provoke the same reaction for use in film scripts

that call for a loose horse rearing without any humans around it.

Stumbling blocks: the main stumbling block with this behaviour is that the horse may become unbalanced and may twist to one side or the other through lack of muscular strength.

General processes in training

Clicker-training: no.

Use of restraints: the horse wears a curb bit (see glossary).

Other equipment: spurs are worn but rarely used, the essence of classical equitation being the minimal use of force. Only advanced horse-riders can sit on such well-trained horses without unwittingly issuing a multiplicity of commands.

Aversive stimuli: the hope is not to have to use the spurs and curb bit, which are used only in later stages of training. Novice riders cannot easily be trusted with this equipment because the risk of making mistakes on such highly conditioned animals is too great.

Auditory cues: up.

Visual cues: the whip is used as a signal when impulsion is required without there being a rider on the horse's back. Arms eventually replace whips as a means of signalling to unridden and unbridled horses.

Use of reinforcers

Rewards used: the neck is scratched as an analogue of mutual grooming in horses. Horses are judging the behaviour of their companions all the time, and they do the same with humans especially during training. They may readily detect the relaxation evident in a trainer who is pleased with his horse's behaviour. Gerard indicates that horses that find ways of reducing tension in their trainers are usually creative animals with positive attitudes.

Variation in the size of a reward: no.

Variety of reward used: no.

Reinforcement schedule: negative reinforcement.

Highlights: horses learn to detect the peculiarities of each rider's signals. This case underlines the complexity of the bond that develops between horses and their riders and why the horse–human bond grows with the number of hours spent in the saddle. As they respond to minute tactile stimuli, horses learn to discriminate between each of the signals and combinations of signals from a single rider. As with all training, this is facilitated by consistency. Good riders are those who remain still in the saddle and do not issue signals inadvertently, e.g. while attempting to balance by pulling on the reins or gripping with their legs. Having a so-called independent seat allows them to issue clear and readily distinguished signals, i.e. to be very consistent.

Conclusions

In this book we have examined interventions that change the frequency with which certain behaviours appear. Unwelcome behaviours can become less likely while desired behaviour can become more likely. This is training.

We have seen that classical and instrumental conditioning may occasionally conflict with one another, but good training is often effective because it allows these two forms of learning to work together. Training takes as many forms as there are trainers, but the best examples are characterised by several common features. These include thoughtful interpretation of what the animals do prior to training (innate responses), accurate timing and almost mechanical consistency.

The cases we have included may be impressive in their variety, but nevertheless we readily acknowledge the limitations on the responses that can be offered, shaped and learned. This reminds us that certain tasks suit certain species and indeed certain animals within a species. Selecting the animals for the task can be approached with insight and forethought. The trainers we have presented in the case histories describe how they identify the best candidates for training in terms of the prerequisites that need to be met and sometimes in terms of the temperaments of the animals.

But what about the trainers themselves? The absence of any self-reflection that examines possible short-comings of a trainer's behaviour seems striking, in that conspicuously few of the trainers we interviewed identified handler error as a stumbling block. To address this potential gap in our story, we would like to distil the desirable characteristics in the outstanding trainers we have met by highlighting a number of ways in which they strike a deal with their subjects and help them to solve the problems they have presented.

The best trainers show exquisite timing. When delivering reinforcement conditional on a response being made when a particular signal is given, precise timing is critical for the development of strong associations between responses and rewards and between the signal and the response. When using classical conditioning, good timing is equally critical for ensuring strong associations between a conditioned stimulus and the reinforcer, or unconditioned stimulus, that follows.

Thoughtful trainers maintain clarity in their training sessions by training one response at a time and training one response for one stimulus. They demonstrate consistency by using uniform cues for responses and so avoid blurring one signal with another. Equally, consistent failure to reinforce is their key to efficient extinction programmes and forms the cornerstone of any attempt to bring a response under stimulus control.

When shaping new or improved responses, top trainers tailor the attempt: reinforcement ratio to suit the individual animal and its stage in training. So, while they reserve reinforcement until an improved response appears, they also demonstrate awareness of how quickly a given animal is going to approximate a given behaviour. To know one's subject in this context is to know how big its strides are likely to be. This allows trainers to keep reinforcements arriving at a rate that avoids the animal losing motivation, that is, giving up on its attempts to solve the current puzzle.

Preparation of animals is usually designed to increase motivation. Training environments are commonly selected not least because they offer a minimum of distractions, especially in the early stages of training. The broadening of contexts in which trained behaviours are offered, along with the reduction of the crudity of discriminative stimuli and the refinement of the responses, are the elements of fine-tuning that appear later in training.

Carrots and sticks are not used in equal measure. As Western cultures have become more humane in their treatment of companion animals and the public have seen what can be achieved in the training of marine mammals, trainers have tended to abandon compulsion and become more sophisticated in the use of carrots. Good trainers seem to use the mildest of sticks to label responses as inappropriate. Having said that, they use even mild punishment (e.g. a verbal non-reward cue) with great care since they recognise that it can destroy an animal's motivation to offer novel responses. These days only the unenlightened use physical punishment in the traditional penal sense, because it amounts to abuse.

Our case histories illustrate how the basic principles have been put into practice by trainers of companion, exotic and working animals. We have aimed to take the mystery out of training by identifying key steps in the training process, but these accounts are offered as exemplars rather than models. We encourage you to experiment and adopt the best characteristics of the training programmes we have showcased when you next present an animal with a learning challenge. The merits of each facet of best practice will depend on the personal preferences of each trainer-animal dyad. When training more than one animal at a time (see figure below), the same principles apply but the need for absolute stimulus control over each animal becomes paramount.

Training animals can be seen as a combination of art and science. Some trainers have argued that to dwell on the latter is to forsake the former, but both elements must be present if we are to get the very best performances from trained animals. Perfect timing and consistency are the mechanisms by which instrumental conditioning takes place, but the detection of mood shifts, individual differences and social relationships demands artful sensitivity. This explains why the individual flare of an elite dressage rider will probably never be matched by a robot. That said, the future is bright for the science of

Fig. Ca and b Numerous dogs being controlled by one handler.

learning and therefore training. Increasingly sophisticated devices to clarify communication between humans and their animals (including remote technologies) encourage hope for an increasingly refined understanding of animal welfare.

As we recognise the similarities between rats, pigeons and monkeys used in laboratory settings and other species, we also begin to appreciate the key differences. Theories based on more than 100 years of experiments on animal learning offer a framework on which we can tailor customised training schemes for our companion, exotic and working animals. This too will mean that we can better undertake to maximise the welfare of animals in various domains.

While this book has naturally concentrated on what we understand about principles of training, we do not wish to convey the impression that this is the end of the story. Predicting the future is always hazardous, but we suspect that a book of this kind in a decade or two will contain important new discoveries about the nature of animal intelligence and how this differs across species. It may also contain additional principles of learning; for example, there is considerable current interest and controversy over whether, and how, animals can change their evaluation of remembered events. Furthermore, recent learning theories have concentrated on how associations between events are formed, but have little to say in general terms about how such associations interact with motivational state to translate into changes in behaviour. Contemporary learning theory can often be wise in hindsight when analysing a change in behaviour, but poor in predicting it. A successor to the present book may well contain sound principles of performance as well as of learning.

Glossary of terms used by trainers, ethologists and psychologists

qv: indicates that a term is defined elsewhere in the glossary.

Active avoidance: training in which a specific response prevents the occurrence of some aversive event that would otherwise occur; thus, an animal receives the aversive event if it does not make a particular response within a certain time.

Advance and retreat: a system of horse training predicated on the likelihood that naive horses move away from humans because of fear (e.g. of predation) especially when approached (advance). Reinforcement in this system involves the human assuming a less predatory posture and the removal of eye contact (retreat).

Agonistic behaviour: any behaviour associated with threat, attack or defence. It includes related aspects of behaviour, including passivity and escape as well as aggression.

Aid: any of the signals used by riders to give instructions to horses. *See also* Artificial aids *and* Natural aids.

Air above the ground: a group of advanced manoeuvres in which the horse rears up in a controlled fashion onto his hind legs, with his forelegs curled under his chest and then either holds this pose, or jumps into the air off his hindlegs. *See also* Ballotade, Capriole, Courbette, Croupade, Levade *and* Mezair.

Allogrooming: grooming action directed from one herdmate to another and most commonly followed by mutual grooming (i.e. in which allogrooming is reciprocated).

Animal cognition: mental processes, such as those involved in memory or problem-solving, in non-human animals.

Anorexia: abnormal reduction of ingestive behaviour, e.g. in depressed and toxic clinical states.

Anthropomorphise: to describe an animal's behaviour or motivation in human terms.

Appetitive: in the broadest sense, appetitive behaviour represents the first phase of a series of behaviours that leads to a consummatory response, and then a refractory period.

Artificial aids: equipment used to alter a horse's behaviour under-saddle or in-hand e.g. whips, spurs and martingales.

Asking with the rein: in horse training, the application of mild pressure to the mouth via the rein.

Associative learning: acquiring associations between related events.

Autoshaping: a form of classical conditioning in which a localised signal is regularly followed by the arrival of a positive reinforcer with the result that an animal increasingly attends to and then approaches the signal. Most commonly used with birds where approach to a visual signal - an illuminated response key - is often followed by pecking at the key; hence 'autoshaped keypecking'.

Aversion therapy: treatment intended to eliminate an unwelcome behaviour by associating it with an aversive stimulus.

Aversive: events that elicit withdrawal and/or reduce the frequency of behaviour that is followed by such an event.

Avoidance learning: training that results in an animal acquiring a response that prevents the arrival of an aversive stimulus (*see* Active avoidance).

Balanced seat: that position of the mounted rider that requires the minimum of muscular effort to remain in the saddle and which interferes least with the horse's movements and equilibrium. (*See also* Independent seat).

Behind the bit: an evasive posture that thwarts the development of impulsion in which the horse persistently draws his nose in, allowing the rein to go slack.

Biological fitness: the ability of an animal to survive and reproduce, a concept referring to one genotype's ability to succeed relative to another's.

Bitless bridle: any of a variety of bridles designed without bits so that pressure is exerted on the nose, poll or curb groove instead of the mouth.

Blocking: the process by which prior conditioning of one stimulus interferes with subsequent conditioning of an added stimulus.

Break: the basic training of a young horse to obey commands and to accept direction and control, for whatever purpose it may be required.

Break point: the point at which an animal stops responding as the number of responses required to obtain a reinforcer is steadily increased (progressive ratio schedule); this provides a measure of the effectiveness of the reinforcer.

Bridge or bridging stimulus: a stimulus that is used by the trainer to fill the gap between a correct response and a delayed primary reinforcer and intended to function as a secondary reinforcer that reduces the otherwise weakening of primary reinforcement by the delay.

Brisket: the sternum of an animal, the body part on which it rests when lying in an upright position.

Circadian rhythm: oscillations in the frequency or strength of behavioural or physiological responses that recur about every 24 hours.

Classical conditioning: a training procedure in which some initially neutral stimulus (conditioned stimulus or CS; e.g. a sound of low to moderate intensity) is paired with a response-eliciting event (unconditioned stimulus or US; e.g. food) with the frequent result that the CS comes to elicit the same or a related response.

Clever Hans effect: the subtle and often barely detectable influence on an animal's behaviour of cues inadvertently produced by a trainer.

Conditioned taste aversion (CTA): an aversion to specific foods or tastes acquired as a result of their association with nausea or malaise.

Conditioning: procedures that promote the formation of associations between events.

Conditioned anxiety: *see* Conditioned emotional response.

Conditioned emotional response (CER): the suppression of ongoing behaviour when a stimulus is presented that has been paired with an aversive event such as shock. (Also known as Conditioned suppression or Conditioned anxiety)

Conditioned reinforcer: *see* secondary reinforcer.

Conditioned response (CR): the response elicited by the conditioned stimulus (CS) as a result of a classical conditioning procedure.

Conditioned suppression: *see* Conditioned emotional response.

Conditioned stimulus (CS): an initially neutral stimulus that comes to elicit a response after it has been paired with an unconditioned stimulus in a classical conditioning procedure.

Conformation: features of the external morphology (viz. relative musculoskeletal dimensions) of a horse that interest breeders and exhibitors, not least because they can affect its performance.

Conspecific: animals belonging to the same species.

Consummatory act, or response: the final response that terminates a sequence of behaviour; contrast with Appetitive response.

Contact: a steady (and preferably light) tension in the rein(s).

Contiguity: the closeness of two events in space or time.

Contingency: the temporal relationship, or correlation, between two repeated events or between repeated responses and reinforcers.

Continuous reinforcement (CRF): the delivery of a primary reinforcer following every correct response.

Coping: the short-term or long-term ability to maintain mental and bodily stability when faced with stressful events.

Cue: stimulus (including command or context) that elicits an instrumental response (*see* Discriminative stimulus) or signals the arrival of a positive reinforcer (*see* Conditioned stimulus).

Curb bit: a type of bit consisting of two metal cheek pieces and a mouthpiece with a central indented section (called the port) used in conjunction with a snaffle bit and a curb chain (qv) in a double bridle (qv).

Curb chain: a chain that lies in the curb groove of the horse's jaw when fitted to a curb or pelham bit and acts by applying pressure to this part of the horse's head in concert with regular bits in its mouth.

Delta: signal used in marine mammal training to alert animal to a least reinforcing stimulus (LRS) (qv). More generally, the term S-delta is used in operant conditioning to refer to a stimulus signalling a period in which reinforcement is unavailable.

Depression: general state of behavioural atony, features of which can include sagged posture and unresponsiveness.

Developmental homeostasis: the phenomenon by which juveniles that have been underexposed to relevant stimuli during socialisation are spared deleterious effects by quite limited contact with other individuals, even ones from another species.

Discriminative stimulus (S^D): an event indicating that an instrumental response will be followed by reinforcement that may come to evoke the response.

Discrimination training: narrowing the range of stimuli that elicit a trained response so that the animal comes to make this response to the specified cue and little else.

Displacement activity: an activity performed in a situation apparently different from the context in which it would normally occur. This term is often of limited use because it depends on the observer's ability to determine the relevance of the behaviour to the current context.

Diurnal: tending to occur during daylight hours, as opposed to Nocturnal. (Diurnal rhythm sometimes refers to behaviours or physiological responses that occur on a daily basis, where the term Circadian rhythm is usually more appropriate.)

Double bridle: a bridle comprising two bits, a curb and a snaffle, which are attached by means of two cheek pieces and may be operated independently.

Down stay: an obedience exercise that involves a dog remaining in the 'down' position (i.e. sternal recumbency or lying on the brisket [qv]) for a defined period with or in the case of advanced dogs without the owner present.

Easy-to-hard transfer effect: the principle that difficult tasks can be shaped by first training an animal to perform easier analogues of those tasks; it usually applies to discrimination training.

Ecological niche: the environment that a species occupies in nature and usually in which it performs best.

Eliminative behaviour: patterns of behaviour connected with the evacuation of faeces and urine.

Epimiletic behaviour: the provision of care and attention such as nursing behaviours.

Errorless learning: successful fading (qv).

Ethogram: a detailed description of the behavioural features of a particular species.

Ethology: systematic observation and description of behaviour intended to improve understanding of its mechanism, function, development and evolution.

Evading the bit: oral behaviours and neck postures that enable horses to reduce the discomfort caused by bits or the extent to which riders can apply tension.

Exploration: any activity that offers the individual the potential to acquire new information about itself or its environment.

Extinction: omission of reinforcement following either classical or instrumental conditioning that results in the eventual weakening of the trained response.

Fading: training designed to ensure that few, if any, responses are made to any stimulus other than the discriminative stimulus (qv).

FEI: The Fédération Equestre Internationale (International Equestrian Federation), body governing the international equestrian sports of show-jumping, three-day eventing, dressage and driving.

Feral: animals that have escaped from domestication and become free-ranging, or their progeny.

Filial imprinting: the process whereby a young animal comes to follow some object (usually the parent or a conspecific under natural conditions) to which it offers species-specific responses.

Fixed action pattern: the unconditioned species-specific response to a particular stimulus.

Fixed interval schedule: a schedule used in instrumental (or operant) conditioning in which reinforcement becomes available only when some fixed time has elapsed since the previous reinforcer was delivered.

Flight distance: the radius of space around an animal within which intrusion provokes a flight reaction.

Foraging: behaviours that increase an animal's likelihood of encountering and acquiring food.

Forehand: those parts of the horse which lie in front of the rider i.e. the head, neck, shoulders, withers and forelegs.

Flooding: the repeated presentation of an aversive stimulus to a confined animal until it no longer shows a fear reaction.

Fraser Darling effect: the stimulation of reproductive activity by the presence and activity of conspecifics in addition to the mating pair.

Frustration: state induced by the non-occurrence of an expected reinforcer.

Frustration effect: a temporary increase in the vigour of an instrumental response in the early stages of extinction (qv).

Gating: returning an animal (usually a marine mammal) to its holding pen as a consequence of its failing to produce a trained response, a form of negative punishment.

Gee: the driving term that signals a turn to the right.

Generalisation: producing a response to a stimulus other than the cue (discriminative or conditioned stimulus) to which the animal has been trained to make the response; failure of discrimination.

Generalisation gradient: function indicating that the ability of a stimulus to elicit the trained response increases with the similarity of the stimulus to the cue used in training.

Geophagia/geophagy: ingestion of soil.

Group effect: a change in the behaviour of a number of animals brought about by common participation.

Habituation: the waning of a response to a repeated stimulus as a result of repeated exposure (not simple fatigue).

Half-halt: a sequential application of rein and leg pressure intended to warn the ridden horse that it is about to be given a new command.

Hard-mouthed: (US cold-jawed, tough-mouthed) term used to describe the 'toughening membrane of the bars of the mouth where the bit rests and the deadening nerves because of the continued pressure of the bit' - more correctly this describes habituation to rein pressure.

Haute école: 'high school', classically the highest form of specialised training of the dressage horse.

Haw: the driving term that signals a turn to the left.

Hedonic conditioning: a type of classical conditioning in which the aim is to increase or decrease liking for (attraction towards) some object or event. For example, a rat's liking for a previously neutral flavour such as almond can be increased by giving it a mixture of almond and sugar water. Also known as hedonic learning and, in a human context, evaluative conditioning or affective learning.

Heel work: the training of dogs to remain close to the handler's leg (the left, by convention).

Herbivores: species that preferentially eat plants.

Imprinting: the development by a young animal of a strong social attachment.

In-hand: in a routine of 'schooling in hand', the trainer works from the ground rather than from the saddle, standing beside the horse and controlling him with rein, voice, and schooling whip.

Independent seat: a rider's ability to maintain a firm, balanced position on a horse's back, without relying on the reins or stirrups. *See also* Balanced seat.

Ingestive behaviour: behaviour concerned with the selection and intake of food, milk and water.

Initiator: the first individual in a social group to react in a way that elicits a new group activity.

Instinct: a term with a variety of related meanings. In the present setting it refers to a tendency of an animal to behave in a way that is characteristic of its species.

Instinctive drift: the spontaneous emergence of species-specific responses appropriate to the reinforcer.

Instrumental conditioning: any training procedure in which the animal's behaviour produces some consequence. This includes reward training, in which positive reinforcement follows the correct response, punishment (qv), in which an aversive event follows an incorrect response, avoidance training (qv) and omission training (qv).

Intention movements: the preparatory activity that an animal may go through when switching from one set of behaviours to another.

Inter-stimulus interval: the time between the start of one stimulus and the start of the next.

Interval schedule of reinforcement: a form of instrumental (operant) training in which there is a fixed or variable time after delivery of one reinforcer before the next becomes available.

Jackpot: an especially strong primary reinforcer that is usually larger than normal rewards.

Latent inhibition: a retarding effect on conditioning that results from prior presentations of a stimulus by itself.

Leaning on the bit: a sign of habituation to bit pressure which manifests with the horse persistently pulling on the rein(s) as though relying on the rider to support the weight of its head.

Learned helplessness: a state produced by exposure to unavoidable and intensely aversive events that is characterised mainly by passivity and subsequent deficits in learning to escape from aversive events.

Learning: the process underlying relatively permanent changes in behaviour or acquisition of knowledge.

Learning set procedure: a training programme in which an animal is given a series of problems, e.g. object discriminations, that are all of the same kind, but with varying content. This can result in increasingly rapid solution of each particular problem as the animal 'learns to learn'.

Least reinforcing stimulus (LRS): a form of negative punishment, this outcome depends on the training system but can include a time out period (qv).

Leg yielding: lateral movement of a horse in response to pressure from the rider's leg, used as a schooling activity before training more complex lateral manoeuvres such as a half-pass.

Long-reining: driving the horse without any vehicle or load. Used to train the horse to move forward without being led, to respond to bit pressures, to habituate it to distractions and to classically condition it to respond to vocal cues.

Lunge (also longe): exercising a horse on the end of a long lead or rope, usually in a circle.

Lures: primary reinforcers placed strategically to attract an animal to an area or piece of apparatus.

Manipulandum: the element of an operant device with which an animal must interact to cause the delivery of reinforcement.

Matching-to-sample: a task that requires an animal to inspect a sample stimulus and a set of comparison stimuli and then to select the comparison stimulus that most closely matches the sample.

Misbehaviour: species-specific responses relevant to the current reinforcer that appear during instrumental conditioning (qv) without being intentionally shaped (qv) and that tend to interfere with the behaviour desired by the trainer.

Motivation: an internal state that impels and directs behaviour.

Natural aids: the body, hands, legs, weight, and voice, as used in controlling a horse.

Need: a deficiency in an animal that can be remedied by obtaining a particular resource or responding to a particular environment or bodily stimulus.

Negative punishment: a procedure whereby a reinforcer is removed or made unavailable if an unwanted response is made. *See also* Omission training (qv).

Neophobia: fear of novel stimuli.

Neurophysiology: the study of nerve function.

Obedience trials: competitions to compare the compliance of dogs to handler's commands in a number of traditional exercises on and off the lead.

Obligate carnivores: species that preferentially eat flesh.

Observational learning: learning that results from one animal observing another rather than on the basis of direct experience.

Omission training: conditioning in which reinforcement is omitted if the target response is made, and thus is contingent on the target response *not* being made.

Omnivores: species that eat a variety of both flesh and plant material.

On the bit: neck and poll flexion that involves the nasal planum being within six degrees of the vertical, a posture intended to improve the extent to which the horse responds willingly to the signals transmitted by the rider through the reins. To most people, 'on the bit' means that the horse is going along with his nose nicely tucked in, moving smoothly from one place to another. However, a vertical nose does not mean that the horse is 'on the bit', although many observers may be fooled by it, a perhaps more elegant term to describe being 'on the bit' is 'direct flexion'.

Off the bit: a lack of at least one of the three prerequisites for 'on the bit' as above.

Operant conditioning: learning that a response elicits an outcome.

Overshadowing: the process whereby the presence of a second stimulus interferes with learning an association between the target stimulus and some important event.

Partial reinforcement (PRF): the reinforcement of some but not all correct responses.

Partial reinforcement extinction effect (PREE): the seemingly paradoxical increase in resistance to extinction (qv) that is normally produced by instrumental conditioning that involves partial reinforcement (qv).

Passive avoidance: training in which an animal receives a shock or some other aversive event if it makes a particular response, but no shock is delivered if it does *not* make the response; equivalent to punishment (qv).

Pecking order: a hierarchy in which each individual is able to threaten, displace or attack individuals lower than itself.

Pica: the searching-for and ingestion of inappropriate substrates that may be toxic and cause obstruction.

Primary (unconditioned) reinforcer: a resource or stimulus that the animal is attracted to and that can serve to strengthen instrumental responding.

Procedural memory: past experience stored in the form of how to perform an action rather than in the form of stored sensory information.

Punisher: any event that makes the preceding response less likely to occur in future.

Punishment: a decrease in the likelihood of a response due to the presentation of an aversive stimulus or, in the case of negative punishment, the removal of a reinforcing stimulus.

Puppy walking: a common habituation exercise in the elementary training of guide dog and foxhound puppies that involves their being placed in homes with stimuli typical of those it will encounter during their working lives.

Ratio schedule of reinforcement: a form of instrumental (operant) training in which a certain number of responses is required before reinforcement occurs.

Redirected behaviour: the direction of an activity away from the primary target and toward another less appropriate substrate; in natural settings this term needs to be used with care because it implies that the observer knows what the primary target is.

Reinforcement: in instrumental conditioning (qv) this refers to the process whereby some event, usually one of some significance to the animal, makes the preceding response more likely to occur in future.

Reinforcer: an event that increases the likelihood that an animal will make a particular response i.e. a reward (positive reinforcer) or removal of a punishment (negative reinforcer).

Reference memory: the information that an animal holds about stable relationships in its environment. In the context of spatial knowledge it is commonly applied to an animal's knowledge about relatively permanent relationships rather than to its knowledge about the temporary location of moveable objects or of resources such as food.

Releasing stimulus: the highly specific signal that is usually needed to trigger fixed action patterns (qv).

Renewal effect: the reappearance in a new context of a response that has been extinguished (qv) only in a highly specific setting.

Response: any behaviour or physiological event.

Response blocking procedure: training designed to produce weakening of some avoidance behaviour by preventing it from occurring when the fear-eliciting stimulus is presented that normally evokes avoidance. It is also often referred to as flooding (qv).

Right shoulder work: a description of the need for guide dogs to learn that since they are always to the left of the handler, they must effectively pivot their owners around their right shoulders when manoeuvring around obstacles.

Ritual behaviour: a fixed and stereotyped sequence of responses that may have lost its original function and instead may have developed a role in communication; e.g. courting displays in many species of birds.

Schedules of reinforcement: the relationship between responding and the delivery of reinforcement in instrumental (operant) conditioning, as in interval (qv) and ratio schedules (qv).

Schutzhund (literal translation from German is 'guard dog'): specialist form of competitive dog training that consists of three phases: tracking (following where a tracklayer has walked and indicating dropped articles); obedience (involving heeling, recall, retrieves on the flat and over jumps, sit, down, stands, send away); and protection (including searching for and guarding a helper without biting, when appropriate to stop attacks on the dog and handler - 'obedience under protection' scenarios).

Secondary (conditioned) reinforcer: a stimulus that has acquired reinforcing properties on the basis of its relationship to a primary reinforcer (qv).

Semantic memory: storage and retrieval processes related to information about the world, as opposed to episodic memory, memory for specific episodes in an individual's past. These terms are more commonly used in the study of human than animal memory; reference memory (qv) is the term commonly used in the study of animal memory that most closely corresponds to semantic memory.

Send away: an obedience exercise that involves a dog travelling away from its handler in a given direction governed by the handler.

Sensitisation: an increase in responsiveness to a repeated stimulus; the opposite of habituation (qv).

Serial reversal task: a series of discriminations, all involving the same stimuli, in which the contingency for each discrimination, e.g. choice of A rewarded; B, not rewarded, is the reverse of that of the previous one, e.g. B rewarded; A, not rewarded. Solving such a task is indicated by a progressive reduction in the errors made in learning successive discriminations.

Sexual imprinting: the process whereby experience during some limited period prior to sexual maturity influences an individual's later sexual preferences.

Shaping: the stepwise reinforcement of responses that increasingly approximate to the target behaviour. Also referred to as the method of successive approximations.

Shell shock/post-traumatic stress disorder: emotional and cognitive deficits following exposure to uncontrollable and intense aversive events; related to learned helplessness (qv).

Short-term memory: the process of storing perceptual events for a limited period until they are either forgotten or transferred into long-term memory.

Simultaneous discrimination training: a task in which on each trial the animal is given access to two or more stimuli at the same time and is rewarded only if it responds to the target, or positive, stimulus.

Sit stay: an obedience exercise that involves a dog remaining in a sitting position for a defined period with or, in the case of advanced dogs, without the owner present.

Social facilitation: when a behaviour is initiated or increased in frequency by the presence of other animals of the same species.

Social learning: learning that results from observing the behaviour of another animal rather than as a result of individual experience.

Social transmission: the process that leads to an increase in the frequency of a particular behaviour throughout a social group and that can occur as a result of social learning or by some less direct route.

Socialisation: exposure of a neonate or juvenile to individuals from the species it is expected to accept as part of its social group. Also any mixing of animals with conspecifics (qv).

Soft mouth: in horse training, a sensitive mouth, responsive to bit pressure.

Spanish walk/trot: extended gaits (usually trained in-hand) in which the forelegs are momentarily held out horizontally forward from the shoulder at each stride, the feet are brought to the ground without the knees bending and head is held high to transfer weight onto the hindlegs.

Spatial contiguity: the extent to which two events are closely located.

Spatial learning: learning that involves spatial relationships.

Spatial memory: stored information about an individual's environment, including the location of resources and aversive stimuli.

Species-specific defence reactions: innate responses to fear-eliciting stimuli that can include flight, fight and freeze responses.

Spontaneous recovery: an increase in the strength of an extinguished response after a rest period.

Station: the place where an animal is routinely given primary reinforcers.

Stimulus control: the degree to which responding occurs in the presence of a specific stimulus and does not occur in the absence of this stimulus; normally results from discrimination training (qv).

Stimulus generalisation: the degree to which a response trained to a specific conditioned (qv) or discriminative stimulus (qv) also occurs to other stimuli. Thus, broad stimulus generalisation indicates poor stimulus control (qv).

Stimulus generalisation test: the presentation of one or more stimuli that differ from the conditioned (qv) or discriminative stimulus (qv) used in training in order to assess the extent to which the test stimuli will also produce the trained response.

Steering: guiding an animal by the application of pressure to a head restraint or with bit pressure via with reins.

Stereotypy: a repeated, relatively invariant sequence of movements that has no obvious function.

Straight line work: the training of guide dogs that focuses on reinforcing them when they resume locomotion in a straight line after some deviation.

Stress: refers either to a set of events, usually aversive ones, that put pressure on an individual or to the state induced by such pressure.

Stimulus: any change in the environment that can be detected by an animal's sense organs.

Stimulus enhancement: increasing an animal's interest in a stimulus by interacting with it or garnishing it with lures (qv).

Successive discrimination training: a task in which an animal is given only one stimulus at a time and is rewarded either for making a single response only to the target, or positive, stimulus (go/no go training) or for making an appropriate response to whichever stimulus is present (e.g. go left to one stimulus and go right to the other).

Target training: conditioning an animal to approach or touch an object that can be moved and thus prompt the animal to change its location.

Temporal contiguity: the extent to which two events occur close together in time.

Terminal bridge: a secondary reinforcer that signals successful completion of a target behaviour.

Territory: the area an animal defends by demarcation or by fighting.

Time out: a period spent without any reinforcement available; a form of negative punishment (qv) or punishment by omission. This can take the form of removal from the training context or even just temporary cessation of attention to the animal by the trainer. In experimental settings with birds such as pigeons time out often consists of switching off all lights within the chamber for a few seconds.

Tonic immobility: a behavioural state of a few seconds or longer during which an animal makes no movement as a result of a pathological condition or an environmental event.

Trial-and-error learning: or more fully, trial-and-error learning with accidental success. Equivalent to instrumental conditioning (qv); now more commonly used in a human context where it implies non-systematic responding with little knowledge beforehand of what is likely to be the critical response needed to attain some goal.

Unconditioned stimulus (US): an event that reliably elicits a response prior to the start of conditioning.

Variable interval (VI) schedule: a form of instrumental (operant) training in which there is a variable time after the delivery of one reinforcer before the next becomes available.

Working memory: stored information about location of currently relevant resources and aversive stimuli.

Working dog trials: competitions designed to show the absolute and relative ability of dogs as they perform specific trained responses in challenges, categorised according to their complexity, which include companion dog (CD), trials dog (TD), working dog (WD) and police dog (PD) classes.

Further reading

Chapter 1 (Instincts and their modification)

Goodenough, J., McGuire, B. & Wallace, R.A. (2001). *Perspectives on animal behaviour*. 2nd edn. New York: John Wiley & Sons.

Chapters 2 and 3 (Learning theory)

Bouton, M.E. (2007). *Learning and behavior: a contemporary synthesis*. Sunderland, Mass: Sinauer Associates.

Lieberman, D.A. (2004). *Learning and memory: an integrative approach*. Belmont, CA: Wadsworth/Thomson.

Chapter 4 (Animal intelligence)

Shettleworth, S.J. (2010). *Cognition, evolution and behavior*. 2nd edn. New York: Oxford University Press.

Wynne, C.D.L. (2004). *Do animals think?* Princeton, NJ: Princeton University Press.

Select bibliography

Barnett, A. (1993). Humanity as homo docens: the teaching species. *Interdisciplinary Science Reviews*, 19(2): 166–74.

Boakes, R.A. (1984). *From Darwin to behaviourism: psychology and the minds of animals*. Cambridge, UK: Cambridge University Press.

Bekhterev, V. (1933). *General principles of human reflexology: an introduction to the objective study of personality*. Translated by E. & W. Murphy. London: Jarrolds.

Breland, M. & Breland, K. (1966). *Animal behavior*. New York: Macmillan.

Breland, M. & Breland, K. (1962) The misbehavior of organisms. *American Psychologist*, 16: 681–84.

Cannon, W. (1932). *The wisdom of the body*. New York: Norton.

Chapuis, N. & Varlet, C. (1987). Short cuts by dogs in natural surroundings. *Quarterly Journal of Experimental Psychology*, 39B: 49–64.

Durrant, M. (Ed.) (1993). *Aristotle's de Anima in focus*. London, New York: Routledge.

Estes, W.K. (1986). Array models for category learning. *Cognitive Psychology*, 18: 500–49.

Fisher, J. (1994). *Why does my dog ...?* With drawings by Ernie Jones. Toronto, London: Bantam.

Harlow, H.F. (1949). The formation of learning sets. *Psychological Review*, 56: 51–65.

Henry, Earl of Pembroke (1761). *A method of breaking horses, and teaching soldiers to ride, designed for the use of the Army*. London: Printed by J. Hughes.

Kamin, L. (1969). Predictability, surprise, attention and conditioning. In B.A. Campbell & R.M. Church (Eds). *Punishment and aversive behaviour*. New York: Appleton-Century-Crofts.

Koehler, W. (1927). *The mentality of apes*. Rev. edn. London: Routledge and Kegan Paul.

Krall, K. (1912). *Denkende tiere*. Leipzig: F. Engelmann.

Ladygina-Kohts, N.N. (2002 [1935]). *Infant chimpanzee and human child: a classic 1935 comparative study of ape emotions and intelligence*. Oxford: Oxford University Press.

Lorenz, K. (1961). *King Solomon's ring: new light on animal ways*. With a new introduction by W.H. Thorpe. London: Methuen.

Maier, S. & Jackson R.L. (1979). Learned helplessness: all of us were right (and wrong): inescapable shock has multiple effects. In G.H. Bower (Ed.). *The psychology of learning and motivation* (Vol. 13). New York: Academic Press.

Morris, R.G.M. (1981). Spatial localization does not require the presence of local cues. *Learning and Motivation,* 12: 239–60.

Mowrer, H.O. (1947). On the dual nature of learning: a reinterpretation of 'conditioning' and 'problem-solving'. *Harvard Educational Review,* 17: 102–50.

Olton, D.S. & Samuelson, R.J. (1976). Remembrance of places passed: spatial memory in rats. *Journal of Experimental Psychology: Animal Behavior Processes,* 2: 97–116.

Pavlov, I.P. (1927). *Conditioned reflexes.* Translated by G.V. Anrep. Oxford: Oxford University Press.

Scott, J.P. & Fuller, J.L. (1965). *Genetics and the social behavior of the dog.* Chicago: University of Chicago Press.

Seligman, M.E.P. (1975). *Helplessness: on depression, development, and death.* New York: W.H. Freeman.

Skinner, B.F. (1938). *The behavior of organisms.* New York: Appleton-Century-Crofts.

Solomon, R. & Wynne, L. (1953). Traumatic avoidance learning: acquisition in normal dogs. *Psychological Monographs,* 67 (4, whole no. 354).

Thorndike, E.L. (1911). *Animal intelligence.* New York: Macmillan.

Pfungst, O. (1965 [1911]). *Clever Hans: (The horse of Mr von Osten).* New York, NY: Holt, Rinehard and Winston, Inc.

Index